THE
HISTORY OF
ROCKET
TECHNOLOGY

President Dwight D. Eisenhower examines a model of the Saturn C-1 space booster at Marshall Space Flight Center, Huntsville, Alabama, as MSFC Director Dr. Wernher von Braun explains the Saturn configuration. In the background are shown the eight engine nozzles, which are covered, of the Saturn C-1 first-stage, and NASA Administrator T. Keith Glennan walking up to join the President. Occasion was the dedication of the George C. Marshall Space Flight Center on September 8, 1960. (NASA Photo)

THE HISTORY OF ROCKET TECHNOLOGY

Essays on Research, Development, and Utility

Edited by Eugene M. Emme

William M. Bland, Jr.
Walter R. Dornberger
John P. Hagen
R. Cargill Hall
Kenneth S. Kleinknecht
Frank J. Malina
Wilfrid J. Mayo-Wells
Wyndham D. Miles
G. Edward Pendray
Robert L. Perry
Arthur G. Renstrom
Robert D. Roach, Jr.
G. A. Tokaty
Wernher von Braun

Published in cooperation with
the Society for the History of Technology

Detroit 1964 / Wayne State University Press

Many of the articles in this book were previously published, in large
part, in Technology and Culture, IV, 4 (Fall, 1963).

CONTENTS

Related Technology

Evolution of Rocketry in the Soviet Union

ILLUSTRATIONS

FIGURES

Preface

From the ancient fireworks of Asia and of Europe, as well as from the better-documented military history of artillery, modern rocketry emerges as a major technological factor in contemporary history. It is a development perhaps only temporarily overshadowed by the impact of nuclear fission and fusion, whose destructive potential has already harnessed rocketry for intercontinental delivery systems. No one seriously questions that the balance of world military power today rests upon a technological fulcrum consisting of intercontinental ballistic missiles armed with nuclear warheads, as well as rockets which can be launched from jet-propelled bombers and from the first true submarines.

The history of rocket technology is not, however, concerned merely with the evolution of military weapons systems in the 1940's and the 1950's nor with the development of space transportation in the 1960's. Rocketry has influenced the entire structure and conduct of national and international politics and economics. It continues to revolutionize the totality and efficiency of a possible unrestrained war among the major powers, thereby confounding the objectives and means for working for effective peace and human freedom throughout the world. The eminence of Western science and technology—and all that this means, including but also beyond the connotations of national power— is not a little dependent upon the short and long-term success of technological progress in rocketry and astronautics.

With our limited perspective it is very clear that rocket technology has had a growing and profound application as a revolutionary tool of science, as an agent of global communications and space mobility, and as a national instrumentality for preserving peace or as a potential weapon of war. How did the technology of rocketry come to this prominent position? What is the real history concerning the rise of this new technology and its associated stimulus to electronics, materials, structures, and most of the other scientific and engineering disciplines? The impact of rocket technology upon society, apparent and portentous, likewise challenges the social sciences and the humanities.

1

The following essays, presented in rough chronological sequence, are the fortunate product of several endeavors. "The History of Rocket Technology" session at the joint American Association for the Advancement of Science–Society for the History of Technology meeting in Philadelphia on December 28, 1962, generated the outstanding attempt by prominent history-makers to set the record straight for historians on key aspects of specific rocket programs. This session included Drs. G. Edward Pendray, Walter R. Dornberger, and John P. Hagen. Second, the Goddard Historical Essay Awards for 1962, the result of a first literary competition sponsored by the National Space Club of Washington, D. C., produced prize-winning essays which add to our knowledge. These were written by historians now associated with industry: R. Cargill Hall, W. J. Mayo-Wells, and Robert D. Roach, Jr.

It was the inspired request of Professor Melvin Kranzberg of Case Institute of Technology, Editor of *Technology and Culture*, that a full issue of the quarterly of the Society for the History of Technology utilize these unpublished papers of high interest to historians. This was done.*

To help insure that the overall historical treatment of representative case studies was not hopelessly disjointed, papers were invited from those who could review with authority major aspects of rocket programs otherwise omitted. Dr. Wernher von Braun, one whose career has been invested in rocketry, kindly wrote on "The Redstone, Jupiter, and Juno." Official governmental historians, Robert L. Perry and Wyndham D. Miles, filled gaps on "The Atlas, Thor, Titan, and Minuteman" and "The Polaris" respectively. And lastly, Dr. G. A. Tokaty provided a historical summary on Soviet rocket technology.

Once the *Technology and Culture* edition appeared, the opportunity to augment this volume was possible. Dr. Frank J. Malina graciously undertook to document the work he and his colleagues initiated with the blessings of Dr. Theodore von Kármán at the California Institute of Technology in 1936. Kenneth S. Kleinknecht and William M. Bland, formerly of the National Advisory Committee for Aeronautics (NACA) and now of the National Aeronautics and Space Administration (NASA), contributed valuable essays on the application of rocketry to manned flight in aircraft and in Project Mercury. It proved infeasible to include representative treatment of the gigantic strides in rocket technology during the past several years. Bibliographical references were most ably collated to date by Arthur G. Renstrom of the Library of Congress for this volume, which remain to

* *Technology and Culture*, Volume IV, No. 4 (Fall 1963).

be detailed as historical research and analysis of rocket technology proceeds.

*   *   *   *   *

Special acknowledgment must be accorded first to the contributors whose essays represent a genuine attempt to further the cause of the history of technology. Future historians are indeed indebted to each of the contributors. Their biographies are found at the places where their helpful essays begin. The Society for the History of Technology, of course, provided the indispensable catalyst for this volume, particularly as personified in the devoted labors of Professor Melvin Krantzberg, Executive Secretary and Editor of *Technology and Culture*. And lastly, the editor of this volume is indebted to those academic and governmental colleagues who provided encouragement by counsel and assistance. While all cannot be cited, the following deserve recognition here: David S. Akens, Historian, NASA Marshall Space Flight Center; Frederick C. Durant, III, Bell Aerosystems, an avid historian of rocketry and former President of the I. A. F. and the American Rocket Society; Mrs. Robert H. Goddard, who blessed the Robert H. Goddard Historical Essay Competition; James Grimwood, Historian, NASA Manned Spacecraft Center; Marvin W. McFarland, Science and Technology, Library of Congress; Ralph Sanders, Industrial College of the Armed Forces; Harold A. Timken, former President of the National Rocket Club, recently renamed the National Space Club; and George L. Simpson, Jr., Assistant Administrator of NASA. The British Interplanetary Society kindly granted permission for the inclusion of Dr. G. A. Tokaty's article on "Soviet Rocket Technology," which appeared in *Spaceflight*, Vol. V, No. 2 (March 1963).

Illustrations and photographs were generously provided, as indicated, by Mrs. Robert H. Goddard, Dr. G. Edward Pendray, the Jet Propulsion Laboratory, Bell Aerosystems Company, Glenn L. Martin Company, F. I. Ordway, Reaction Motors of the Thiokol Chemical Corp., the Smithsonian Institution, the Department of Defense, and the National Aeronautics and Space Administration. And finally, the editor received the time and opportunity for many unlogged hours in the countdown for this manuscript from Ruth Rance Emme and our children.

EUGENE M. EMME

Introduction

EUGENE M. EMME*

> "It is difficult to say what is impossible, for the dream of yesterday is the hope of today and the reality of tomorrow."
> —Robert H. Goddard, 1904

> "The earth is the cradle of the mind, but one cannot live forever in a cradle.
> "To set foot on the soil of the asteroids, to lift by hand a rock from the moon, to observe Mars from a distance of several tens of kilometers, to land on its satellite or even on its surface, what can be more fantastic? From the moment of using rocket devices a new great era will begin in astronomy: the epoch of the more intensive study of the firmament."
> —Konstantin Ziolkovsky, 1899

OF RENEWED INTEREST as an intellectual launching pad for historians of technology today is the classic thesis of the late William Fielding Ogburn on the "cultural lag" in human affairs.[1] Traditionally, mankind as a whole has reluctantly understood and accommodated itself to dynamic changes in scientific knowledge about nature as well as the technological means available to exploit it. This "cultural lag" has been rather well documented for the sailing vessel, the telescope, the steam engine, the airplane, and nuclear fission. Ogburn's thesis might well be revisited now, when the pace and the breadth of contemporary technical changes present a wholesale challenge to society in these middle decades of the twentieth century.

Until the balloon and the airplane opened up the air space medium, man's physical mobility was only two dimensional. The techniques of

---

* Historian of the National Aeronautics and Space Administration (Washington, D. C.), Dr. Emme is editor of *The Impact of Air Power: National Security and World Politics* (Princeton: 1959) and author of *Aeronautics and Astronautics: 1915-1960* (Washington, 1961). He is Chairman of the History Committees of the National Space Club and the American Institute of Aeronautics and Astronautics, and is on the History Committee of the International Academy of Astronautics.

[1] *Cf.* Otis D. Duncan, "An Appreciation of William Fielding Ogburn," *Technology and Culture*, Vol. I No. 1 (Winter, 1959/1960), pp. 94-99.

war and peace as well as scientific inquiry were thereby constrained. Technologically improved air vehicles, however, exercised a three-dimensional influence upon the pursuits of earth-bound mankind.

Within the past two decades, moreover, the fourth dimension has been brought sharply into the realm of human comprehension and utility by the release of nuclear energy and the advent of astronautics. These made their appearance in a rapidly thickening atmosphere of scientific understanding and technological competence and, at the same moment, in a near vacuum of humanistic and philosophic comprehension of their basic import. The full significance of the application of rocket technology beyond military utility to space flight—the first breaching of the last barrier to man's mobility into the universe itself— seemed less appreciated in the Sputnik birth of the space age than was loud public debate on the "missile gap," the "space race," and "national prestige."

*   *   *   *   *

Revival in the twentieth century of the ancient festival and military art of rocketry was initially closer to speculation concerning space mobility than is generally conceded. Once the financial and organizational interest of the major nations was drawn to rocket development for military applications, the technology of rocket propulsion was ultimately advanced to fulfill many of the speculations of Ziolkovsky, Goddard, and Oberth. Ziolkovsky, as is well known, wrote about the colonization by mankind *Beyond the Planet Earth* (1903), and he understood the performance of reactive propulsion in the near-vacuum of space. Goddard, as is not yet well known, was keenly interested in the exploration of space before turning to rocket development. First proving in a laboratory that rocket propulsion would function in a vacuum before World War I, Goddard's patriotic development of a successful solid-fuel ballistic rocket by 1918 lay unused for twenty-five years. Launching the world's first liquid-fuel rocket on March 16, 1926, Goddard was supported throughout the 1920's and the 1930's by the Smithsonian and Carnegie Institutions and the Guggenheim family to develop a rocket means of exploring the atmosphere. It was the German Society for Space Travel which picked up the notions of Goddard and Oberth regarding space and initiated serious rocket work in Germany, as did the British Interplanetary Society and the American Rocket Society later. Enthusiasm by a few, public derision, and a lack of financial means characterized the primitive era of modern rocketry.

It was the military potential of rocket propulsion, an art lost to artillery in the 19th century, which created missilery as a strategic weapons system and brought forth the technology making possible the birth of practical astronautics. The Treaty of Versailles prompted the German Army in 1931 to initiate a serious, albeit modest and secret investment in the possible military potential of rocketry, an effort uncurtailed by the Third Reich. In 1931 also, the Soviet Union established the famous Group for the Study of Rocket Propulsion Systems (G. I. R. D.), later renamed the State Rocket Scientific Research Institute. Not until July 1, 1939, did the U. S. National Academy of Sciences sponsor a $10,000 project at the California Institute of Technology to develop rockets suitable to assist bomber take-offs, the first Federal rocket program as such. The spectacular appearance of the German V-2 ballistic rocket in 1944, demonstrated a technological jump at the same time that German and British operational jet-propelled aircraft appeared. After the dramatic events at Hiroshima and Nagasaki in 1945, the history of rocket technology entered the phase culminating with the launching of the first manmade earth satellite on October 4, 1957.

It is significant that the finish line in the race for the first-generation intercontinental ballistic missile and the dawn of the so-called " space age " occurred at virtually the same historical instant. Strategic requirements of national security enforced and continue to enforce high priorities for the development of effective military systems. The full impact of the first Sputniks, however, triggered a chain-reaction of events beyond military considerations to explore and to exploit the newly accessible environment of space, an effort growing to dimensions unforeseen by even the most enthusiastic advocates of space mobility. Scientific, engineering, political, and dramatic challenges of the space venture of mankind have thus far prevailed. The first phase of the Space Age was largely based on the missile-derived technology while genuine space transportation systems are now well underway.

*   *   *   *   *

As the telescope placed the earth in orbit around the sun for thinking men in the seventeenth century, so rocket propulsion in the twentieth century enables scientists to test and augment their basic knowledge beyond the cataract of the earth's atmosphere that not only filters their optical vision of the solar system, but also shields mankind from the deadly solar radiations whence life-giving energy derives.

Six years ago no one knew about the Van Allen radiation belts or was actively searching for extra-terrestrial life. Today the feasibility of operational communications and weather satellites has been fully demonstrated. Within the past 36 months, astronauts and cosmonauts have orbited weightless above the earth's atmosphere and gravitational force and returned safely to *terra firma*. Within recent months, the first hard data concerning the atmosphere and surface of Venus were acquired by the *Mariner II* space probe and Ranger VII made close-up moon pictures. These new data were added to the knowledge acquired by over 200 scientific satellites and space probes launched by the United States and the Soviet Union during the past half dozen years.

In the present kindergarten era of astronautics, with its tender philosophy, perhaps a new renaissance of the mind and spirit of mankind may be in the making—a renaissance sparked as when the new geography of Columbus and Magellan and the new astronomy of Copernicus and Galileo helped loosen Europe from the Middle Ages; or when the new biology of Darwin for the physical organism, the new challenges of Marx and the new psychology of Bergson and Freud for the conscious man assisted the great intellectual stimulus of the late nineteenth century as well as the humanitarianism and technological boom of the twentieth century.

As in most man-made ventures, there was a small band of zealous prophets who anticipated a science and technology of rocketry and astronautics that they themselves could not achieve or fully explain. So also the new cosmology animated by Ziolkovsky, Goddard, and Oberth and postulated by Clarke and Dryden and Von Braun and Van Allen and Urey and Lovell and others—in suddenly expanding man's domain from this planet to a whole solar system and beyond—has sown seeds for a dynamic revolution in man's comprehension and exploration of reality. Now the frontiersmen of the co-mingled disciplines of the space sciences foretell a wholesale acquisition of new understandings of the meaning of space, time, energy, motion, and life processes. Historically, as we shall examine, man's new accessibility to the space environment stemmed from the evolution of rocket technology, first prodded by military conflict and yet animated by crucial requirements for national survival in a very troubled world.

Just ten years ago, man grappled with a shrunken and bipolarized air-age world, this with an aeronautical technology exploiting a usable atmospheric medium only twice as high as his mountains. Intercontinental air power and global-legged statesmen, businessmen, politicians, artists, scholars, and tourists quickly made their mobility felt in human affairs on earth. Yet less than ten years hence, we are told, man will have stood on the moon while confidently preparing to voyage to nearby planets in this solar system. His radio telescopes and orbiting laboratories and space stations will have already charted much of the new cosmography (i. e., the geography of space). Our present primitive level of understanding of the true nature of the universe beyond our appreciations of the unique environment of the earth will have

been grossly expanded as the cosmic jigsaw puzzle of the space environment is pieced together.[2] Then man's outermost horizons may truly
be infinity.

In his stimulating earlier essays on the impact of science on society,
Bertrand Russell pointed out:

> Man has existed for about a million years. He has possessed
> writing for about 6,000 years, agriculture somewhat longer, but
> perhaps not much longer. Science, as a dominant factor in deter-
> mining beliefs of educated men, has existed for about 300 years.
> In this brief period it has proved itself as an incredibly powerful
> revolutionary force. When we consider how recently it has risen
> to power, we find ourselves forced to believe that we are at the
> very beginning of its work in transforming human life. . . .[3]

Although specialized historians may find chronological exceptions to
Lord Russell's thesis, his central point of the recency and pace of
social change because of technological progress seems reasonable in
the light of Western experience.

The Administrator of the National Aeronautics and Space Administration, James E. Webb, recently said to a select audience of social
scientists:

> Every thread in the fabric of our economic, social and political
> institutions is being tested as we move into space. Our economic
> and political relations with other nations are being reevaluated.
> Old concepts of defense and military tactics are being challenged
> and revised. Jealously guarded traditions in our educational insti-
> tutions are being tested, altered, and even discarded. Our economic
> institutions—the corporate structure itself—are undergoing re-
> examination as society seeks to adjust itself to the inevitability of
> change.[4]

Whether or not the future bears out this stimulating thought, there
is no question but that general technological progress, of which
space exploration is a part, spurs on. It also appears that historians
today and tomorrow could easily become the greatest victims of
"cultural lag."

[2] *Cf.* Hugh L. Dryden, "Future Exploration and Utilization of Outer Space,"
Technology and Culture, Vol. II, No. 2 (Spring 1961), pp. 112-26; "The Lunar
Exploration Program," *Vital Speeches* (March 15, 1962), pp. 336-40; and "Foot-
prints on the Moon," *National Geographic* (March 1964), pp. 356-401.

[3] Bertrand Russell, *The Impact of Science on Society* (New York, 1951), p. 9.

[4] James E. Webb, Conference on Space, Science, and Urban Life (Washington:
NASA SP-37, 1963), pp. 93-102. *Cf.* "New Age of Discovery," *Airpower Historian* (July 1964), pp. 81-86.

Historians of today are swept along in the great tide of swiftly unfolding events shaped by the recent forces unleashed by what many blandly call the "technological explosion." Historians of the future will, of necessity, have to grapple with the ever-increasing acceleration of technical change as well as with the philosophical complexities inherent in the conceptual convulsions concerning the nature of universal nature and man's scientific techniques to understand and exploit it. If the historians of technology today are at long-last marshalling a methodology—one gaining recognition from their fellow political, diplomatic, economic, and social disciples of Clio—then indeed future historiography may be destined for shattering upheavals prompted by the pace and the breadth of major technological innovations now well underway but hitherto relatively ignored by serious scholars.

*   *   *   *   *

The central purpose of this volume is to present a preliminary historical assessment of rocket technology. It is neither a definitive treatment of the evolution of modern rocketry nor of its application as a tool of science, as a military weapon, or as a means of transportation in space. Further, none of the essays pretends to be a final evaluation of the chapters or case-studies of the over-all history of rocket technology. What is usefully evident throughout the volume is the accelerating nature of the unprecedented technological development associated with rocket propulsion, as well as the evolution of complex interactions between scientific, engineering, and industrial activities in their full political, economic and strategic context at both the national and the international level.

Primitive experiments have rapidly given way to complicated test and operational systems. Engines, pumps, turbines, valves, tubing, tanks, gyroscopes, accelerometers, guidance, and computers—all adapted to rocket propulsion—have been manufactured in large quantity. An urgent need also developed for mechanical and electronic instruments, pressure and strain gauges, transducers, beacons, and recorders. New material processes and tools were modified or created—explosive forming, chemical milling, electron-beam welding, and so forth. New combinations of high stress, heat extremes, vibration harmonics demanded new alloys and new structures of steel and aluminum as well as greater use of other metals—tungsten, molybdenum, beryllium, titanium —better insulators of resins, glass, graphite, and rubber. Specialized ground servicing and launch-associated equipment had to be designed and produced, often with unique mobility and dimensions. Rocket propulsion fuels, solid and liquid, have been produced in great tonnages: composite double-base solid fuels; liquid oxygen, kerosene, nitric acid, hydrazine, fluorine, and, most recently, hydrogen. Also, nuclear and electric propulsion offer promising results in space applications.[5]

Virtually a new industry has coalesced rapidly—indeed, several new industries. Technical personnel in missile and space programs expanded from a few hundred persons in the late 1930's to several hundreds of thousands. The broad front of rocket technology is based upon constant refinements of manifold systems and sub-systems, innumerable tests and repeated modifications, all aimed at the improvement of performance and reliability of operations, often leading to new techniques.

Most importantly, historians of technology should not miss the central theme and opportunity submitted here: the vast host of important and new historical problems awaiting detailed research and scholarship, perhaps new techniques for documentation and analysis as well as less laggard initiation.[6] By definition, historians always come after the event. But in the dynamic field of rocket technology, with its inherent implications concerning "cultural lag," perhaps we will not be too laggard for the cause of accurate and reliable documentation of technical change and its social influence in its own historical context.

[5] See Milton W. Rosen, "Big Rockets," *International Science and Technology*, Vol. I (December 1962), pp. 66-71.

[6] The case for contemporary history, with its attendant challenge and hazards, has been stimulatingly discussed in the A. H. A. Presidential Address by Carl Bridenbaugh, "The Great Mutation," *American Historical Review*, Vol. LXVIII (January 1963), pp. 315-31, and Arthur M. Schlesinger, Jr., "The Historian and History," *Foreign Affairs*, Vol. XLI (April 1963), pp. 491-97.

EARLY DEVELOPMENT

" He suggested the Brick Moon. The plan was this: If from the surface of the earth, by a gigantic pea-shooter, you could shoot a pea upward from Greenwich, aimed northward as well as upward; if you drove it so fast and far that when its power of ascent was exhausted, and it began to fall, it should clear the earth, and pass outside the North Pole; if you had given it sufficient power to get it half round the earth without touching, that pea would clear the earth forever . . .

" ' But a pea is so small! '

" ' Yes,' said Q., ' but we must make a large pea.' "

—Edward Everett Hale, The Brick Moon (1869)

1. *Dr. Robert H. Goddard* standing beside the world's first liquid-fuel rocket. This liquid oxygen-gasoline rocket was successfully fired on March 16, 1926, at Auburn Massachusetts, an event now called the "Kitty Hawk of Rocketry." (Smithsonian Photo)

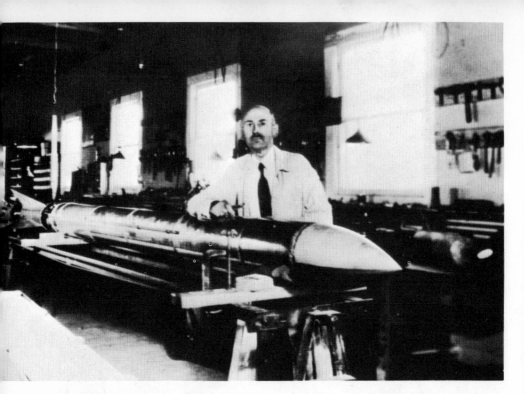

2. *Dr. Goddard* with his 1940 rocket, in a photograph taken by Mrs. Goddard at the Mescalero Ranch near Roswell, New Mexico. Esther C. Goddard's still and movie cameras were an important part of assessing each test flight. (Printed by permission of Mrs. Goddard)

3. *G. Edward Pendray (right) and Bernard Smith* (left) prepare A. R. S. Rocket No. 2 for launching at Marine Park, Staten Island, on May 14, 1933. Designed by H. F. Pierce and Pendray after German concepts, it rose about 250 feet at which point the liquid-oxygen tank burst. Two tubular fuel tanks are mounted on either side of a small cast-aluminum motor immersed in a container of water to serve as coolant. Damaged in a static test as A. R. S. No. 1, this rocket was completely rebuilt by Smith. (Pendray photo by permission)

4. *Cutaway diagram of German A-4 rocket* showing structural details of the V-2. (Photo supplied by F. I. Ordway, III) **5.** *V-2 being launched* at White Sands Proving Ground (now W. S. Missile Range), N. M., by the U. S. Army in 1946. (U. S. Army Photo)

6. *Captain Homer Boushey (AAF)* in Ercoupe makes first JATO (jet-assisted take-off) with solid-propellant GALCIT rockets from March Field, California, in July 1941. (JPL Photo) **7.** *Dr. Theodore von Kármán (center)* with GALCIT project before historic JATO flights in 1941. To the right of Dr. von Kármán are Frank J. Malina and Captain Homer Boushey. To his left (right to left) are Martin Summerfield, Dr. Clark Millikan, and an unidentified man. (JPL Photo)

8. *Army Air Force Douglas A-20 attack bomber* taking off with GALCIT liquid-fuel JATO unit in 1942. (JPL Photo) 9. *First launching from USAF Long Range Proving Ground*, Cocoa, Florida, Bumper-Wac No. 8 on July 12, 1950. LRPG was later the Atlantic Missile Range of the Department of Defense and known as Cape Canaveral, and more recently as Cape Kennedy. (JPL Photo)

10. *Army-JPL Bumper Wac* (V-2 first stage, Wac Corporal second stage) lifts from White Sands Missile Range, N. M. (U. S. Army Photo)

Pioneer Rocket Development
in the United States

G . EDWARD PENDRAY*

THE WORK OF Dr. Robert H. Goddard, the American rocket pioneer, and the early experimental work of the American Rocket Society, both of considerable interest in the evolution of modern rocket technology, were quite different and independent. Goddard's was not only of longer duration—beginning about 1898 and ending only a brief time before his death in 1945—but was of incomparably greater fundamental importance as a contribution to the space age. The American Rocket Society's period of experimentation was contemporary with some of Goddard's work, extending as it did from about 1931 through 1941, and also resulted in some notable contributions.

I knew Dr. Goddard—at first through correspondence and later by personal acquaintance. As for the work of the Society, I was one who helped organize and direct it, serving throughout the period as chairman of the A. R. S. Experimental Committee. I personally helped to design and construct two of the A. R. S. rockets—and assisted in the testing of all of them.

The Work of Robert H. Goddard

It is generally conceded that there were three great pioneering pro-

* Mr. Pendray (Pendray and Co., Bronxville, N. Y.) has been closely associated with the development of rockets since 1929, being one of the founders and a director and advisor of the American Rocket Society (which merged in January 1963 with the Institute of the Aerospace Sciences to form the American Institute of Aeronautics and Astronautics). His influential book, *The Coming Age of Rocket Power* (New York, 1945) was read by Robert H. Goddard, and, with Mrs. Esther C. Goddard, he edited a collection of Dr. Goddard's research notes published as *Rocket Development: Liquid-Fuel Rocket Research, 1929-1941* (New York, 1948). With Mrs. Goddard he is currently editing the papers of Dr. Goddard.

This paper was presented at the program on "The History of Rocket Technology" at the meeting of the Society for the History of Technology cosponsored by Section L (History and Philosophy of Science) and Section M (Engineering) of the American Association for the Advancement of Science on December 28, 1962, in Philadelphia.

genitors of the modern space age: Konstantin Ziolkovsky, Robert H. Goddard, and Hermann Oberth.[1]

The earliest, by a few years, was the Russian Konstantin Eduardovich Ziolkovsky (1857-1935). He was an obscure schoolteacher who, in 1898, after some years spent in calculations and reflection, sent his first exploratory work on space ships to the Russian magazine, *Science Survey*, which finally published it in 1903.[2]

The second was Dr. Robert H. Goddard (1882-1945), a professor of physics at Clark University, Worcester, Massachusetts, who as a very young man independently began speculating about means of reaching high altitudes and interplanetary space. In 1919 he published his classic paper: *A Method of Reaching Extreme Altitudes.*[3]

The third was Dr. Hermann Oberth, born at Sibiu, on the northern slopes of the Transylvania Alps in 1894, and who is today living in West Germany. Oberth began his study of the space flight problem about the time of the first World War and presented his first treatment of it in *Die Rakete zu den Planetenraumen*, published in 1923.[4]

Of these three pioneer thinkers, the first to undertake specific translation of his theories into shootable rockets and patentable devices was Goddard. While Oberth later had some connection with rocket development projects, including some association with the Germans at Peenemuende, Goddard was the only one of the three personally to reduce rocket theory to actual practice. He developed the basic mathematical and physical concepts which today underlie rocketry and space flight, and much of the engineering as well.

It has been said that one cannot today design a rocket, construct a rocket, or launch a rocket without infringing one or more of the 214 Goddard patents. Unusual recognition was given to this fact by the United States Government, when in 1960 the Army, Navy, Air Force,

[1] General biographies are in B. Williams and S. Epstein, *The Rocket Pioneers* (New York, 1955); H. Gartmann, *The Men Behind the Space Rockets* (New York, 1956); and Shirley Thomas, *Men of Space*, Vol. I (Philadelphia, 1960).

[2] See Y. I. Perelman, *Tsiolkovsky* (in English, Moscow, 1932); "An Autobiography," trans. by A. N. Petroff, *Astronautics* (May 1959), pp. 48-49, 63 ff.; *Beyond Planet Earth*, trans. by K. Syers (New York, 1962); and F. J. Krieger, ed., *The Men Behind the Sputniks* (Washington, D. C., 1958). Also see chapter by Tokaty below.

[3] Smithsonian Institution, *Miscellaneous Collections*, Vol. 71, No. 21 (1919). Select references to the writings by and on Robert H. Goddard are listed at the end of this paper.

[4] See H. Oberth, "From My Life," *Astronautics* (June 1959), pp. 38-39 ff.; *Wege Zur Raumschiffahrt* (Munich, 1929); *Menschen im Weltraum* (Düsseldorf, 1954), trans. by G. P. H. de Freville as *Man Into Space* (New York, 1957).

and National Aeronautics and Space Administration, after long study, jointly awarded $1,000,000 to the Goddard estate for the use of his patents.

In the course of his pioneering work, Dr. Goddard:

- Was the first to develop a rocket motor using liquid propellants (liquid oxygen and gasoline) (1920-1925).
- Was first to design, construct, and launch successfully a liquid-fuel rocket (March 16, 1926, at Auburn, Mass.).
- First developed gyro-stabilization apparatus for rockets (1932).
- First used deflector vanes in the blast of the rocket motor as a method of stabilizing and guiding rockets (1932).
- Received the first U. S. patent on the idea of multi-stage rockets (1914).
- First explored mathematically the practicality of using rocket power to reach high altitudes and escape velocity (1912).
- Was first to publish in the U. S. a basic mathematical theory underlying rocket propulsion and rocket flight (1919).
- First proved experimentally that a rocket will provide thrust in a vacuum (1915).
- Developed and demonstrated the basic idea of the "bazooka" during World War I (November 9, 1918)—though his plans lay unused in the U. S. Army files until they were put to use in World War II.
- First developed self-cooling rocket motors, variable-thrust rocket motors, practical rocket landing devices, pumps suitable for liquid rocket fuels, and forecast jet-driven airplanes, rocket-borne mail and express, and travel in space.

Goddard began speculating about rockets as a means of reaching high altitudes as early as 1899, when he was a 17-year old schoolboy in Worcester, Mass. A notebook of his, dating back to October of that year, contains several entries about rockets for the exploration of the upper atmosphere and space. In 1907 he prepared and submitted for publication a manuscript suggesting that heat and radioactive materials could ultimately be used to propel rockets through interplanetary space. This precocious manuscript was forthrightly rejected by the *Scientific American, Popular Science Monthly*, and *Popular Astronomy*. In 1909 he began to speculate about using liquid hydrogen and liquid oxygen as rocket propellants. In that year he also hit on the scheme of using step-rockets—or rockets consisting of multiple stages—on which he later obtained a patent.

His actual experimental work began about 1914, when he was an instructor at Clark University, in Worcester, Massachusetts. His first tests were made with various types of ship rockets and with larger solid-fuel rockets constructed by himself. These were followed during the first World War by experiments on the grounds of the Mount Wilson Observatory in California. Sponsored by the Smithsonian Institution and the U. S. Signal Corps, the purpose of these war-time tests was to develop rockets useful in warfare, and they resulted in successful prototypes of the modern bazooka and solid-propellant bombardment and anti-aircraft rockets.

From the point of view of space flight, the most productive period of Goddard's life began about 1925, when he first commenced serious work on the actual design of liquid propellant rockets, culminating in the world's first flight of a liquid fuel rocket, on a farm near Auburn, Mass., on March 16, 1926.

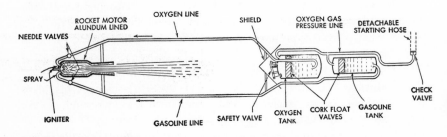

Fig. 1   Cross section of Goddard's historic 1926 liquid-fuel rocket. This drawing was made by Dr. Goddard for inclusion in G. Edward Pendray's *Coming Age of Rocket Power* (New York: Harpers, 1945, p. 98). Reprinted by kind permission of Dr. Pendray.

Other liquid fuel rocket shots followed, including a rather spectacular one on July 17, 1929. In this one he placed history's first rocket-borne instrument payload—an aneroid barometer, a thermometer, and a camera focussed on both instruments to record their readings. The rocket fired only 18½ seconds, rose about 90 feet, and flew a horizontal distance of 171 feet—but was almost a "shot heard 'round the world," for it made so much noise the neighbors telephoned for ambulances, believing an airplane had crashed. The resulting publicity caused Goddard to be called to the office of the Massachusetts Fire Marshal, and he was thereafter enjoined from making further tests in that state.

But the nationwide publicity which had caused such harm also opened new doors. Col. Charles Lindbergh, then at the height of his fame following his solo Paris flight, saw the "Moon Rocket Man" news stories, discussed the experiments with Goddard, and suggested to members of the famous Guggenheim family that these researches were worth supporting. The result, in 1929, was a grant from Daniel Guggenheim, and later a series of grants from The Daniel and Florence Guggenheim Foundation, of which Harry F. Guggenheim, son of Daniel Guggenheim and himself a pioneer naval aviator, is president. These grants enabled Goddard, aided by a small team of assistants, to set up a more ambitious experimental program at a site near Roswell, New Mexico.

In the succeeding 11 years, from 1930 until October 1941, Goddard brought his liquid rockets to a high degree of development. They contained virtually all of the devices later to appear on the larger German V-2 rockets. In one form or another, Goddard tried practically every one of the ideas that have since been developed in rockets and guided missiles, including gyrocontrols, clustered engines, research instrumentation, turbine-driven propellant pumps, gimbal-mounted tail sections for steering, automatic firing and releasing devices, and numerous other schemes.

In his theoretical writing he also forecast, speculated upon, and drew up preliminary plans for the application of atomic power to rocket flight, the use of ion propulsion, solar energy, and many other advanced rocket and space flight ideas, some of which are still far in the future.

The culmination of Goddard's work in New Mexico was a rocket that made a successful shot some 9,000 feet high. In 1941, he volunteered his talents for a second time to the Armed Services; almost until the time of his death in 1945 he worked at Annapolis, Md., for the Navy and Army on liquid propellant jet-assisted takeoff for aircraft and variable thrust liquid rocket motors.

The Work of the American Rocket Society

Goddard's lifework was already well launched by the time the rest of us in the United States—and for that matter in Germany and Russia—got into the act. The burst of publicity in the early 1920's that followed publication of Goddard's Smithsonian paper, *A Method of Reaching Extreme Altitudes*, started a sort of psychological chain reaction all over the world. Many a young man with an inventive or romantic turn of mind was set to dreaming by Goddard's ideas and the speculation that filled the press in the wake of his accomplishments.

The American Rocket Society—at first called the American Interplanetary Society—was born in that wave of Goddard-engendered enthusiasm; but the beginnings of its experimental program did not stem directly from Goddard's work. When Goddard in his desert fastness in New Mexico proved uncommunicative, those of us who wanted to do our part in launching the space age turned to what appeared the next best source of light: the *Verein für Raumschiffahrt*—the German Interplanetary Society—in Berlin. Following a visit to Berlin in the spring of 1931, during which we saw a proving-stand test of a very small liquid motor, Mrs. Pendray and I helped organize the Experimental Committee of the Society.

The Society's first rocket was designed by H. F. Pierce and myself, generally following the ideas of the Germans. Known as ARS Rocket No. 1, the rocket had two tubular propellant tanks, mounted on either side of a small cast aluminum motor, immersed in a container of water to serve as coolant. A static test at Stockton, New Jersey, on November 12, 1932, developed sufficient lift for a flight, but the rocket was very fragile and was damaged during handling following the test.

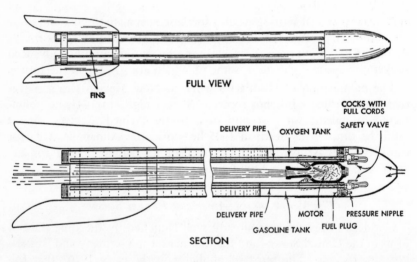

Fig. 2 Design of American Rocket Society's Rocket No. 2. Reprinted by permission of Dr. Pendray (*Coming Age of Rocket Power*, New York: Harpers, 1945, p. 124)

It was then completely rebuilt by Bernard Smith and became the Society's second rocket, unimaginatively known as ARS Rocket No. 2. A flight test took place at Marine Park, Staten Island, on May 14, 1933. It rose about 250 feet, at which point the liquid oxygen tank burst, terminating the flight. However, for the time and state of the art, it seemed to us a wildly successful project.

The Society's third rocket was a strange device, designed jointly by Bernard Smith and myself. ARS Rocket No. 3's propellants were contained in two concentric cylindrical tanks, one inside the other, with the liquid oxygen tank outside. The motor was located near the ogival head of the rocket, with a long nozzle running from one end of the rocket to the other; the tail was terminated by a cylindrical thrust augmenter, into which the nozzle exhausted.

This rocket turned out to have one major draw-back: it could not readily be fueled. The oxygen tank had so much internal surface of warm metal that the liquid simply evaporated faster than it could be forced in by the crude means at our disposal. Had the rocket been larger, so as to increase the ratio of tank volume to surface, it would have been a practical and successful design.

Firing this rocket was abandoned after several attempts, but it did yeoman service just the same. It looked more like a rocket should look than any we made either before or afterward, and it was therefore in much demand at exhibits, including the New York World's Fair of 1939. On one journey to an exhibit, in the early 1940's, it was lost, and has never been heard of since. Possibly it is in orbit.

The most triumphant ARS liquid rocket was No. 4, designed and built primarily by John Shesta. Like all the other ARS rockets, it had its motor mounted at the forward end. The motor of ARS No. 4, however, had four nozzles slanting downward and slightly outward to project the flame free of the cylindrical fuel tanks below, which were arranged in tandem. Ahead of the motor was a parachute folded into a cylindrical container.

This rocket was static tested several times at Marine Park, Staten Island, and finally was launched there on September 9, 1932. It was a beautiful flight. The rocket rose 382 feet and traveled a distance of 1,585 feet, the altitude and distance being measured by theodolite.

Calculations indicated that at one point the speed may have exceeded that of sound. The parachute unfortunately did not open, and the rocket struck the surface of New York Bay off Staten Island at full speed. It was not too badly damaged, however, and the propellant tanks were later used in the first ARS proving stand.

Making and testing these early rockets had convinced the members of the Experimental Committee by the fall of 1934 that building rockets without first developing reliable components was unprofitable business. There followed a long series of static tests of liquid motors of many kinds, sizes, designs, and materials. These tests culminated in the development of what may have been the world's first successful regenerative motor. It was devised by James Wyld, one of the members of the Experimental Committee. A regenerative liquid motor is one in which incoming liquid propellants are used to cool the motor—thus permitting it to be operated at temperatures above the melting point of the materials of which it is made.

The new type of motor was first tested at New Rochelle, New York, on December 10, 1938, and was subsequently tested a number of times without a single burnout. On the basis of this motor design, four members of the Experimental Committee—Lovell Lawrence, John Shesta, James Wyld and H. F. Pierce—formed Reaction Motors, Inc. in 1942.

During this same period of static testing, a number of individual theorists, experimenters, and inventors were also carrying on developments and testing—some quite independently, and some in conjunction with the ARS, which had made its testing facilities available to all Society members.

One independent development was the effort by F. W. Kessler, Willy Ley, and Nathan Carver to send mail across the New York-New Jersey state line at Greenwood Lake by means of a small glider powered by a liquid rocket motor. On the second test, February 23, 1936, one glider travelled about 1,000 feet over the ice-bound lake, successfully satisfying the requirements for an interstate mail flight. The motors used on these planes were developed by Nathan Carver.

In the following year, on May 9, 1937, H. F. Pierce independently launched a liquid rocket to about 250 feet altitude at Old Ferris Point, in the Bronx, New York. A tubular motor designed and built by Pierce was also tested on the ARS proving stand at New Rochelle, New York, on October 22, 1938. On December 10 of the same year, at New Rochelle, a series of liquid motors designed by ARS members were ground tested—including one designed and built by Robert Truax, later to become an important figure in Navy rocket development. This early Truax motor developed a thrust of 20 pounds before burning through the thrust chamber.

The long series of liquid rocket motor tests with the ARS proving stand continued, in various localities, until September 1941. In the latter year there were three significant series of the tests at Midvale, New Jersey; motors of Piercewiez and Carver, and of Wyld on June 8; motors of Africano, Youngquist, and Wyld on June 22; and three runs of the Wyld regenerative motor on August 11.

Meanwhile, the society had also been flight testing small solid fuel rockets, principally to study dynamic stability and aerodynamic effects of various forms of rocket bodies. Two such series of solid propellant tests were held—one at Pawling, New York, on September 12, 1937, and another two years later at Mountainville, New Jersey, on September 10, 1939.

In Retrospect

Since, as history would have it, the Germans were the first to develop really large, practical liquid rockets, it may be asked what this pre-war American work really accomplished, if anything. My own feeling is that it was the invaluable and necessary background to all that has happened since.

The work of Dr. Goddard, of course, underlies all modern developments in rocketry and space flight. And the efforts of the ARS Experimental Committee and independent experimenters served to develop a vital body of knowledge about what will and will not work in this new field of technology.

These efforts also brought forth a group of men with experience and know-how who were ready and willing to take leadership positions in the modern rocket and missile age. And perhaps equally important, the early rocket experiments helped to promote an ever-mounting pitch of interest and enthusiasm, and stirred large portions of the human race to desire the eventual conquest of space—thus generating the broad public support which for any great and costly new project is a vital necessity for success in a democratic society.

SELECT REFERENCES ON THE WORK OF
ROBERT H. GODDARD

Emme, Eugene M., "Yesterday's Dream . . . Today's Reality," *The Airpower Historian* (October 1960). Brief biography of Goddard with 19 bibliographical references.

Goddard, Robert H., *A Method of Reaching Extreme Altitudes* and *Liquid Propellant Rocket Development*, originally published by the Smithsonian Institution in 1919 and 1936; republished by the American Rocket Society in one volume entitled *Rockets* in 1945, with a new Foreword by Dr. Goddard and G. Edward Pendray (N. Y., Prentice-Hall, 1961).

Lehman, Milton, *This High Man, The Life of Robert H. Goddard* (N. Y.: Farrar, Straus, & Cudahy, 1963).

Pendray, G. Edward, "Rocketry's Number One Man" *Astronautics*, No. 37 (American Rocket Society, July 1937).

Pendray, G. Edward, *The Coming Age of Rocket Power*, Chap. VII, "The Persistent Man" (N. Y.: Harper & Brothers, 1945).

Rosenthal, Alfred, *The Early Years of the Goddard Space Flight Center*, Chap. I, "From Robert H. Goddard to the International Geophysical Year," (Greenbelt, Md.: NASA GHM-1, 1964).

Thomas, Shirley, *Men of Space*, Volume I, "Robert H. Goddard, Father of Modern Rocketry" (Philadelphia: Chilton Company, 1960).

Williams, Beryl and Epstein, Samuel, *The Rocket Pioneers*, Chap. 5 "Robert Hutchings Goddard, Father of American Rocketry." (N. Y.: Julien Messner, 1955).

SELECT REFERENCES ON THE AMERICAN ROCKET SOCIETY

Astronautics, Publication of the American Interplanetary Society, Nos. 26 (May 1933), 27 (October 1933), 28 (March 1934).

Astronautics, Publication of The American Rocket Society, Nos. 29 (September 1934), 30 (October-November 1934), 31 (June 1935), 32 (October 1935) 33 (March 1936), 34 (June 1936), 35 (October 1936), 36 (March 1937) 37 (July 1937), 38 (October 1937).

Pendray, G. Edward, *The Coming Age of Rocket Power*, Chap. IX (N. Y.: Harper & Brothers, 1945).

Pendray, G. Edward, "The First Quarter Century of the American Rocket Society" 25th Anniversary Issue, *Jet Propulsion*, Journal of the American Rocket Society (November, 1955).

Pendray, G. Edward, "32 Years of A. R. S. History," *Astronautics and Aerospace Engineering*, Vol. I (Feb. 1963), pp. 124-28.

Williams, Beryl, and Epstein, Samuel, *The Rocket Pioneers*, Chap. 8, "The American Rocket Society" (N. Y.: Julian Messner, 1955).

The German V-2

WALTER R. DORNBERGER *

THE DESIGN FEATURES and performance data of the V-2, one of the outstanding innovations of the last war, are well known and have been described extensively in many books and articles.[1] Less well known is the inside story of this weapon—how the Germans came to build it, what inspired them, how they succeeded, and especially why this weapon, in spite of all efforts, failed to become what its creators intended.

In the fall of 1929, the Research and Development Department of the German Army Board of Ordnance, under its chief, Colonel Professor Dr. Karl Becker, began to investigate jet propulsion as a possible means to propel an explosive carrier.[2] They uncovered more fiction than fact, no exact data from which they could come to any conclusion. What they found was technically unconquered land hidden in a foggy, sometimes stormy, atmosphere.

* Dr. Dornberger was chief of the German Army Board of Ordnance rocket development group from its beginning in 1931. In 1937 this group established the Experimental Test Station at Peenemuende and developed a series of test rockets culminating in the A4, later known as the V-2. After the war, he came to the United States and has served as a technical consultant to government and industry. He is now Vice President and Chief Scientist for Textron's Bell Aerosystems, Buffalo, N. Y.

This paper was presented at the program on "The History of Rocket Technology" at the meeting of the Society for the History of Technology cosponsored by Section L (History and Philosophy of Science) and Section M (Engineering) of the American Association for the Advancement of Science on December 28, 1962, in Philadelphia.

[1] See Walter Dornberger, *V-2* (New York, 1954); W. J. Craven and J. L. Cate, eds., *The Army Air Forces in World War II*, Vol. III (Chicago, 1951), pp. 84-85, 525-46; British Ministry of Supply, *Report on Operation "Backfire"* (London, War Office SPOG/500/12, January 1946); U. S. War Department, *Handbook on Guided Missiles of Germany and Japan* (Washington, February 1, 1946); L. E. Simon, *German Research in World War II* (New York, 1947); U. S. Army Air Forces, *The Story of Peenemuende—Interviews on German Rocket Research* (Washington, 1945); J. M. J. Kooy and J. W. H. Uytenbogaart, *Ballistics of the Future* (New York, 1948); and W. G. A. Perring, "A Critical Review of German Long Range Rocket Development," *Journal of the Royal Aeronautical Society* (July 1946).

[2] Alfred R. Weyl, *Guided Missiles* (London, 1949).

On the other hand, the time was ripe. Since the early 1920's, with the development of inexpensive, mass-produced light metals, highly efficient oxidizers which could be handled, and reliably accurate electronic equipment, three fundamentals were available for the revival of the ancient art of rocketry.

The history of technology proves that when the time is ripe, people are thinking about or working on the same problems in almost all civilized countries. So we see in 1930, private groups, inventors, and engineers in many countries were working on rocket propulsion, even designing and fusing first samples of liquid-fuel rockets. Experimenting in the United States was Professor Robert H. Goddard, in Romania Professor Hermann Oberth, in Russia Professor Konstantin E. Ziolkovsky, in Germany Max Valier, Engineer Johannes Winkler, Rudolf Nebel, and others.

One thing was common to all of them—their funds were extremely limited. In part, they had excellent ideas, imagination, and even skill, but they failed to perceive the development costs and the amount of hard work required before attaining convincing results. As late as 1941, Professor Oberth, the outstanding rocket theorist, who had no knowledge of the German efforts in this direction, suggested a 200-mile range single-stage rocket for whose development he asked $10,000. These men lacked one thing—none had a financially strong sponsor. Eccentric inventors with new ideas usually do not get such sponsors.

Role of the German Army

Why, then, did the German Army become a sponsor of rocket development? The answer is to be found in another question: Why should it have been different with the rocket than with atomic energy, with the airplane, or with most other revolutionary technical inventions? The big boom in aircraft development began from the moment the armed forces all over the world became interested in it, not as a means of transportation for peaceful purposes, but as a weapon carrier. The rocket, too, had to find its way into modern technology by its first application as a carrier of explosives. Private industry or government would not have spent hundreds and hundreds of millions of dollars for a new technical idea which, in the foreseeable future, would not produce any profit. The Germans were looking for a new superior weapon system which was not prohibited to them by the Treaty of Versailles.

It remains to be explained why the German Army later became its own contractor in the rocket field, doing the research and development work in a military installation without letting big private industry in on this new business. Up to 1930, all development divisions of the German Army carried on their developmental work, as in the United States, with the assistance of competent industries. Only for the development of solid and liquid-fuel rockets did the Army set up its own engineering staff and its own workshops and facilities. There were two reasons: (1) no competent industry was interested; and (2) secrecy. If the German military wanted a truly secret weapon, they had to develop it within military facilities where strict security regulations could be enforced.

Their obvious success was proof of the correctness of their thinking at that time. Hardly anyone in the world, not even most of the top officials of the Third Reich, knew before the spring of 1943 that such a development was under way at the Army Experimental Station at Peenemuende. Yet, by 1945 the Germans had a rocket lead of approximately ten years.

But in the early 1930's there was no such thing as Peenemuende, only confusion. On the one hand, theorists and university professors quarreled about the sixth decimal behind the comma in the calculation of a flight path to Mars and Venus. On the other, a branch chief in the Board of Ordnance made a written report to his supervisors in 1931 that a liquid fuel rocket could never take off from the ground on its own. He came to this conclusion—which almost killed the development of liquid propulsion for rockets—from early test results. The ballistics branch of the Army's Board of Ordnance at that time experimented with a combustion chamber which produced 60 lbs. thrust. But the weight of the power plant package with its tanks was 400 lbs., and such a device presumably could never take off.

Rocket development in Germany owed its later progress to the initiative and foresight of the chief of the development department of the Army Board of Ordnance, Major General Karl Becker, at that time one of the outstanding ballisticians of the world. (In the spring of 1940, he committed suicide after a quarrel with Hitler). General Becker established in 1930 the first goal in the field of modern military rockets: to make a saturation weapon out of solid rockets and to find out what could be done with a first prototype of a liquid-fuel rocket.

When the German military realized they could not get industry to do the development job for them, nor induce different groups of inventors to concentrate on hard study and work and forget about publicity stunts, the Board of Ordnance was forced to start initial work on a small scale in a corner of Kummersdorf, an Army proving ground near Berlin.

At that time, four men formed the nucleus of an enterprise which

later, in 1943, employed almost 17,000 men in Peenemuende alone:
a 19-year old student, later Chief Engineer at Peenemuende, Wernher
von Braun, now NASA's director of booster development at the
Marshall Space Flight Center in Huntsville, Alabama; a young technician with some experience in liquid-fuel rocket powerplants and
especially in the handling of liquid oxygen, later chief designer at
Peenemuende, Walter Riedel, now in England; a highly skilled fore-
man, later chief of the experimental shop in Peenemuende, Heinrich
Grunow; and myself, at that time Captain in the German Board of
Ordnance and assistant in the ballistics branch.

The first rocket static test stand was built at this proving ground
in the fall of 1932; it was a test stand for a maximum thrust of 3000 lbs.
only. It was in this test stand that the first hot run with a 600 lb.
combustion chamber was tried the day before Christmas 1932. This
attempt ended in a big explosion, and it took three months to repair
the facility.

How did it happen? We weren't so wise at that time as we are now.
We tried to ignite the liquid propellants, oxygen and alcohol, gorging
out of the nozzle by a torch on a long stick, held near the nozzle
mouth. The fuel ignited all right, but the static test stand was completely destroyed.

It would be foolish to think that at that time the Germans had any
definite idea about what would later evolve from their work. Yes, the
initial, small group dreamed about long-range rockets and space ships.
But they did not know and they did not care what would happen
later. They just started with a power plant. From 1932 until 1945, they
never received any specific written requirement of any kind for a
weapon system from their military superiors or anybody else. Later
on, this group had to make up their own minds how a military rocket
should perform. I can assure you, if we had known at that time, what
amount of work, what trouble, what desperation—but happiness too—
was hidden in the lap of the future, we would have stopped our work
immediately. We approached the rising problems with the courage of
the innocent and the dumb. A step in any direction was a step on
virgin soil. As we progressed we enjoyed our work more and more.
Everyone became enthusiastic. There was no obstacle which we would
not try to overcome. We learned to know the feelings of great inventors who see their dream finally take shape and come true.

In this connection, I would like to correct an error which you find
in a number of stories about the V-2, namely that the V-2 was Hitler's
devilish idea, designed to conquer the world. Up to 1943 Hitler had
absolutely nothing to do with the rocket program. In September 1944,

he named the first operational rocket: "Vengeance Weapon 2"
(V-2). *We* called the rocket the A4. The A4 was the first weapon
version of a long line of experimental rockets, which were developed
by my division in the Army Board of Ordnance. Hitler never saw
the A4 except in movies, nor had he ever been in Peenemuende. He
simply was not interested. We could not understand it, because he was
very much interested in the technical details of all other weapons. He
had a phenomenal memory for all types of guns and for any kind of
weapon; he knew their performance data, weight, and number better
than any expert, but he was not interested in our work. My only
explanation is that he put great store in his intuitions and dreams. Since
he had dreamed that such a weapon would never be fired against
England, he had made up his mind that it was unwise to put effort and
money into such a project.

Besides struggling with the technical complexity of this weapon,
we therefore, until 1943, had also to struggle against this dream of the
Fuehrer. Not until July 1943, when we finally convinced him with
facts, did he see any usefulness in our rockets, and then not as a weapon
but as a war-preventive means. "Why didn't I believe in the success
of your work?" Hitler asked me. "If we had had this weapon in
1939, we never would have had this war. Now and in the future,
Europe and the world are too small for a war. With such weapons
available war will become unbearable for the human race."

Some hours later, he told me, "I have to apologize only to two
people in my life. One is Field Marshal von Brauchitsch. I did not
listen to him when he pointed out over and over again the importance
of your development. And the second is you. I did not believe in any
success for your work."

Evolution of the V-2

Now, I would like to describe how the A4 concept was actually
conceived. In the Board of Ordnance rocket development started in
1930, before Hitler came to power. At that time it was very difficult
to obtain money and facilities. It was a constant struggle, and only
through the support of General Becker, who allocated money from
other divisions, could work continue. As this brainchild of Becker's
grew rapidly, requiring more and more money, new ways to raise
funds had to be found. Becker told me in January 1936, "If you want
more money, you have to prove that your rocket is of military value."

Up to that time only a powerplant had been developed, and a small
rocket in two versions had been assembled, the A1, which shortly
afterwards was modified into the A2. The latter was a sounding rocket,

which was first launched in December 1934 to an altitude of 1½ miles. A new project, the A3, was another experimental rocket which, it was hoped, would break the sonic barrier.

We knew from the beginning that if we really wanted to develop big operational rockets we would have to have our own research and development center; it must be large and self-sufficient, with all laboratories, wind tunnel, work shops, and test facilities at a remote spot, far away from any large city, near the seashore, so we could test-fire over the sea. By December 1935, we found such a place near Peenemuende, a very small fishing village on a large island in the Baltic Sea. Planning such a station, we had to fix the requirements for big test stands. Now we had to think about what we really wanted to put into operation. We proposed liquid-fuel propelled rockets for use as jato's (jet assisted take off rockets for aircraft), rocket powerplants for airplanes, and powerplants for heavy shells with short range, but the big rocket was only a somewhat hazy dream.

One day, in March 1936, I sat with von Braun and Riedel in our small office on the proving ground near Berlin, talking about the size of the planned test facilities at Peenemuende. After listening for an hour to their fumbling around, I planted my fist on the table and told them what I wanted and how this rocket should look.

I am an old long-range artillerist. And, the most famous gun until 1936 was the Parisian gun, dating from the end of the first World War. This gun fired 22 lbs. of explosives over a range of 78 miles, but it was too heavy in the firing position and was terribly inaccurate. This weight in the firing position, necessary for long-range guns, had to be eliminated by using a single-stage rocket to be launched vertically and to be programmed later on into an elevation angle of 45°. This rocket should carry 100 times the weight of the explosives in the shell of the Parisian gun and have a range twice that of the gun, or 156 miles. The accuracy of the rocket should be three tenths of one per cent of the range, compared with four to five per cent of conventional guns. This rocket should be small enough to be shipped in one piece on normal roads, even through small villages, without jamming traffic, or on one single railroad car, through all European railroad tunnels. Thus, the over-the-fins diameter of not more than nine feet and the overall length of not more than 42 feet was established. It was quickly calculated that a burn-out speed of 3,600 miles per hour could do the job. Finally, after years of jumping in all directions, a mission for a large rocket was found.

During the next few days, thrust, combustion time, and mass ratio were calculated. Much thought was given to the overall configuration, to guidance and control, and to structural problems. With these calculations and considerations, troubles began. There was no solution to all our problems. We had violated one of the fundamental laws of realistic engineering: " Don't project your thinking too far into the future." What was needed was 55,000 lbs. thrust for 65 seconds, and the biggest combustion chamber at that time had a thrust of only 3,300 lbs. A kind of radio control had to be developed which would allow cutting off the thrust at the right moment with an accuracy of 1/1000th of the velocity. We did not know at that time what an accelerometer looked like nor did we have the faintest idea about an integrating accelerometer. There were thousands of major problems for which there was no answer at that time.

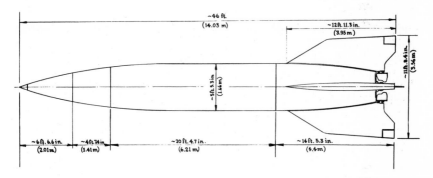

Fig. 3   Cross section of German A-4 rocket (V-2). Provided by Dr. Dornberger.

In addition, I should like to mention one more problem for whose solution we had to break through conventional scientific thinking. At that time it was allegedly a proved fact that an aerodynamically-controlled body could not fly stably at supersonic speed, yet a Mach 4.5 fin-stabilized body was anticipated. [Mach number, after Austrian Ernst Mach (1838-1916), expresses speed of a body with respect to the surrounding air relative to the speed of sound. Hence, Mach 4.5 is a speed four and one-half times the speed of sound (Ed.)].

The question may be asked: who is the actual inventor of the V-2? There is no single inventor who had a brilliant brainstorm leading to the V-2. Invention and development of modern, complicated machines such as guided missiles, which comprise in their design and performance all branches of science and technology, bring into being a new type of collective inventor, the team. Modern invention is hard, scientific, and technical work by a whole group of intelligent, dedicated people. It is a matter of progressing step by step, examining the testing in different institutes and facilities, weighing the feasible against the hoped-for in many proposals. Last, but not least, it is the successful perseverance of all workers, of their unshakable faith, of sufficient means, of luck, and of one single, hard will to fulfill the task.

There were at least a dozen outstanding people working at that time in Peenemuende, each an expert in his special field. Without a single one of them, modern rocketry would certainly have been delayed for decades. Therefore, if an inventor has to be named, I should call him: The Peenemuende Team.

Rocket propulsion is not an invention of modern times. It can be found in nature. Human beings used this type of propulsion for hundreds of years. When Sir Isaac Newton fixed his third law of motion, propulsion by reaction had been theoretically proved as one of the few possible drives for space craft. The basic principles were well known for centuries, but the time was not yet ripe to start the development of big rockets until the three fundamentals, as I mentioned before, were available. So, all over the world, between 1900 and 1920, rocketry was revived, this time on a big scale.

Professor Goddard was one of the first who realized the new possibilities. There were others, in different countries, even in Germany. Naturally, the German Board of Ordnance studied all available literature. But what was available? A few books, some articles in trade papers, and much wishful thinking. Technical facts and data could not be found. Almost 90 per cent of Goddard's patents were, we later learned, not available, and the Germans never saw them. This is particularly true regarding the use of jet rudders, film cooling, stabilization, and control.

It is my view that any group of interested and skilled people, no matter from what country in the world, which had to handle the same problems that we had to handle in Germany, under the same conditions, and which had to solve the pending task by conscientious, hard labor, necessarily would have come to the same solutions.

We had transferred our activities from this small proving ground near Berlin to Peenemuende on the Baltic Sea. In August 1936 we broke the ground and in May 1937 we moved in with approximately 300 men. Peenemuende was a self-sufficient research and development center for rockets. It remained such a center until January 1945, when its personnel and mobile facilities were transferred to Thuringia.

It was a research and development center in the good and bad sense of the word. The V-2 was never mass-produced in Peenemuende, only the first blocks of experimental rockets were manufactured. All in all, only 250 V-2's were built in Peenemuende.

During the preparations for mass-production, it was not easy to stop scientists from thinking and creative engineers from inventing, otherwise they would not be scientists and creative engineers. They always had new ideas and they felt production should wait until they were ready. A lot of technical knowledge, common sense, and experience must be expected from the chief of such an organization to guide these people, to determine the correct moment to freeze development, and to start production. This transition period, from development to mass-production, was by far the most trying in the entire program. There were no qualified people available for that, and the job had to be accomplished with people not qualified for this task. In fact, we had to release about 60,000 design changes from the moment we thought we were ready to freeze the design for mass production until the end of the war.[3]

Peenemuende

Peenemuende was set up in two main parts. In one part the Air Force established a large airfield and test facilities for the V-1, the glide bombs, jato's, Me-163, Me-262, and later for air-to-air and ground-ground remote controlled anti-aircraft guided missiles. The other part, by far the bigger one, was for the Army. Three hundred million marks were spent altogether by the Army to establish and operate these facilities. At its peak, the Army Experimental Station occupied an area of approximately 18 square miles and employed about 17,000 engineers and workers. The most significant factor in the successful development of the rockets proved to be that the research institutes, the engineering departments, the static test facilities, the oxygen generating plants, the work shops, and the launching sites were all at the same location and under one management. No time losses could occur.

Peenemuende, although a military installation, was set up like a private enterprise. And even with 4000 soldiers with engineering background, Peenemuende was organized like a private factory. The chiefs of all departments, divisions, and branches were civilians. With the exception of some accounting and administrative military personnel

[3] Wernher von Braun, "Survey of Development of Liquid Rockets in Germany and Their Future Prospects," *Journal of the British Interplanetary Society* (March 1951), pp. 78-80.

for the base, the only military office was that of the Military Commander, who was at the same time military and technical chief.

Why were those 4000 soldiers at the Research and Development Center? The reason was lack of support of the rocket program by the Armament Ministry and by Hitler himself. During the war, both were responsible for manpower and raw material distribution. Although the experimental station in Peenemuende was fully supported by our military chiefs right up to the Chief of the Army High Command, we could get no personnel and no materiel from the high offices of the Reich. In November 1939, Hitler dropped Peenemuende from the priority list. To continue work, I asked the Chief of the German Army High Command to release from his front-line troops several thousand soldiers with engineering background on whom the authorities of the Reich could not lay their hands. I got them.

Within the factory these soldiers were civilians and received the same pay as civilian employees. Outside the plant they were front-line troops on temporary duty inside Germany. These soldiers became the backbone of Peenemuende, and later on, when the A4 troop formations were established, they were the skilled nucleus of these troops, trained during long years at Peenemuende. By July 1943, when Hitler finally acknowledged Peenemuende, enough manpower was allocated to finish the development and to start mass production.

An article in *Fortune Magazine* about the RAND Corporation, stated that Hitler, by looking into his crystal ball and supporting the V-2 program, had essentially contributed to the defeat of Germany.[4] Had Germany put the same amount of effort into the manufacture of airplanes as it did into the V-2 program in order to achieve air supremacy in Europe, the article stated, the outcome of the war would have been different. Such a statement is very debatable and may lead to false conclusions. The historical facts are these:

(1) Hitler did not support Peenemuende at all, not until it was too late (July 1943). American aircraft production at that time could never have been rivaled by Germany's aircraft production. It was only a question of time before the Allies would have air supremacy over Europe and Africa.

(2) Up until the end of the war it was not aircraft production that caused the Germans trouble. Underground factories in aircraft production ran full blast up to the final days. What was lacking was fuel, not airplanes. Germany could not protect the oil fields under its control nor the factories producing synthetic

---

[4] *Fortune Magazine* (August/September 1946).

gasoline. They were destroyed by bombing from the air. Lack of foresight about the effectiveness of subsonic and supersonic anti-aircraft missiles and high-speed interceptors kept the development of these defensive weapons back for at least two to three years. Then it was too late. From 1938 until 1942 such weapons were proposed by the Army Experimental Station; even in 1942, when such a proposal was again presented, the Air Ministry replied that air defense would be handled by German fighters and anti-aircraft guns.[5]

(3) The V-2 was developed as an artillery weapon with high accuracy to surpass the range of long-range guns. In 1940 and 1941, when a German bomber could not fly over England more than three times before being shot down, the question of whether such a weapon as the V-2 could take over some tasks of the bombers became urgent. The advantage of a big long-range rocket, costing only about $38,000, became evident when compared with the $1,250,000 cost of a bomber, not to mention the loss of its crew.[6]

(4) What would have happened if, starting in 1942, the Germans had fired such long-range rockets against England in increasing number, with greater range and accuracy; or if the German High Command had followed our advice to develop and mass-produce anti-aircraft guided missiles in sufficient quantities so that they could go into action in 1942? It can be assumed that the outcome of the war would have been quite different; at least, there would not have been the devastating bombing of German cities, industries, and the synthetic gasoline generating plants. Germany would have kept air supremacy over Europe not with fighters and bombers but with anti-aircraft guided missiles and long-range missiles. Under their protection a new, powerful bomber fleet could have been built up in order to carry the war over enemy territory.

Until the late fall of 1939, it was expected that the big rocket could be developed without the help of universities and industry. After war broke out, time became all important. Many universities and institutes, which were threatened with closure, and industries were given a list of some hundred specific problems requiring urgent solutions. The response was overwhelming, and through the resulting cooperation large strides were made. By June 1942, the first rocket was launched,

---

[5] Sir Philip Joubert, *Rocket* (New York, 1958).

[6] Rudolf Lusar, *Die deutschen Waffen und Geheimwaffen des 2. Weltkrieges und ihre Weiterentwicklung* (Munich, 1962), p. 157; David A. Anderton, *Aviation Week* (September 24, 1957), p. 130.

although it proved to be a flop. By October 3, 1942, with the third missile on the launcher, all records in range, altitude, and speed had been broken. The feasibility of big liquid propelled rockets had been proved.

However, even after this success, not everything went well. We went from success to failure and back again. In July 1943 we had four explosions in a row on the launching pad. We learned the hard way that such an automatic weapon is as good, bad, or even worse than its smallest, most insignificant component part. Even the tiniest failure of a part resulted in total loss of the missile. And most of the time we had no idea what caused the failure. Telemetering equipment was not available before the end of 1943, and then only for a few important check points.   Therefore, we had to rely on long and thorough testing of all component parts and of the completely assembled missile under simulated flight conditions. It was also learned that reliability, based on simplicity and foolproofness, should be the first and principal law in the development of these new weapons.

Air Attacks on Peenemuende

Development was in its final phase, and the underground facilities for mass-production at Nordhausen in Thuringia were almost ready for operation, when the famous British air attack on Peenemuende occurred in the night of August 17-18, 1943. We knew it could be expected and we were prepared as best we could.

In the spring of 1943, the British Government received for the first time factual intelligence reports that rockets were being developed in Peenemuende.[7] The characteristic vapor trail in the air during the launchings could not be avoided and could be seen from Sweden. In addition, German propaganda boasted too much about all the coming wonder weapons. The Royal Air Force photographed the entire German Baltic seashore from Denmark to Poland, and in spite of all camouflage, the type of activity at Peenemuende was revealed by these pictures.

After two months training, about 600 British bombers began their attack on Peenemuende during a full moon. By radar they found the location, which was covered by thick, artificial fog. In one hour they dropped more than three million pounds of explosives and an enormous quantity of incendiary bombs. Only 47 bombers were shot down. The day before, the heavy anti-aircraft defense of Peenemuende had

[7] Terence Robertson, "The War Against Von Braun," *MacLean's* (Canada, March 1962), pp. 17-21; cf. Thomas F. Dixon, "Solving the V-2 Mystery in 1944," *Airpower Historian*, Vol. X (April 1963), pp. 46-49.

been withdrawn by an order from Hitler. Peenemuende lost 735 lives that night, 210 Germans, mostly women, girls, and children, and more than 500 foreign construction workers in a big camp between Peenemuende and Zinnowitz, the next town on the shore. At first the damage looked extensive, but soon it was discovered that the vital buildings—the electronic division, wind tunnel, oxygen generating plants, the 12 big static test stands, and big work shops for the test series—were not hit at all. Only wooden barracks and replaceable buildings in the plant were destroyed. The living quarters of our workers and employees were wiped out. But after four weeks of clean-up work, Peenemuende worked full-time again. Most of the vital equipment and production drawings had been moved to other places in the neighborhood before the attack.

The air attacks on Peenemuende continued with four day-time raids by the United States Air Force during 1944. They consisted mostly of pin-point attacks on unfinished static test facilities. No vital damage and no casualties were incurred. The completion of the work to be done on the long-range rocket could not be prevented, nor could the later incessant bombing of the launching sites at the front delay its entry into action. In the case of the V-2 offensive, the bombing neither delayed it nor reduced it to any extent.[8] However, it was decided to be careful, and during the following months no rockets were launched from Peenemuende at all. The impression of complete annihilation was created. By order from Headquarters, experimental firing was moved to Poland, where the rockets were fired over ground.

After the first successful launchings of a radio-guided ballistic missile in 1937, we had started looking seriously into the future. Up to that time it had not been proved that a ballistic rocket, built more or less according to well known design principles, could operate in space. For many years from that date, the advanced planning and preliminary design departments were busy with drafts and first lay-outs for intercontinental missiles (the A9/A10), winged missiles to increase the range (A4B), and bigger load-carrying rockets for the establishment of space stations, circling the globe. It was a difficult decision for me to stop this future planning in the fall of 1943, after the attack on Peenemuende. It was found out, by firing over land, how many problems still had to be solved before the V-2 could become operational.

Until the attack, we had fired only over water, along the shore where the tracking stations were established. The colored spots in the gray Baltic Sea, originating from dye-bags carried with the missile, were regarded as the presumable impact point of the complete missile.

[8] Sir Norman H. Bottomley, *Flight* (London, February 25, 1948), p. 226.

Test and Actual Firings

Now came the usual set-backs as the first production series were tested and experimental firings increased. Up to ten missiles a day were fired from three launching tables for training purposes and also to put the finishing touches to the missile. Ten per cent of these stopped short after launch, the thrust failed, and the missile dropped back on the launching site, causing much damage. Twenty per cent exploded in the ascending branch of the trajectory, and forty per cent exploded two to three miles above the ground after travelling over the entire course without any trouble. For a long time, no reason could be found for these failures. From the small amount of telemetering data available at that time, we could determine only what happened after the primary failure had occurred.

Finally, after many test firings, the reasons were found. Though minor, they had big consequences. First, a dropping relay caused by resonance vibrations; second, a loosening of fittings in the propellant pipe lines, also caused by vibration and a weak spot in the design and structure of the outer skin at the ogival forward section. When the missile re-entered the atmosphere, some fluttering of the skin, already weakened by air friction heat, which increased the temperature to approximately 600° centigrade, occurred. The skin burst, air rushed in, and the missile blew apart. However, this was found out only in the last months of the war. A rivetted cuff around this section improved the situation noticeably.

But before these problems were solved, the rocket was already deployed. On September 6, 1944, the first rocket was launched against a military camp near Paris. Two days later, the first V-2's were fired against London and targets in the southern part of England. Altogether, 3,745 of these flying laboratories were successfully launched between September 6, 1944 and March 27, 1945. Some 1,115 fell on England, 2,050 on targets on the Continent. For development, improvement, and training of the troops 580 rockets were used. Of all launched rockets, 74 per cent went within a target circle of 18 miles, from these 44 per cent within a six mile circle. In November, December, and January, an average of 140 missiles a week were launched. Twenty-five percent of all missiles were beam-riders during the powered part of the trajectory, resulting in a lateral dispersion in the impact area of only ± one mile.

During the deployment at the front, the losses in the firing positions by enemy action were nil. Some casualties occurred among the supply formations. Never was a single rocket intercepted by enemy action, nor did we discover any radio counter-measures. It may be that the well-known erroneous shot to Sweden in June 1944 led British intelligence in the wrong direction. That time an A4 was used as a carrier for the radio guidance equipment for the supersonic anti-aircraft rocket "Wasserfall." This missile went out of control and dropped on Swedish soil, thus prematurely revealing this secret weapon.[9]

The lack of casualties on the launching sites may be explained by the rocket's mobility. The missile could be launched from unprepared, hidden firing positions, out of a forest, out of a burned-out barn, or from side roads. The firing position could be changed after each shot. But it was not necessary. One beam-rider regiment stood in one firing position near Zwolle in Holland for four months without ever being attacked.

Besides technical trouble, there were plenty of other worries. The Peenemuende group were considered utopians and fantasts, even among the upper echelon of the Reich. But from the moment success was evident, their product was no longer considered the work of some crazy Army people, but the deed of the German intellect and belonged to the German people. Then the Ministry of Ammunition wanted to take over, big industrial concerns wanted the lead, party organizations and the SS claimed the rocket for their own personal benefits, or at least wanted to share in the rewards. This struggle worried us for years after the first successful launchings. Partly we lost, partly we won. But this situation was far from being helpful.

Hopes and Failures

It must be explained, also, why the V-2 failed to become what official German propaganda hoped and the Allies feared.

(1) This new rocket, from a military viewpoint, was intended as an important addition to the already available military arsenal to increase the range of the artillery and to provide some advantages which could never be obtained by heavy guns.

(2) This new weapon, with its 1,650 lbs. payload of explosives could only have the effect of a normal bomb of the same size. The German Board of Ordnance was completely aware of that. It was never intended to develop this weapon with an annihilating effect; there was no nuclear warhead development in Germany. The pretense of the German propaganda machine that the outcome of the war could be changed fundamentally by these so-called wonder weapons, accepted so readily by the Allies, put the German Board of Ordnance in a very difficult position. It also

---

[9] See Dixon, *loc. cit.*

aroused hopes in Germany which the creators of this modern rocket never intended. Anybody trained in weapon technology could see that this weapon was a new and outstanding weapon, as were so many others during the last war, and only a useful combination of all of them could turn events decisively.

(3) The deployment of this weapon occurred at least two years too late. The war in 1944 could not have been won by firing 900 V-2's per month as planned, on mainly two targets, not even with the combination of all so-called "vengeance weapons." Lack of foresight and knowledge of U. S. potentialities in aircraft production prevented the German leadership from giving early and sufficient support to this program in order to help win the war in Western Europe before the masses of the American Air Force could go into action. General Eisenhower wrote in his memoirs, *Crusade in Europe*, if the V-2 weapon would have gone into action six months earlier, the landing in Normandy would have been almost impossible.[10]

(4) The weapon was not fully developed when it was forced into action by a decision of Hitler:

(a) The high drift rate of the gyro axis, which could not be improved further at that point of the war, did not allow an accuracy of three tenths, of one per cent of the range, as had been specified in 1936. However, the dispersion of the A4 was much better than that of any other weapon built up to 1945, considering the range.

(b) The airbursts, which we still had when the A4 went into action, did not allow the use of highly sensitive fuses which could detonate the missile on the first slight contact with the ground. Instead, we had to use a very insensitive fuse which withstood the stresses of a possible airburst. Therefore, the result was mostly a big hole in the ground.

(c) The development of a proximity fuse, which could detonate the rocket 30 to 60 feet above ground, could never be completed in Germany so that it could be mass-produced.

Nevertheless, a new weapon system was used for the first time in history. In spite of its imperfection, this will always remain one of the outstanding technical achievements of modern times. By wrong timing and lack of support it came too late to play a decisive military role in the last war.

In Retrospect

When we forget for a moment what was expected from this technological newcomer in the weapon field on both sides, then this new

[10] Dwight D. Eisenhower, *Crusade in Europe* (Garden City, N. Y., 1952), p. 294.

weapon was the first operational sample of a new generation of weapon systems—ballistic long-range rockets—which, in their achieved perfection decades later, are bound to determine the future of mankind.

It is self-evident that in technical pursuits, the first idea put into practice can never be perfect—and can never mean the end of the work. Mistakes are made, difficulties are not completely overcome. Complicated early solutions are not replaced by simple and reliable ones. And above all, the new device does not make the impression of a perfect, rounded-off, and finished product. Criticism from hindsight comes easy at this stage. However, the first application of a big rocket power plant in a supersonic carrier, flying through free space, is now recognized in its pace-setting importance to the history of rocket technology.

Those looking at the V-2 rocket only as a weapon system should not forget that rocket propulsion proved for the first time its possible application for future space flight. For this future—the utilization of space for mankind—the Peenemuende crew worked as well. In March 1944, the director of engineering of Peenemuende, Professor von Braun, and two of his leading men were put in jail by the German Gestapo because they had thought and talked too much about space travel and not about the rocket as a weapon. Therefore, they allegedly committed sabotage. It was not easy to get them freed. They were released only by explaining to Hitler that everyone working on the big rocket was indispensable to the V-2 program and had become a space fanatic who looked at the V-2 only as a first step into the future of space travel.

Origins and First Decade of the Jet Propulsion Laboratory

FRANK J. MALINA*

THE GUGGENHEIM AERONAUTICAL LABORATORY (GALCIT) of the California Institute of Technology (Caltech) in the mid-1930's, a few years after its founding, was recognized as one of the world's centers of aeronautical instruction and research. It was my good fortune to become a GALCIT graduate student in 1934.[1] Under the leadership of Theodore von Kármán, GALCIT specialized in aerodynamics, fluid mechanics, and structures.[2] Von Kármán's staff included Clark B. Millikan, Ernest E. Sechler, and Arthur L. Klein, and a group of graduate students who later were to be found in leading aerospace posts in many parts of the world.[3] The outstanding contributions to rocket technology and the space sciences by the Jet Propulsion Laboratory (JPL) of Caltech during the past quarter of a century stem from the GALCIT tradition of utilizing fundamental conceptions, and of applying most recent advances in the various branches of science. Those of us who began a modest and very austere effort were guided by these principles from the inception of our work.

* Dr. Frank J. Malina was a co-founder of the Jet Propulsion Laboratory at the California Institute of Technology, of the Aerojet General Corporation, and of the International Academy of Astronautics. He is Chairman of the Academy's Lunar International Laboratory (LIL) Committee and a member of its Committee on the History of the Development of Rockets and Astronautics.

[1] At the outset of this historical account I desire to point out that since I played a role in the story it is unavoidable that there should be subjective overtones in the text. Because of the unusually close relationship between me and the late Theodore von Kármán, with whom I first studied and then worked intimately for over twenty-five years, it is not always possible to separate the contribution either of us often made to technical and organizational progress. Finally, there are undoubtedly aspects of the story of which I am unaware. For his suggestions, I am indebted to Martin Summerfield.

[2] H. L. Dryden, "The Contributions of Theodore von Kármán: A Review," Astronautics and Aerospace Engineering, Vol. I, No. 6 (July 1963), p. 12; and F. J. Malina, "Theodore von Kármán, 1881-1963," Revue Française d'Astronautique, No. 1963-4 (July-August 1963) p. 149, also Technology and Culture, Vol. V, No. 2 (Spring 1964), pp. 241-46.

[3] Guggenheim Aeronautical Laboratory—The First Twenty Five Years (Pasadena, California Institute of Technology, 1954).

In 1934 at GALCIT serious studies were getting under way on problems of high speed flight, and the limits of the propellor—engine propulsion system for aircraft were beginning to be clearly recognized. Furthermore, at Caltech, research in meteorology under Irving P. Krick, and on cosmic rays, posed problems of making measurements at high altitudes. Robert A. Millikan, then the head of Caltech, was a member of a committee appointed by the Daniel and Florence Guggenheim Foundation to advise on the support being given by the Foundation to Robert H. Goddard for the development of a high-altitude sounding rocket.

In 1935, I conducted experimental research with William W. Jenney on the characteristics of propellers for a masters' thesis. During these studies, my mind began turning more and more to the subject of rocket propulsion.

A considerable body of literature on rocket propulsion and its possible application to space flight already existed at this time, consisting mainly of contributions from Ziolkovsky, Goddard, Esnault-Pelterie and Oberth—the first generation of space-flight pioneers.[4] In scientific circles, this literature was generally regarded more in the nature of science fiction, primarily because the gap between the experimental demonstration of rocket-engine capabilities and the actual requirements of rocket propulsion for space flight was so fantastically great. This negative attitude extended to rocket propulsion itself, in spite of the fact that Goddard realistically faced the situation by deciding to apply this type of propulsion to a vehicle for carrying instruments to altitudes in excess of those that can be reached by balloons—an application for an engine of much more modest performance. It is true that Goddard's sounding rockets had reached an altitude of only some 7,500 feet by 1935.

Early in 1936, at one of the weekly GALCIT seminars, William Bollay (then a graduate assistant to von Kármán) gave a lecture on the possibilities of a rocket-powered airplane, based essentially on studies made by Eugen Sänger in Vienna. A Pasadena newspaper published an article on Bollay's seminar, which resulted in attracting to GALCIT two rocket enthusiasts—John W. Parsons and Edward S. Forman. Parsons was a self-trained chemist who, although he lacked the discipline of a formal training, had an uninhibited fruitful imagination.[5] Forman, a skilled mechanic, had been working with Parsons for some time constructing small black-powder rockets. They wished to

---

[4] Th. von Kármán and F. J. Malina "Los Comienzos de la Astronautica," *Ciencia y Tecnologia del Espacio*, Madrid, I. N. T. A. E. T., 1961, p. 7.
[5] Parsons was killed by an explosion at his private workshop in 1952.

test a liquid-propellant rocket motor, but found that they lacked adequate technical and financial resources for the task. They hoped to find help at Caltech.

The GALCIT Rocket-Research Project

After discussions with Bollay, Parsons, and Forman, I prepared in February 1936 a program of work whose objective was the design of a high-altitude sounding rocket propelled by either a solid- or a liquid-propellant rocket engine. In March, von Kármán agreed to my proposal that the subject of my doctorate thesis be on rocket propulsion and rocket-flight performance, and that Parsons and Forman could work with me, even though they were neither students nor on the professional staff at Caltech.[6]

The initial program we set for our GALCIT Rocket-Research Project consisted of two parts: (a) theoretical studies of the thermodynamical problems of the reaction principle, taking into account available literature, and of the flight performance of a sounding rocket; and (b) elementary experiments of liquid- and solid-propellant motors to determine the problems to be met in making static tests.[7]

For the experimental part of our program we lacked money and a suitable place to work. During the first year, the three of us scraped together a few tens of dollars to buy materials, and we selected for our tests the area of the Arroyo Seco back of Devil's Gate Dam on the western edge of Pasadena, California—a stone's throw from the present day Jet Propulsion Laboratory. I learned several years later from Clarence N. Hickman that he and Goddard had conducted smokeless-powder armament rocket experiments at this same location during World War I.

We began construction of an uncooled rocket motor similar in design to that previously tried by the American Rocket Society, and of a primitive transportable test stand. For propellants we chose gaseous oxygen and methyl alcohol.

In the spring of 1936, Apollo M. O. Smith, a GALCIT graduate student, joined our project, and I began with him a theoretical study of the flight performance of a sounding rocket.

In August, Goddard made a visit to Caltech. R. A. Millikan arranged for me to have a short discussion with him during which I told him of our hopes and plans. Goddard invited me to visit him at Roswell, New

---

[6] Excerpts from "Letters Written Home" by Frank J. Malina (unpublished collection).

[7] Frank J. Malina, "Rocketry in California," *Astronautics*, No. 41, July 1938, p. 3.

Mexico, the next month when I was going for a holiday to my parents' home in Texas.

Goddard and his wife received me cordially at Roswell. I was shown the machine shop where his rockets were built, the tower for launching the sounding rockets, and a static test stand for motors up to 2,000 lbs. thrust. I was not however shown any rocket models or rocket engines, or given any experimental results that had been obtained in static tests of his liquid oxygen-gasoline engines. Goddard

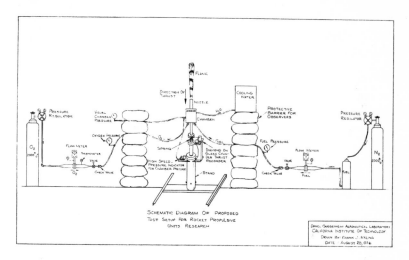

Fig. 4   Schematic Diagram of Proposed Setup for Rocket Propulsion Units Research by Frank J. Malina, August 28, 1936 (JPL photo)

stated that he was not ready to release details of his work. As I departed, he suggested that I should come and work with him at Roswell when I had finished my studies at Caltech.

Upon my return to Pasadena we completed preparations for our first firing of the gaseous oxygen-methyl alcohol motor. Several tests were made, the first on October 29, 1936, and the last in January 1937.

In March, Smith and I had completed our analysis of the flight performance of a sounding rocket.[8] The results of this study were so encouraging that our "Project" obtained from von Kármán the continued support of GALCIT in every way except that no funds could be found for us in the budget of the laboratory. We were authorized to conduct small-scale rocket-motor tests at the laboratory, and I was

[8] F. J. Malina and A. M. O. Smith, "Flight Analysis of a Sounding Rocket," *Jour. Aero. Sci.*, Vol. 5, 1938, p. 199.

asked to give a report on the results of our first year's work at the GALCIT seminar at the end of April.

The unexpected result of the seminar was the offer of the first financial support for our project. Weld Arnold, then an assistant in the Astrophysical Laboratory at Caltech, came to me and said that in return for his being permitted to work with our group he would make a contribution of $1,000 to the project. Also at this time the group gained the very keen mind of Hsue Shen Tsien, a graduate student from China, who was one of von Kármán's outstanding pupils. What has frequently been called the original GALCIT rocket-research group was now complete. It consisted of Tsien, Smith, Parsons, Forman, Arnold, and me. In June studies made by members of the group, including an unpublished paper by Bollay on "Performance of the Rocket Plane," were collected together into what the group called its "Bible."

One of the principal conclusions reached at this time was that on the basis of information in the *published* literature it was not possible to design a solid- or liquid-propellant rocket engine to given specifications. The published reports of Goddard, Sänger and other experimental investigators indicated, at most, that it was possible to construct successful liquid-propellant rocket engines. There were no systematic experimental results available giving design criteria for propellant injection, combustion-chamber volume, nozzle dimensions and motor cooling.

When von Kármán gave the group permission to make small scale experiments of rocket motors at GALCIT it was decided to mount a small motor utilizing methyl alcohol and nitrogen dioxide as the bob of a 50-foot pendulum, using the deflection of the pendulum to measure thrust. The pendulum was suspended from the third floor of the laboratory with the bob in the basement. Tests began in August. One of the first tests misfired with the result that a cloud of NO_2- alcohol mixture permeated most of the laboratory, and left behind a thin layer of rust on much of the equipment. We were told to move our apparatus outside the building at once. The group was now called the "suicide squad."

Although only a limited amount of useful information was obtained with this apparatus, it did represent the first, or one of the first, experiments in America with a rocket motor using a storable liquid oxidizer. On the basis of the experience with nitrogen dioxide, Parsons later proposed the use of red-fuming nitric acid as an oxidizer.

During this period Tsien and I had been making theoretical studies of the thermodynamic characteristics of a rocket motor.[9] To check the results, steps were taken to design and construct a test stand with a small rocket motor burning gaseous oxygen and ethylene. The exhaust nozzle and combustion-chamber lining were made of carbon. Experiments with the apparatus began in May 1938, and during the next two years many useful data on motor characteristics were obtained. Studies were also carried out by Parsons and Forman on a smokeless-powder rocket motor of the impulse type previously described by Goddard in his Smithsonian Institution report of 1919.

During the summer of 1938, Smith and Arnold left Caltech, and Tsien was able to devote less time to the work of the project. I struggled on with Parsons and Forman, little suspecting that in the next few months the project would become a full-fledged GALCIT activity supported financially by the Federal Government.[10]

An indication that our work was having some impact came from the aircraft industry. The Consolidated Aircraft Co. of San Diego, California, appears to have been the first American commercial aeronautical organization to recognize the potential importance of rocket assisted take-off. Its President, Ruben Fleet, turned to GALCIT for advice, which resulted in my being invited to San Diego to discuss the matter. I prepared a report giving encouraging prospects for this type of rocket-engine application.[11]

The possibility of arranging active collaboration with Goddard was a recurring subject at Caltech. In September 1938, Harry F. Guggen-

[9] F. J. Malina, "Characteristics of the Rocket Motor Unit based on the Theory of Perfect Gases," *Jour. Franklin Inst.*, Vol. 230, No. 4, 1940, p. 433.

[10] As part of the effort to increase the financial resources of our group, I entered the competition for the REP-Hirsch International Astronautics Prize which was administered by the Astronautics Committee of the Société Astronomique de France. The Prize was named for the French astronautical pioneer Robert Esnault-Pelterie (1881-1957) and the banker rocket-enthusiast of Paris, André Louis-Hirsch (1900-1962). In 1912, Esnault-Pelterie wrote a historically important paper on manned travel by rocket to the moon and to the planets. In order to present his paper before the French Physical Society he had to give it the neutral title "Considerations of the Results of the Indefinite Decrease in the Weight of Engines." After the lecture the Society would publish only a summary of the paper. In 1930 he published a book giving the results of his studies of the exploration of space by rocket. The book was entitled *L'Astronautique*. The word "*astronautics*" was coined in 1927 by the writer J. H. Rosny, Sr., a member of the Astronautics Committee. I did not learn until 1946 that I had been awarded the REP-Hirsch Prize in 1939. The outbreak of World War II had prevented the Committee from informing me of the award.

[11] F. J. Malina, "The Rocket Motor and Its Application as an Auxiliary to the Power Plants of Conventional Aircraft," GALCIT Rocket Research Project, Report No. 2 August 24, 1938 (Unpublished).

heim brought together Goddard with von Kármán and C. B. Millikan, in New York, to see if an arrangement might be made. The result of the meeting was negative for Goddard did not feel that he could accept von Kármán's condition of full disclosure of information on all aspects of a problem which was to be studied cooperatively.

In December 1938, after giving a lecture to the Caltech chapter of *Sigma XI* on the " Facts and Fancies of Rockets," I was informed by von Kármán, R. A. Millikan and Max Mason, that I was to go to Washington, D. C., to give expert information on rocket propulsion to the National Academy of Science (NAS) Committee on Army Air Corps Research of which R. A. Millikan and von Kármán were members. In May, von Kármán had obtained a first indication that the Army Air Corps was getting interested in rocket propulsion.[12] One of the subjects on which Gen. Henry H. Arnold, at that time Commanding General of the Army Air Corps, asked the Academy to give advice was the use of rockets for the assisted take-off of heavily loaded aircraft. I prepared a report on jet (rocket) propulsion, and presented it to the Academy committee on December 28.[13]

Air Corps Jet Propulsion Research—GALCIT Project No. 1

My report to the NAS committee evidently made a good impression, for in January 1939 the Academy decided to accept the offer of von Kármán to study with the GALCIT rocket research group the problem of assisting the take-off of aircraft on the basis of available information, and to prepare a proposal for a research program. A sum of $1,000 was provided for this work. The Academy also appointed von Kármán chairman for a sub-committee on Jet Propulsion of the committee on Air Corps Research.

It is interesting to note that at this time when Caltech obtained the first federal support for its rocket-research project, Jerome C. Hunsaker, of the Massachusetts Institute of Technology, volunteered to study the de-icing of windshields, which was then a serious aircraft problem. He told von Kármán, " You can have the Buck Rogers job." [14]

The remark made by Hunsaker reflected the general attitude which prevailed in engineering circles as regards rockets and rocket propulsion. The word " rocket " was of such bad repute that von Kármán

---

[12] War in Europe appeared inevitable.

[13] F. J. Malina " Report on Jet Propulsion for the National Academy of Science Committee on Air Corps Research," December 21, 1938 (Unpublished).

[14] Review by Th. von Kármán of C. M. Bolster's James Cabot Lecture on *Assisted Take-off of Aircraft*, in *Jour. Amer. Rocket Soc.*, No. 85 (June 1951), p. 92.

and I felt it advisable to drop the use of the word. It did not return to our vocabulary until several years later, by which time the word "jet" had become a part of the name of our laboratory and of the Aerojet Engineering Corporation.

Air Corps Jet Propulsion Research, GALCIT Project No. 1, came into being on July 1, 1939 when a contract for $10,000 was granted by the NAS to Caltech. Under the contract studies were to be made of a number of basic problems connected with the development of jet propulsion for application to the "super-performance" of aircraft. The term "super-performance" was defined to include: (a) shortening of the time and distance required for take-off; (b) temporary increase of rate of climb; and (c) temporary increase of level-flight speed. The contract also wisely authorized work to be done on both liquid– and solid–propellant rocket engines.[15]

Von Kármán, then 57 years of age, became actively committed to the development of rocket propulsion by taking over the direction of the project with Parsons, Forman, and me forming the nucleus of the staff. He brought to the work his vast experience of utilizing mathematics and fundamental physical principles for the solution of difficult engineering problems, and his rare skill in negotiation and organization.

Several acres of land for the experimental work of the project were leased by Caltech from the City of Pasadena on the west bank of the Arroyo Seco, where the present Jet Propulsion Laboratory is now located.[16]

In October I prepared a study of the application of rocket propulsion to a radio-controlled flying torpedo as a report of the GALCIT Rocket Research Project.[17] In a letter of 25 February 1958, Rear Admiral D. S. Fahrney informed me that he was preparing a history of "Radio Controlled Aircraft and Guided Missiles" for the Bureau of Aeronautics of the Navy. In a subsequent letter of March 27, 1958, he stated: "My earliest comments on your work concern the study on rocket propulsion you made in 1939 (GALCIT Rep. No. 3) and gave a copy to Commander R. F. (Bobby) Jones. Jones forwarded this to me as head of the guided missile project. It was based on your

[15] F. J. Malina, J. W. Parsons and E. S. Forman, "Final Report for 1939-40 of the Air Corps Jet Propulsion Research Project, GALCIT Project No. 1," Report No. 3, June 15, 1940 (Unpublished). The reader will be aware that technical literature written during wartime years remained unpublished.

[16] World War II began in Europe on September 1, 1939.

[17] F. J. Malina, "Report on Application of Rocket Propulsion to a Radio Controlled Flying Torpedo," GALCIT Rocket Research Project, Report No. 3, October 5, 1939 (Unpublished).

findings that we produced the first jet-propelled guided missile in this country, the GORGON, powered with the Naval Engineering Experiment Station liquid rocket."

In June 1940, the GALCIT Project was able to report to the Academy and the Army Air Corps a number of positive results obtained during the first year of the contract. I had accumulated considerable data on rocket-motor design utilizing the gaseous-propellant testing apparatus. The desire of the Air Corps for a storable liquid oxidizer to replace liquid oxygen, which at that time was not readily stored and transported, was met by Parsons who found that red-fuming nitric acid would serve satisfactorily. Preliminary experiments with long-duration solid-propellant rockets made by Parsons and Forman showed promise.

The group had confidence that a liquid propellant rocket engine could be constructed, for, Goddard and other investigators had demonstrated that it was possible to do so.[18] On the other hand, up to this time long-duration (10 seconds or more) solid-propellant engines had not been built anywhere, and there was great doubt among experts on explosives that it was physically possible to build them. Von Kármán, in the spring of 1940, after listening to both the opinion of the experts and the repeated explosions of Parsons' rockets on the test stand, one evening at his home wrote down four differential equations which he asked me to solve. He said to me: " Let us work out the implications of these equations; if they show that the process of a restricted burning-powder rocket is unstable, we will give up, but if they show that the process is stable, then we will tell Parsons to keep trying." [19] Parsons was told to keep trying, and some months later the first experimental Jet-Assisted Take-off (JATO) rockets, with a duration of about twelve seconds, were built. The present-day American large solid-propellant engines are direct descendants of these first primitive restricted-burning JATO rockets.

The Air Corps decided upon receiving the report, at the initiative of Benjamin Chidlaw (then major), to assume direct sponsorship of the GALCIT Project. The program for the next year called for continued fundamental studies of the design of solid- and liquid-propellant engines and for preparations to be begun for flight tests of a small

---

[18] F. J. Malina, " A Short History of Rocket Propulsion up to 1945," *Jet Propulsion Engines, High Speed Aerodynamics and Jet Propulsion*, Vol. XII, (Princeton Univ. Press, 1959), p. 3.

[19] Th. von Kármán and F. J. Malina " Characteristics of the Ideal Solid Propellant Rocket Motor," *Collected Works of Theodore von Kármán*, Vol. IV, (London, Butterworth Scientific Pub., 1956), p. 94.

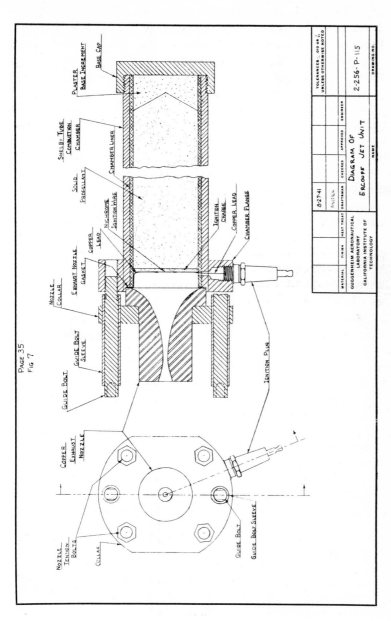

Fig. 5 Diagram of Ercoupe Jet Unit, August 27, 1941 (JPL photo)

aircraft equipped with JATO units. Close liaison was begun with the Air Material Command at Wright Field, Dayton, Ohio, which gave the GALCIT Project the designation Aircraft Laboratory Project MX121.

The facilities and equipment of the project were considerably expanded, and the staff was increased. In July 1940, Martin Summerfield joined the project to take over supervision of the development of a liquid-propellant rocket engine. The senior staff now consisted of von Kármán, Director; me as Chief Engineer; Summerfield, Head of Liquid Propellant Section; Parsons, Head of Solid Propellant Section, and Forman, Head of Machine Shop and Maintenance.

By the beginning of 1941 sufficient progress had been made in the development of the solid propellant JATO to permit plans to be made for flight tests. In January, C. B. Millikan and Homer J. Stewart made an extensive aerodynamic analysis of take-off and initial climb of aircraft as affected by auxiliary rocket propulsion. The Air Material Command selected the low-wing monoplane, known as the Ercoupe, for the tests, and designated Homer A. Boushey, Jr. (then a captain) as the test pilot.[20]

The first successful American rocket assisted take-off was accomplished with the Ercoupe aircraft at March Field, California, on August 12, 1941 with Boushey at the controls. The JATO units used contained a compressed solid propellant developed by Parsons (designated as GALCIT 27) and delivered a maximum thrust of 28 pounds for 12 seconds.[21]

The first successful American flight of an aircraft with rocket power alone was made by Boushey on August 23, 1941. The Ercoupe was equipped with 12 of the JATO units and an initial boost was given by towing the aircraft with an automobile. Over the nose of the Ercoupe, where the propeller had been, a safety poster was pasted. It read: "What about tomorrow if I meet with an accident today?"

The flight tests were a great satisfaction to all; however, the elation lasted but a short time. The JATO units with the GALCIT 27 propellant upon being exposed to accelerated storage tests were found to explode in almost every case. It was therefore necessary to continue the search for a propellant that would be suitable under service conditions. The search was finally rewarded when Parsons, together with

[20] "Research and Development at the Jet Propulsion Laboratory, GALCIT," May 17, 1946 (Unpublished).

[21] F. J. Malina and J. W. Parsons, "Results of Flight Tests of the Ercoupe Airplane with Auxiliary Jet Propulsion supplied by Solid Propellant Jet Units," Air Corps Jet Propulsion Research, GALCIT Project No. 1, Rep. JPL R-1-9, September 2, 1942 (Unpublished).

Mark M. Mills and Fred S. Miller, in June 1942, developed the asphalt-potassium perchlorate castable propellant GALCIT 53.[22] (In 1946 an important development in composite solid propellants was made at JPL by Charles E. Bartley when he replaced asphalt with a polysulfide material which became the basis of propellant manufacture by the Thiokol Chemical Corp.)

Early in 1942, the Navy upon the recommendation of Calvin M. Bolster (then commander) and of C. F. Fisher (then lieutenant) of the Bureau of Aeronautics, who had witnessed the Ercoupe tests, placed a contract with Caltech for the project to develop for experimental purposes a JATO unit delivering 200 pounds of thrust for eight seconds. The new plastic propellant GALCIT 53 was developed in time to be used in these units.[14]

Paralleling the work on the solid-propellant JATO unit, the development of a red-fuming nitric acid (RFNA)-gasoline engine was proceeding apace. In July 1941 a program of testing was initiated on an uncooled motor delivering 500 lbs. thrust. By September, except for one explosion, a successful series had been completed, justifying von Kármán to recommend to the Air Material Command that preparations be initiated for flight tests of a liquid-propellant JATO unit. It was decided to construct two units, each delivering 1000 lbs. thrust for 25 seconds, which would be mounted in the nacelle tail cones of the A-20A bi-motor Douglas bomber.

In October tests began on the 1000–lb. motor. Summerfield, Walter B. Powell, and Edward G. Crofut, who were given the task of designing and testing the JATO unit, encountered from the first experiments ignition difficulties and combustion throbbing which led to blowing up of the motor. For four months attempts were made without success to overcome the difficulties of igniting and burning the RFNA-gasoline propellant combination.[23]

During a visit in February 1942 to the rocket research group at the Naval Engineering Experiment Station at Annapolis, I discussed the combustion problem with Robert C. Truax (then lieutenant), the officer in charge of the group, and his chemical engineer, Ray C. Stiff (then ensign). Stiff had found in the literature that aniline had the property of igniting spontaneously with nitric acid, and wondered if it could be used as an additive to gasoline to overcome motor throbbing. During the overnight train trip from Annapolis to Dayton, Ohio, it occurred to me to try replacing gasoline with aniline as a fuel. I sent

[22] Mills was killed in a helicopter crash at Eniwetok Island in 1958.
[23] On December 7, 1941, the United States entered World War II.

a telegram immediately to Summerfield with the suggestion. When I returned to Pasadena a few days later I learned from Summerfield that aniline had eliminated all combustion throbbing and, further, its property of spontaneously igniting with RFNA had made it possible to do without an auxiliary ignition system.

Considerable resistance came from the military services to accepting aniline, a toxic liquid, as a replacement for gasoline. The Air Material Command finally accepted the suggestion when it became evident that the A-20A flight tests, scheduled to start two months later, could not be made without risk of catastrophe, if gasoline was used as a fuel. The Navy Bureau of Aeronautics resisted the use of aniline as a fuel by the Annapolis group for almost another year.

The first successful American take-off of an aircraft assisted by liquid-propellant rocket engines was made on April 15, 1942, at the A. A. F. Bombing and Gunnery Range, Muroc, California. The test pilot was Paul H. Dane (then major) and the operator of the rocket engines in flight was Beverly M. Forman. The 1000 lb. thrust-25-second-rocket engines utilizing RFNA and aniline functioned without failure 44 times. The flight-test program included the measurement of increase of maximum speed of the aircraft.[24, 25]

Following the successful flight tests of the Ercoupe and in view of the good progress being made in the development of a liquid-propellant engine, it became evident that steps would soon have to be taken for the production of solid- and liquid-propellant engines for the Air Force and the Navy. Caltech being an institution for basic research and instruction was not appropriate for undertaking engineering development and production on a large scale. Furthermore, I shared the opinion of Parsons and Forman that after the efforts we had made during the previous five years we should participate in the exploitation of the ideas we had developed. Summerfield was in agreement with us.

When I came to von Kármán in September 1941 with the proposal that we initiate the production phase of rocket engines, I found him sympathetic. We approached several aircraft companies, but found that we could not make a satisfactory arrangement. Then, upon the counsel of Andrew G. Haley, von Kármán's attorney, it was decided to found a company of our own. The Aerojet Engineering Corpora-

[24] F. J. Malina, "An A-20A Airplane as Affected by Auxiliary Propulsion Supplied by Liquid Propellant Jet Units" JPL Report No 1-12, Calif. Inst. of Tech., June 30, 1942 (Unpublished).

[25] M. Summerfield, W. B. Powell and E. G. Crofut, "Development of a Liquid Propellant Jet Unit and Its Operation on an A-20A Airplane," JPL Report No 1-13, Calif. Inst. of Tech., Sept. 14, 1942 (Unpublished).

tion, now called Aerojet General Corporation, was formally incorporated on March 19, 1942 with the following officers: von Kármán, President and Director; Malina, Treasurer and Director; Haley, Secretary and Director; Parsons, Summerfield and Forman, Vice-Presidents.[26]

By the end of the year Parsons, Summerfield, and Forman were devoting much of their time at Aerojet assisting with the transition from the experimental stage to pilot scale and to full-scale production of solid– and liquid–propellant rocket engines. In September, Haley took over as president of Aerojet, and von Kármán and I again concentrated our efforts on the continually expanding research program at GALCIT Project No. 1.

In February 1943, von Kármán and I submitted a proposal to the Armament Laboratory of the A. A. F. Air Technical Service Command at Wright Field for under-water jet-propulsion research and for the design and construction of a towing channel. Preliminary experiments had been made in the autumn of 1942 by Summerfield on the operation of solid- and liquid-propellant rocket engines submerged under water with encouraging results. In view of the interest of the A. A. F. in the development of a missile to be launched from a bombing plane and to be propelled at high speed under water a contract was arranged, and Louis G. Dunn was put in charge of the Underwater Propulsion Section. The work carried the designation Armament Laboratory Project MX363. Under Dunn's supervision a towing channel was built having a length of 500 feet, width of 12 feet, and depth of 16 feet. The first towing carriage used on the channel was propelled by a RFNA-aniline rocket engine up to speeds of about 40 miles per hour.[27]

The research on this program in the first phase was carried out in cooperation with the Westinghouse Manufacturing Company and the United Shoe Machinery Company which were selected by the Armament Laboratory to build prototype hydro-bomb models.

At the request of the Air Technical Service Command, Army Air Forces, in the summer of 1943, von Kármán organized for the Caltech academic year 1943-44 the first American graduate course in jet propulsion for Army and Navy officers assigned to GALCIT for study. In 1946 the Air Technical Service Command published the lectures under the title *Jet Propulsion*. The 799 page volume was edited by

[26] A. G. Haley, *Rocketry and Space Exploration* (Princeton, N. J., Van Nostrand Co., 1958), p. 157.
[27] Th. von Kármán and F. J. Malina "Memorandum on the Design, Construction and Operation of a Towing Channel for Under-Water Jet Propulsion Research," JPL Misc. 2, February 20, 1943 (Unpublished).

H. S. Tsien and contained contributions from: P. Chambre, J. V. Charyck, L. G. Dunn, A. Hollander, N. Kaplan, Th. von Kármán, F. J. Malina, C. B. Millikan, M. M. Mills, A. J. Phelan, W. D. Rannie, H. S. Seifert, H. J. Stewart, R. F. Tangren, and H. S. Tsien.

The Jet Propulsion Laboratory, GALCIT

A new impetus was given to the work of GALCIT Project No. 1 when three British intelligence reports were received by von Kármán in the summer of 1943 giving the first indication of large-scale German missile development at Peenemünde. These reports were studied by von Kármán, Tsien and myself. At the suggestion of Col. W. H. Joiner, A. A. F. Material Command Liaison Officer at Caltech, a review and a preliminary analysis of performance and design of long-range projectiles was prepared by Tsien and myself. This study together with a memorandum by von Kármán outlining the possibilities of long-range rocket projectiles was transmitted to the military services in November 1943.[28] This was the first document to carry the designation " Jet Propulsion Laboratory."

In January 1944 Gladeon M. Barnes (then Major General) of the Army Ordnance Department requested JPL to undertake a research and development program on long-range jet-propelled missiles.

This led to the consummation of a contract for research on long-range rocket missiles between Caltech and the Ordnance Department (the ORDCIT Project) after arrangements for cooperative utilization of the staff and facilities of JPL had been made with the Army Air Forces.

The primary purpose of the contract was to develop a jet-propelled missile together with suitable launching equipment in accordance with the following objectives:

(a) Minimum weight of high explosive payload, 1000 lbs.
(b) Range of missile 75 to 100 miles.
(c) Dispersion at maximum range not in excess of 2 per cent or missile suitable for direction by remote control.
(d) Velocity sufficient to afford protection from fighter aircraft.

The scope of the contract included fundamental research on propel-

---

[28] Th. von Kármán, " Memorandum on the Possibilities of Long-Range Rocket Projectiles," and H. S. Tsien and F. J. Malina, " A Review and Preliminary Analysis of Long-Range Rocket Projectiles," Memorandum JPL-1, Jet Propulsion Lab., Caltech, 20 Nov. 1943 (Unpublished). Summary in *Collected Works of Theodore von Kármán*, Vol. IV, (London, Butterworth Scientific Pub. 1956), p. 206.

lants and materials involved in rocket and ramjet units, on remote-control equipment, and on high-speed aerodynamic problems, and provided for the engineering design and fabrication of prototype missiles suitable for firing tests.

Steps were immediately taken to expand the staff and facilities of JPL, which was to become America's first center for space research and long-range missile development.

Von Kármán, towards the end of May 1944, had a serious operation in New York which kept him from returning to Pasadena until September. It was while he was recuperating that Gen. H. H. Arnold approached him to undertake the creation of the Scientific Advisory Board to the Chief of Staff, U. S. Army Air forces, "to investigate all possibilities and desirabilities for postwar and future war's development as respects the A. A. F." [29]

In December von Kármán went to Washington, D. C., to carry out this task, and I took over the direction of the Laboratory with Dunn as Assistant Director. An Executive Board was established headed by C. B. Millikan, Laboratory administration was in the charge of Eugene M. Pierce, and the key research staff consisted of the following persons:

H. J. Stewart	Chief,	Research Analysis, Section 1
L. G. Dunn	"	Underwater Propulsion, Section 2
H. S. Seifert	"	Liquid Propellant Rocket, Section 3
M. M. Mills	"	Solid Propellant Rocket, Section 4
P. Duwez	"	Materials, Section 5
N. Kaplan	"	Propellants, Section 6
W. A. Sandberg	"	Engineering Design, Section 7
J. A. Amneus	"	Research Design, Section 8
W. H. Pickering	"	Remote Control, Section 9
R. F. Tangren	"	Ramjet, Section 10
S. J. Goldberg	"	Field Testing, Section 11
M. Serrurier	"	Facility Design, Section 12

When World War II ended in Europe, a year after the ORDCIT Project got under way, JPL had a staff of 264. The facilities and

[29] E. M. Emme *Aeronautics and Astronautics—An American Chronology of Science and Technology in the Exploration of Space 1915-1960*, (Washington, National Aeronautics & Space Administration, 1961), p. 48 (Ed. Note: The series of 26 technical reports of the AAF Scientific Advisory Board, entitled *Towards New Horizons*, were to underwrite post-war aerospace research and development planning for almost a decade.)

equipment on 32 acres at the Arroyo Seco location in Pasadena were valued at about $3,000,000.[30]

JPL continued to benefit greatly from the possibility of arranging at Caltech for the use of special laboratory equipment and for expert consultation by staff members. A chemistry group under the direction of Bruce H. Sage of the Department of Chemical Engineering began working on chemical problems of propellants for JPL in 1942.

In the summer of 1944 work was begun on rocket missiles propelled by solid- and liquid-propellant engines. The solid-propellant engine

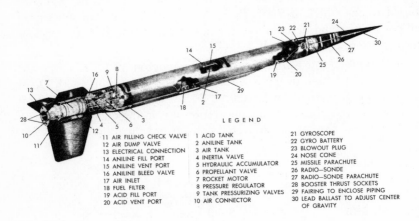

LEGEND

11 AIR FILLING CHECK VALVE	1 ACID TANK	21 GYROSCOPE
12 AIR DUMP VALVE	2 ANILINE TANK	22 GYRO BATTERY
13 ELECTRICAL CONNECTION	3 AIR TANK	23 BLOWOUT PLUG
14 ANILINE FILL PORT	4 INERTIA VALVE	24 NOSE CONE
15 ANILINE VENT PORT	5 HYDRAULIC ACCUMULATOR	25 MISSILE PARACHUTE
16 ANILINE BLEED VALVE	6 PROPELLANT VALVE	26 RADIO—SONDE
17 AIR INLET	7 ROCKET MOTOR	27 RADIO—SONDE PARACHUTE
18 FUEL FILTER	8 PRESSURE REGULATOR	28 BOOSTER THRUST SOCKETS
19 ACID FILL PORT	9 TANK PRESSURIZING VALVES	29 FAIRING TO ENCLOSE PIPING
20 ACID VENT PORT	10 AIR CONNECTOR	30 LEAD BALLAST TO ADJUST CENTER OF GRAVITY

Fig. 6   Sketch of JPL Wac Corporal, 1946 (JPL photo)

missiles were the finned PRIVATE A, and the same missile, except that the symmetrical tail fins were replaced by a vertical fin and wings, became the PRIVATE F. Neither of these missiles had a guidance system. Both were launched by solid-propellant booster rockets.

The liquid-propellant missiles were the CORPORAL E with a gas-pressure feed system engine and the CORPORAL F with a turbine-driven pump-feed system engine. The design of the guidance system for the missiles was assigned to the Sperry Gyroscope Company. Work on guidance-system components at JPL was carried out under William H. Pickering, present director of the laboratory. The CORPORAL E was to have a gross weight of 11,000 lbs. and a range of 40 miles. The engine was to deliver 20,000 lbs. thrust for 60 seconds.

[30] "The Jet Propulsion Laboratory, GALCIT," Memorandum No. JPL-3, Calif. Inst. of Tech., June 25, 1945 (Unpublished).

The PRIVATE A was successfully fired during the period December 1-16, 1944, only 11 months after the start of the ORDCIT Project. The maximum range of the missile was about 11 miles. The PRIVATE A was the first American missile propelled by a long-duration solid-propellant engine.

Paralleling research work on liquid- and solid-propellant engines, studies had also been initiated in 1944 on ramjet propulsion. In March 1944, von Kármán, Summerfield, Tsien and I made a comparative study of jet-propulsion systems as applied to missiles and transonic aircraft.[31] This was followed by a contract from the Power Plant Laboratory, Air Technical Service Command of the A. A. F., for the study of ramjet engines for aircraft and missiles. The project, designated "Power Plant Laboratory Project MX527," was carried out in conjunction with the ORDCIT Project.

In December 1944, I returned from a mission to Europe where I had studied for the Ordnance Department rocket developments in Britain and German V-1 and V-2 installations in the Pas-de-Calais area of France. It occurred to me on the return journey that the original dream of the GALCIT Rocket Research Project to construct a high-altitude sounding rocket could now be technically fulfilled. I stopped off in Washington, D. C., where I obtained the approval for such a project from Gervais W. Trichel (then colonel), of the Rocket Research and Development Division of the Ordnance Department.[32] In accordance with a requirement of the Signal Corps, the sounding rocket was to be capable of carrying 25 pounds of meteorological equipment to an altitude of at least 100,000 feet. The name WAC CORPORAL was given to the rocket because it was thought of as the little sister of the CORPORAL E. (The letters WAC stand for Women's Auxiliary Corps). Work on the rocket began immediately.

From April 1 to 13, 1945, firing tests were made on the PRIVATE F at Fort Bliss, Texas. Also at this time, Pickering carried out the first experiments of a rocket airfoil tester built around a five-inch high-velocity aircraft rocket, the HVAR, which had been built by the National Defense Research Committee group working on armament

[31] Th. von Kármán, F. J. Malina, M. Summerfield, and H. S. Tsien, "Comparative Study of Jet Propulsion Systems as Applied to Missiles and Transonic Aircraft," Memorandum JPL-2, Jet Propulsion Laboratory, Calif. Inst. of Tech., March 28, 1944 (Unpublished). Summary in *Collected Works of Th. von Kármán*, Vol. IV (London, Butterworth Scientific Pub., 1956), p. 209.

[32] F. J. Malina and H. J. Stewart, "Considerations of the Feasibility of Developing a 100,000 ft. Altitude Rocket (THE WAC CORPORAL)," Memorandum no. JPL 4-4, Calif. Inst. of Tech., January 16, 1945 (Unpublished).

rockets at Caltech under Charles C. Lauritsen. The forces acting on the airfoil model were reported to the ground by a telemetering system.[33]

By July the design features of the WAC CORPORAL were outlined and confirmed by the tests from July 3 to 5 at Goldstone Lake, California, on a ⅕ scale model. The full-scale rocket had a length of 16 feet, a diameter of one foot and a weight of 665 pounds. It was provided with three instead of the usual four tail fins, and to avoid the complications and weight of flight-control equipment it was accelerated to stable flight out of a 100-foot launching tower by a Tiny Tim booster rocket. The WAC CORPORAL was powered by a RFNA-aniline gas-pressure feed-system engine delivering 1500 pounds thrust for 45 seconds. The motor was constructed by the Aerojet General Corporation and the vehicle final assembly was carried out by the Douglas Aircraft Co. The team which designed and tested the sounding rocket under my direction consisted of the following JPL staff members: S. J. Goldberg, P. J. Meeks, M. M. Mills, W. A. Sandberg, H. J. Stewart, and R. C. Terbeck. Leslie A. Skinner (then colonel) and Benjamin S. Mesick (then colonel) acted as liaison officers between the Ordnance Department and JPL.[34]

Firing tests of the WAC CORPORAL were made as the first program at the newly built White Sands Proving Ground in New Mexico between September 26 and October 25, 1945. On October 11 the rocket set an altitude record of 235,000 feet. Thus, only 10 months after the project had been approved by the Ordnance Department, and 10 years after the GALCIT rocket research group started its work, a successful sounding-rocket flight had been achieved.[35]

A somewhat larger sounding rocket using the design features of the WAC CORPORAL was developed subsequently by Johns Hopkins University's Applied Physics Laboratory working with the Aerojet General Corporation. It was named the AEROBEE, and versions of it are still in use today.

At JPL, after the WAC CORPORAL tests and with detailed information available on the performance of the German V-2, our thoughts began to turn to the concrete possibilities of space flight. Together with Summerfield I began a study of the problem of escape from the earth by rocket. I gave our conclusions to the U. S. War Department's

[33] World War II ended in Europe on May 7, 1945.

[34] World War II ended with the surrender of Japan on August 14, 1945.

[35] F. J. Malina, "Development and Flight Performance of a High-Altitude Sounding Rocket, the WAC CORPORAL," Report No. JPL 4-18, Calif. Inst. of Tech., January 24, 1946 (Unpublished).

Stillwell Committee on January 3, 1946. At the end of September 1946, I presented to the Sixth International Congress for Applied Mechanics in Paris a paper Summerfield and I had prepared on the " escape " problem which gave a criterion for the design of step-rockets and also preliminary estimates of a rocket engine using nuclear energy to heat hydrogen.[36] It is interesting to note that America's first satellite EXPLORER I launched January 31, 1958, had a payload of a weight and instruments for the measurement of cosmic-ray intensity as proposed in this paper. The EXPLORER I was a cooperative venture of JPL and the Army Ballistic Missile Agency.

In the July-August (1946) issue of the *Army Ordnance Journal*, I had included an idea of Summerfield that the WAC CORPORAL be used as a second stage with the V-2 as the mother vehicle. We estimated that the WAC would reach an altitude of around 375 miles.[37] The Ordnance Department upon the initiative of Col. Messick started the Bumper Project in October to test the staging of the two rockets. The Ordnance Department in conjunction with JPL, which was then under the direction of Dunn, launched the Bumper WAC to an altitude of 244 miles at White Sands Proving Ground on February 24, 1949. The WAC CORPORAL thus became the first man-made object to enter extra-terrestrial space. On July 24, 1950, a Bumper-WAC was the first missile launching from Cape Canaveral.

As JPL entered its second decade of work the situation in the world of men and in the world of science differed greatly from the one that prevailed in 1936. As far as rocket technology was concerned, it had been demonstrated that rocket engines, whether they used liquid or solid propellants, could be built which were reliable and which possessed characteristics that could not be met by any other type of existing power plant. Rocket engineering rested on a scientifically and technically sound foundation. Many problems had been solved or formulated for further study. Unfortunately, for example, throbbing difficulties of certain types of liquid-propellant engines are still with us in 1964, especially in large engines required for space vehicles.

One might say that the era of rocket-propulsion development, which began with the Chinese powder rocket around the 11th century, was now giving way to the era of the development of guidance and control systems for missiles and space vehicles, and of finding methods

[36] F. J. Malina and M. Summerfield, " The Problem of Escape from the Earth by Rocket," *Jour. Inst. of Aero. Sci.*, Vol. 14, No. 8 (August 1947) p. 471.

[37] F. J. *Malina*, " Is the Sky the Limit? " *Army Ordnance*, Vol. XXXI, No. 157 (July-August 1946) p. 45.

for permitting man to live under conditions existing in extraterrestrial space.

In 1946 much that previously had been regarded as science fiction was established fact. It was then only necessary to stimulate the imagination of those who still could not understand why man needed to escape from the earth—which was and is today perhaps the most difficult problem of all.

Early U.S. Satellite Proposals

R. CARGILL HALL

AT THE END of World War II the United States stood pre-eminent in the world in political influence, in industrial productivity, and in sheer military power. The United States alone emerged virtually unscathed from the conflict and, more significantly, was the sole possessor of the atomic bomb. Her European allies were financially and materially prostrate, Germany and Japan lay in ruins. Soviet Russia, having had a substantial percentage of her industrial and agricultural capacity destroyed as well as having suffered innumerable casualties, faced the monumental task of rebuilding simply to attain pre-war levels of productivity.

International rivalry, which has frequently acted as the catalytic stimulus to technological advance, was replaced by a victorious enthusiasm and ephemeral unity of the Allied powers. An emergency climate which would sustain continuous experimentation and investigation leading to advancement in the state-of-the-art in rocketry and astronautics no longer existed in this country at the conclusion of hostilities in August 1945. To the United States, sole possessor of atomic weapons and global air supremacy, a military threat from a foreign power was difficult to visualize. Wartime military and civilian programs were subject to a return to " normalcy "—to peace-time operation.

The layman's inherent skepticism, manifested by his reaction in 1920 to Robert H. Goddard's " moon-impact proposal " (and his daring suggestion that rocket thrust could operate in a vacuum),[1] was displayed

* Historian and Operations Research Analyst at Lockheed Missiles and Space Company (Sunnyvale, California), Mr. Hall is the author of numerous monographs on Air Force satellite programs. This article is the winning essay of the Robert H. Goddard Historical Essay Competition for 1962, sponsored by the National Space Club, Washington, D. C. The paper was submitted in October 1962 under the title " World-Circling Spaceships: Satellite Studies in the U. S. during the 1940's." It is based upon material from a projected book by the author with W. H. Ramsell on *Astronautics and the War for Space.*

[1] On January 12, 1920 the *New York Times* had castigated Goddard for the proposals he outlined in his Smithsonian paper, " A Method of Reaching Extreme Altitudes " (1919).

once again in 1945, at a more critical time in our history, by an influential member of the scientific community and a U. S. defense policy maker. Dr. Vannevar Bush, Director of the Office for Scientific Research and Development, and Chairman, Joint Committee on New Weapons of the Joint Chief of Staff (1942-1946), made the following comments before the Special Senate Committee on Atomic Energy in December 1945:

> Let me say this: There has been a great deal said about a 3,000-mile high-angle rocket. In my opinion such a thing is impossible and will be impossible for many years. The people who have been writing these things that annoy me have been talking about a 3,000-mile high-angle rocket shot from one continent to another carrying an atomic bomb, and so directed as to be a precise weapon which would land on a certain target such as this city.
>
> I say technically I don't think anybody in the world knows how to do such a thing and I feel confident it will not be done for a very long period of time to come. I think we can leave that out of our thinking. I wish the American public would leave that out of their thinking.[2]

America's global power, her demobilization—the return to " normalcy "— and the influence of decision-makers in the same frame of mind as Dr. Bush determined to a great degree the course of events which were to follow for the first rocket and satellite programs initiated after the end of the war.

Regardless of thinking at higher levels, within several months after the conclusion of hostilities in 1945, the Armed Services of the United States did embark upon a number of advanced rocket and satellite programs. However, these programs, which might well have cul-

---

[2] *Inquiry into Satellite and Missile Programs,* Part I, Preparedness Investigating Subcommittee, Senate Committee on Armed Services, 85th Congress, 1st and 2d sessions, November 1957-January 1958, p. 283.

It is to Dr. Bush's credit that he adjusted to the inevitable evolution of astronautics and, in November 1957, a month after Sputnik was launched, testified before the Senate Committee on Armed Service: " I am quite frank to say that when this (ICBM/Satellite) work began soon after the war, I was exceedingly skeptical whether that tough problem could be solved." Dr. Bush then proceeded to make a plea for the " eccentric," saying, " What he wants more than anything else is the respect of his peers, the respect of his fellow scientists. . . . he wants to feel that he is working in an area where the public about him, the businessman, the men he meets casually, think of him as a fellow worker for the good of the country, and not as a highbrow or egghead that is off somewhere on a pedestal and not to be approached." *Ibid.,* p. 65.

minated in the orbiting of an American satellite by 1951, were not to receive the support of the War Department.[3]

Satellite Studies In The United States, 1945-1947

The first formal studies of earth satellite vehicles made with government funds in the United States were conducted during the 1940's by the Navy and the Army Air Force. However, knowledge of this early work has been limited. Available information concerning these studies, although now unclassified, has been published in disrelated segments, scattered widely, and has contained no unifying historical thread bonding a relationship between the parallel work. As an example, a recent reference to one of the major satellite studies conducted in the mid-1940's appeared inconspicuously within the *Chronology of Missile and Astronautic Events*, published by the House Committee on Science and Astronautics: " May 12, 1946: Project RAND presented its report to the Army Air Force entitled Preliminary Design of an Experimental World-Circling Spaceship." [4]

While the U. S. Congressional Chronology mentions the 1946 Army Air Force-Project RAND satellite study, no mention was made of the satellite study conducted by the Navy which had begun the year before, in 1945. Insight into this unique phase of American astronomical endeavor has been provided by Dr. Harvey Hall, who was instrumental in starting the original Navy satellite study and remained with the program until its termination in late 1948.[5]

In early October 1945, a Committee for Evaluating the Feasibility of Space Rocketry (CEFSR) was established in the Navy Bureau of Aeronautics.[6] This group performed calculations and profile analysis on a proposed liquid hydrogen-oxygen single stage earth satellite vehicle, and, in late October 1945, the CEFSR submitted the satellite proposal to the Navy Bureau of Aeronautics with the strong recommendation that an experimental program be adopted for the explicit objective of constructing and launching an earth satellite vehicle to carry electronic equipment for scientific test purposes.

[3] Prior to 1947, the Department of Defense (and a separate Air Force) had not been established.

[4] *A Chronology of Missile and Astronautic Events*, Report of the Committee on Science and Astronautics, U. S. House of Representatives, 87th Congress 1st Session, 1961, p. 9.

[5] Subsequent Navy Satellite documentation cited in this paper is noted in Dr. Hall's memorandum, " Early History and Background on Earth Satellites," ONR:405:HH:dr, November 29, 1957.

[6] BuAer Memo Aer-E-203-KWM, of 3 October 1945.

This early Navy satellite proposal, (not to be confused with the later " Vanguard " Program) was based upon a contemporary hydrogen rocket motor development program then being conducted by the Navy Bureau of Aeronautics. Late in 1945 under the BuAer program, personnel of Aerojet succeeded in actually burning gaseous hydrogen and oxygen in a rocket motor for the first time, and shortly thereafter, under the same Navy auspices, the largest hydrogen liquefier in the world was placed in operation at Aerojet, an early rocket propulsion firm, where liquid hydrogen was successfully stored, pumped and burned in what became routine test operations.[7] At this early date the BuAer effort on large rocket propulsion systems was composed of several serious " hardware " development contracts. Other contracts were also undertaken for the study of boro-hydride fuels and for electronic components that could be employed in rockets.

As a result of the CEFSR satellite recommendations, the Navy Bureau of Aeronautics placed a contract with the Guggenheim Aeronautical Laboratory at the California Institute of Technology in December 1945 to conduct research on the relationship between the orbit (altitudes), rocket motor and fuel performance, structural characteristics (mass ratio), and payload.[8] The results of these calculations, implementing those already made within the BuAer, confirmed the feasibility of a single stage liquid hydrogen-oxygen earth satellite rocket vehicle provided: (1) the fuel and engine combination would perform according to theory and (2) that the assumed structure (mass ratio) could actually be realized. Consequently, a contract was awarded to Aerojet in order to determine whether a test stand value of the specific impulse of liquid hydrogen-oxygen was sufficiently near the theoretical value to justify these conclusions of satellite feasibility. This propulsion system contract led to the construction of the large hydrogen liquifier and actual test stand operation of liquid hydrogen-oxygen rocket engines which verified theoretical performance specifications. Verification of the second condition on structures was undertaken later in 1946.

Even before some of these early investigations had been completed, support for the satellite project was solicited from many individuals and at many levels in the Navy. It soon became apparent to BuAer personnel involved in the project that full Navy support for an actual

[7] The availability of this hydrogen liquefier was later to fill an important requirement in the AEC's hydrogen bomb development program, after the Navy Bureau of Aeronautic's hydrogen rocket program had been terminated.

[8] California Institute of Technology Contract and Report NOa(S)7913 of 10 December 1945.

flight test vehicle program would not be forthcoming. Cost estimates for the preliminary design phase of the project had been set between $5,000,000 and $8,000,000 in November 1945.[9] In early 1946 there were clear indications that whatever progress could be attained would have to be done on a great deal less than $5,000,000.

Faced with this unpromising situation, members of the Navy CEFSR approached the Army Air Force in the hope of establishing a joint earth satellite project. The first meeting between representatives of the two services took place in Washington, D. C., on March 7, 1946. At this meeting the status of the Navy BuAer rocket and satellite developments was reviewed, and a plan was presented to serve as the basis for the proposed joint Army Air Force-Navy experimental program. Reception of the Navy proposal by the Army Air Force representatives was most favorable, and a tentative arrangement was established:

> It was agreed at the conference that the general advantages to be derived from pursuing the satellite development appear to be sufficient to justify a major program, in spite of the fact that the obvious military, or purely naval applications in themselves, may not appear at this time to warrant the expenditure.
>
> On this basis, the Army representatives agreed to investigate the extent of Army interest by discussions with General LeMay and others, after which a future joint conference is planned.[10]

For several days in March 1946, it appeared that a satellite project might possibly commence in the United States. Ten years were to lapse, however, before an American satellite program was ever accorded an official go-ahead.

After review of the Navy proposal at higher levels, General Carl Spaatz designated General Curtis E. LeMay to represent the Army Air Force before the Navy satellite proposal team. In mid-March Dr. Harvey Hall was summoned to the office of General LeMay and was informed by the General that the Army Air Force would not support the proposed Navy satellite project, although the possibility for further discussion on the subject of earth satellites was left open.

[9] BuAer Memo Aer-E-31T-HH, CX-281360, 27 November 1945.

[10] BuAer Letter to Commanding General, Army Air Forces, Aer-EL-1-HH, F 41(1), ser. CO2262, 15 March 1946. (With encl. memo of Committee of 7 March, copy to Maj. General Curtis E. LeMay, Maj. General E. M. Powers, CNO, ORI.) Members attending the conference of 7 March were: Major General H. J. Knerr, AAF; Major General H. M. McClelland, AAF; Brig. General W. L. Richardson, AAF; Captain W. P. Cogswell, USN; Commander H. Hall, USNR.

Personnel at the Navy BuAer returned to continue work on their single-stage satellite investigations. In the meantime the Army Air Force turned to the Project RAND [11] research group quartered on the West Coast. This consultant organization was instructed to perform a separate earth satellite feasibility study.

Further attempts by the Navy Bureau of Aeronautics to arrange another conference with the Army Air Force on a joint satellite proposal met with repeated delays. The second meeting was finally held in early June under the War Department's Aeronautical Board. This board, formed during World War II, was composed of representatives from the Army and Navy Air Forces to review new developments and coordinate similar requirements for the two air corps. (Later in 1946 this organization was supplanted by the Joint Research and Development Board (JRDB) [12] of the War Department which expanded and formalized the functions performed by the Aeronautical Board.) At this second joint meeting the Army Air Force representative, General Laurence Craigie, introduced the Project RAND satellite study report " on which the ink was hardly dry, as the basis of a bargaining position that the AAF was on an equal or similar developmental position with the Navy. From this point on, no further progress was made towards a joint project." [13]

The Navy Bureau of Aeronautics satellite vehicle, designated High Altitude Test Vehicle (HATV), was to have been a single stage " multimotored liquid oxygen-hydrogen rocket craft capable of achieving orbital motion about the earth. It is 86 feet long and has a maximum diameter of 16 feet. It is constructed of stainless steel and has nine

[11] Project RAND was established in late 1945 and initially operated as a semi-autonomous branch of the Douglas Aircraft Corporation, responsible directly to the Vice President, Engineering. Qualified physicists, engineers, and mathematical analysts were drawn from Douglas and other aircraft firms, and assembled at Santa Monica in separate quarters. The original concept was that several companies would get together and set up an advisory type function which, in turn, would allow RAND to advise the various services on what they should procure, so that the services would not request the " impossible " from industry in the area of aircraft armaments. In November 1948, the RAND Corporation was created and became a completely autonomous non-profit research institution.

[12] The chief responsibility of the JRDB was the preparation of an integrated program of research and development, in the light of which individual projects of the Army, Navy, and Air Force could be evaluated. The Board decided who developed what weapons. It made sure that there was no unnecessary duplication in the activities of the services, although it could permit competition which promised to produce a better result. By the late 1940's the principle of preventing duplication of effort had been seriously eroded.

[13] Hall, *op. cit.*, p. 4.

individual thrust motors. The vehicle is capable of attaining a maximum velocity of 25,400 feet per second at an altitude of about 150 miles." [14] North American Aviation (NAA) performed the CEFSR studies on the HATV structures in mid-1946. The HATV was designed to weigh 101,400 pounds initially, broken down into several components: propellants, 89,000 lbs.; payload, 1,000 lbs.; motor and accessories, 5,000 lbs.; and structure, 6,400 lbs.

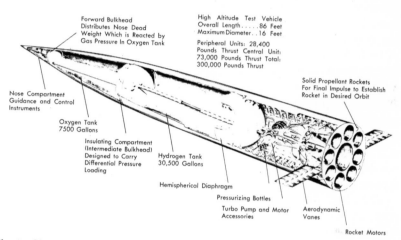

Fig. 7 Sketch of U. S. Navy High Altitude Test Vehicle (HATV), 1946). Design included eight peripheral rocket engines of 28,400-lbs. thrust each, and a central engine of 73,000-lbs. thrust. A secondary engine propulsion system for circularizing the initial eliptical oribit was to consist of four solid-propellant rockets. Overall length: 86 feet; maximum diameter: 16 feet. (U. S. Navy)

The ratio of propellant weight to initial gross weight was .89. Previous investigations by the California Institute of Technology had established that " if a rocket ship could be built composed of .89 per cent oxygen and hydrogen in liquid form as fuel, and 11 per cent as dead weight, then the craft could attain free flight orbital movement around the earth at an altitude which would allow a number of revolutions before its energy is decreased due to atmospheric drag. . . ." The starting weight required an initial thrust of 233,000 pounds,

[14] *Structural Design Study, High Altitude Test Vehicle*, Contract NOa(s)-8349, North American Aviation, Incorporated; Report No. NA 46-758, September 26, 1946, p. 1-1.

varying to about 308,000 pounds at altitude.[15] Since the structures portion of this single stage vehicle could not weigh much more than five per cent of the total weight of the rocket, the specifications called for a mass fuel-to-structure (content-to-shell) ratio approaching that which exists in an egg.[16]

The engineers at North American Aviation were aware at that early date that a satellite could be made by multi-staging conventional (V-2) rockets, but they were responding to the Navy's requirements to see if a single-stage satellite could be made. With the exception of the extensive work on the propulsion system, the satellite studies conducted for the Navy BuAer in 1946 were not hardware contracts, but rather substantial preliminary feasibility studies for the purpose of evaluating the upper limit to which a single-stage liquid hydrogen-oxygen booster-satellite design could be carried. For the NAA engineers, answers to this problem came out in the affirmative: with appropriate extension in rocket engine burning time and with small improvements in metallurgy, a single-stage satellite vehicle was definitely a feasible device. In addition to the NAA design study, the Navy also found confirmation of the concept in two additional design studies: one by the BuAer design group under Abraham Hyatt; and one under a joint contract to the Glenn L. Martin Co. and Aerojet.

Project RAND

In the Army Air Force satellite studies which commenced in 1946, as a direct result of the Navy satellite efforts, no predetermined specifications were imposed upon Project RAND. However, this consultant group was instructed to complete its satellite feasibility study in three weeks—because the Air Force and the Navy were scheduled for a presentation of their respective cases for unmanned satellites before the next monthly meeting of the Aeronautical Board of the War Department. Ultimately this unrealistic date was postponed and extended by the Army Air Force for about three months. In 1946 the separate satellite studies being conducted by the Navy and Army Air

[15] *Ibid.*, p. 3-1.

[16] Ultimately the United States approximated just what the CEFSR had proposed when "Project Score" guided an entire Atlas ICBM into orbit in late 1958. The "single-stage plus" Atlas ICBM is a pressure-stabilized structure and in itself an extremely light weight vehicle. Moreover, the Air Force Atlas employs conventional propellants (kerosene and liquid oxygen) which do not approach the higher specific impulse delivered by liquid hydrogen-oxygen, in many ways making that vehicle a more difficult engineering achievement than the original Navy Bureau of Aeronautics single-stage HATV rocket proposal.

Force had assumed the character of programs undertaken to demonstrate to the War Department that one or both of the two services had
a feasible satellite program, and thus might lay claim to weapon
developments in the medium of space.

Administratively the early RAND project was managed through
the Douglas Aircraft Company. Actually, however, there was participation by North American and Northrop. Although the three-way
venture did not reach maturity until early 1947, there was sufficient
technical interchange among the three participating companies to make
the Douglas/RAND group keenly aware of the difficult engineering
problems inherent in the Navy's single-stage satellite specification.
Project RAND also knew of a possibly easier solution to the problem:
the staging of conventional fueled rockets.

Even with a common knowledge of fundamentals and a free exchange
of technical information within aircraft engineering circles in 1946,
it was not an easy task for the Project RAND group to produce its
first satellite feasibility study within the time limits. Finally on May
12, 1946, twenty copies of a document entitled *Preliminary Design of
an Experimental World-Circling Spaceship* were rushed from Project
RAND to the Air Materiel Command at Wright Field, Dayton, Ohio.

" Prophetic " is the only term which can be applied to the following
excerpts from the introduction to this unique engineering report:

Although the crystal ball is cloudy, two things seem clear—

1. A satellite vehicle with appropriate instrumentation can be
   expected to be one of the most potent scientific tools of
   the Twentieth Century.
2. The achievement of a satellite craft by the United States
   would inflame the imagination of mankind, and would probably produce repercussions in the world comparable to the
   explosion of the atomic bomb. . . .

Since mastery of the elements is a reliable index of material progress, the nation which first makes significant achievements in space
travel will be acknowledged as the world leader in both military
and scientific techniques. *To visualize the impact on the world,
one can imagine the consternation and admiration that would be
felt here if the U.S. were to discover suddenly, that some other
nation had already put up a successful satellite.*[17] (Italics added.)

That the author of these statements was correct in his prophecy was

[17] From Project RAND engineering report *Preliminary Design of an Experimental World-Circling Spaceship*, Santa Monica, May, 1946. Subsequent quotes
in the following sections are from the same report unless otherwise noted.

evidenced by the state of shock in which the free world found itself on October 4, 1957, when Sputnik I rocketed into orbit, propelled by a missile with ICBM characteristics.

Feasibility of a World-Circling Spaceship

After carefully analyzing the state-of-the-art and potential developments, the men working at Project RAND stated that "technology and experience have now reached the point where it is possible to design and construct craft which can penetrate the atmosphere and achieve sufficient velocity to become satellites of the earth." This statement was well documented in the RAND report which, admittedly, was a feasibility study for a satellite vehicle "judiciously based on German experience with the V-2," and which relied for its success on "sound engineering development which could logically be expected as a consequence of intensive application to the effort."

Although deemed feasible as a satellite per se (it was felt that a 500-pound satellite could be placed on a 300-mile orbit *within five years*, or *by 1951*), Project RAND ruled out the satellite as a military "ballistic weapon," i. e., a device which would carry a destructive payload. No known propulsive system could lift a heavy A-bomb to orbital altitude, and any explosive force less than atomic could not inflict enough damage on an enemy to make worth while the expense of transporting it via a satellite. Here the status-quo of military feasibility was to remain for some years. The problem was not a lack of the wherewithal to orbit a satellite vehicle, but rather the problem of devising a *useful function for the satellite to perform once it was in orbit.*

The satellite, therefore, had been determined a feasible device, but not a military weapon. Because it was not a "weapon," no funds were available for its development. Personnel at Project RAND were aware of this condition, and yet, through logical extrapolation of potential based upon the standpoint of feasibility, the mathematicians and engineers knew that a satellite would provide scientific and psychological advantages which would transcend the utility of such a vehicle as a mere weapons carrier. In an attempt to circumvent contemporary War Department rationale and establish a secondary basis for evaluation and review of "radical" proposals, and at the same time gain official sanction to proceed with its development, the report went on to urge the early adoption of a satellite program:

> In making the decision as to whether or not to undertake construction of such a craft now, it is not inappropriate to view our

present situation as similar to that in airplanes prior to the flight of the Wright brothers. We can see no more clearly now all of the utility and implications of spaceships than the Wright brothers could see flights of B-29's bombing Japan and air transports circling the globe. . . .

The technicians at Project RAND who might at first have been intrigued with the novelty of an unmanned satellite turned to plead

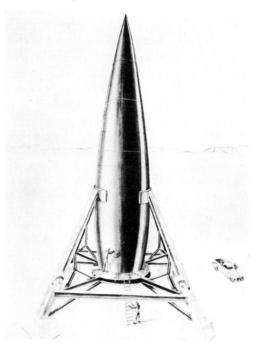

Fig. 8 Design of the RAND "World-Circling Spaceship"—1946. This satellite launching rocket was to be a four-stage liquid alcohol-oxygen vehicle, while a three-stage rocket would be optimum for a liquid hydrogen-oxygen fueled vehicle. (USAF)

the case for continued work on the satellite program regardless of its non-military nature, thereby following the earlier lead of the Navy Bureau of Aeronautics. To establish the case for the usefulness of a satellite vehicle, the Project RAND summary went into considerable detail on non-military uses for such a device including astronautical observation of cloud patterns and short-range weather forecasting, as well as biological observations in a gravity-free environment. Heavy emphasis was placed on the possibilities of the satellite as a *communica-*

tions relay station. And, as in the case of the Navy personnel in the Bureau of Aeronautics, the plea to justify further fixed effort also fell on barren ground.

Project RAND Conclusions Concerning World-Circling Spaceship

One of the important conclusions of the Project RAND design study was that it would be highly advantageous to have *multi-stage rockets* utilizing given types of liquid propellant in order to achieve the required performance, i. e., alcohol-oxygen, or, as in the case of the Navy proposal, hydrogen-oxygen. As a refutation of the Navy's case, the study further sought to prove that neither hydrogen-oxygen nor alcohol-oxygen would be capable of accelerating a single-stage, unassisted vehicle to orbital speeds. Further analysis of the propellant combinations for staged vehicles revealed that four stages were optimum for conventional fueled liquid alcohol-oxygen rockets. The gross weight of such a vehicle was listed at 233,669 pounds with a final fourth-stage payload—or satellite—of 500 pounds.

> The work has been based on our present state of technological advancement and has not included such possible future advancements as atomic energy. If a vehicle can be accelerated to a speed of 17,000 mph and aimed properly, it will revolve on a great circle path above the earth's atmosphere as a new satellite. The centrifugal force will just balance the pull of gravity. Such a vehicle will make a complete circuit of the earth in approximately 1½ hours.

Three stages were determined to be optimum for a liquid hydrogen-oxygen rocket. However the report was published with all data based on a two-stage liquid hydrogen-oxygen rocket (an addition of one more stage over the original Navy proposal). A postscript was added explaining that time did not permit the substitution of data, but that the addition of a third stage would afford substantial weight savings.

> It is planned to fire the rocket vertically upward for several miles and then gradually curve the flight path over in the direction in which it is desired that the vehicle shall travel. In order to establish the vehicle on an orbit at an altitude of about 300 miles without using excessive amounts of control, it was found desirable to allow the vehicle to coast without thrust on an extended elliptic arc just preceding the firing of the rocket of the last stage. As the vehicle approaches the summit of this arc, which is at the final altitude, the rocket of the last stage is fired and the vehicle is accelerated so that it becomes a freely revolving satellite.

It was also planned that the launching of a satellite would be made from one of the Pacific islands near the equator in a west-to-east plane [18] and that a series of telemetering stations would be established around the equator to obtain the data from the scientific apparatus contained in the vehicle. "The first vehicle will probably be allowed to burn up on plunging back into the atmosphere. Later vehicles will be designed so that they can be brought back to earth. Such vehicles can be used either as long range missiles or for carrying human beings."

Note of Warning

In a chapter entitled "The Significance of a Satellite Vehicle," Dr. L. N. Ridenour, another member of the original group of consultants to Project RAND, emphasized that by creating a satellite and booster system one has at the same time developed the requirements for an intercontinental ballistic missile:

> There is little difference in design and performance between an intercontinental rocket missile and a satellite. Thus a rocket missile with a free space trajectory of 6,000 miles requires a minimum energy of launching which corresponds to an initial velocity of 4.4 miles per second, while a satellite requires 5.4. Consequently, the development of a satellite will be directly applicable to the development of an intercontinental rocket missile.

More than a decade later, at the conclusion of the Senate's special 1958 investigation of Sputnik and America's lagging space effort, Senator Lyndon Johnson belatedly paraphrased Dr. Ridenour when he noted that "it [Sputnik] demonstrates beyond question that the Soviet Union has the propulsive force to hurl a missile from one continent to another." [19]

Dr. Ridenour stressed the possibility of a military use for the satellite in a passive capacity: "It should be remarked that the satellite offers [itself as] an observation 'aircraft.' . . . Perhaps the two most important classes of observation which can be made from a satellite are the

---

[18] An eastward firing from a 30 to 45 degree latitude yields a velocity increment of 1000 to 1300 feet per second as a performance margin due to the earth's peripheral velocity. This is equivalent to several hundred pounds of additional payload capacity. This approach was that employed in the NASA Project Mercury launches.

[19] *Inquiry into Satellite and Missile Programs*, Part 3, Hearings before the Preparedness Investigating Subcommittee of the Committee on Armed Services, U. S. Senate, Eighty-Fifth Congress, First and Second Sessions, February 26, April 3, and July 24, 1958, p. 2428.

spotting of points of impact of bombs launched by us, and the observation of weather conditions over enemy territory."

Ridenour saw the impending decline in the importance of the manned bomber, and it is evident that he recognized the significance of the satellite as a means of surveillance. These speculations which had arisen in the "crystal ball gazing" of 1946 were reiterated by General James Gavin in a less subtle manner a decade later:

> The ICBM is the consequence of manned bomber obsolescence . . . not the cause. The manned bomber will become obsolete when effective [armed] surface-to-air missiles can be employed against it . . . as soon as they are on site in numbers.

> If manned bombers cannot penetrate enemy territory [in the future] then certainly manned observation aircraft cannot.[20] Observation must be provided by an unmanned reconnaissance vehicle . . . for a short-range missile it will be a recoverable drone operated by remote control; for an ICBM it will, in time, be a satellite.[21]

Time—The Essence

Time is impartial and indiscriminate, and does not wait for individuals, nations, or ideologies. Subsequent to the release of the initial satellite study in May, RAND issued on October 18, 1946, a special report, *The Time Factor In The Satellite Program*, written by Dr. James Lipp (who is considered to have been Dr. Hall's equivalent on the Air Force Satellite program) in support of *The World-Circling Spaceship*. Excerpts from this report contain several rather accurate guesses as to immediacy of satellite developments and the trends to expect in competition from foreign powers:

> The possibility of constructing a satellite has been well publicized both here and in Germany and the data of the Germans are available to various possible enemies of the United States. Thus, from a competitive point of view, the decision to carry through a satellite development is a matter of timing, depending upon whether this country can afford to wait an appreciable length of time before launching definite activity. . . .

---

[20] This point was brought home to a startled American public in 1960 when a CIA U-2 "weather observation" aircraft fell to earth near Sverdlosk in Central Russia, victim of a Soviet anti-aircraft rocket. Although details are not available, and even pilot Powers appears uncertain, it is believed that it was indeed the close proximity explosion of a surface-to-air rocket which brought the plane down.

[21] General James Gavin, *War and Peace in the Space Age*, (New York, 1958), p. 11.

Since the United States is far ahead of any country in both airplanes and sea power, and since others are abreast of the United States in rocket applications, we can expect strong competition *in the latter field as being the quickest shortcut for challenging this country's position.* (Italics added.)

Another implied advantage of satellite development which transcends any financial commitments was touched upon:

> The psychological effect of a satellite will in less dramatic fashion parallel that of the atom bomb. It will make possible an unspoken threat to every other nation that we can send a guided missile to any spot on earth. Combined with our present monopoly of the atom bomb such a threat in being will give pause to any nation which contemplates aggressive war against the United States. It will be necessary to produce such deterrents from time to time because of the probability that other nations will eventually produce atom bombs of their own.

From a purely psychological standpoint the author noted that ". . . as an aid to maintaining the present prestige and diplomatic bargaining power of the U. S., it would be well to give the world the impression of an ever-widening gap between our technology and any other possible rivals since other nations are obviously hoping to play for time in an effort to overcome the existing lead."

The special report stated that the United States might conceivably have to be content with spending anywhere from $50 to $150 million to orbit a satellite by the early 1950's. Recognizing the underdeveloped state-of-the-art in this country, the report concluded on this terse note:

> It is hardly necessary to point out that most of the reasons for beginning a satellite development program cannot be assigned values in terms of dollars and cents lost in each year of delay. It is equally clear that some of the items discussed are of sufficient importance that the probable cost of the project becomes insignificant. . . .
> It is therefore recommended that the satellite be considered not as an academic study but as a project which merits planning and establishing of a priority in the research program of the Army Air Force.

Following the Navy and Army Air Force satellite presentations in June 1946, the Aeronautical Board arrived at an agreement to let the services pursue their independent studies separately and postponed any jurisdictional assignment—thereby confirming the situation established by General LeMay in March of that year. Regardless of the Aeronautical Board's failure to authorize a single formal program, the Navy satellite studies were ordered to continue. Evidently having received word of the Army Air Force study prior to its formal presentation, the Chief of Naval Operations directed the Bureau of Aeronautics to proceed with further preliminary investigations of an earth satellite vehicle in May 1946. The stated purpose of the continuing investigation was to " contribute to the advancement of knowledge in the field of guided missiles, communications, meteorology, and other technical fields with military applications." [22] The Navy single-stage rocket satellite study was to continue through mid-1948, conducted by the structures division in the BuAer, and under a joint contract by Glenn L. Martin—Baltimore Company and Aerojet, in addition to the NAA structural study already noted. Further investigation of borohydride fuels as an alternative for hydrogen had been disappointing in spite of the optimistic early estimates of high specific impulse based on results of theoretical chemistry.

Project RAND also commenced a second study in mid-1946, directed toward preparing more detailed specifications which would set forth minimum requirements for achieving a successful satellite vehicle. This work was completed in late 1946, and the reports were published in April 1947. General conclusions resulting from these studies pointed to an optimum arrangement for a satellite booster as a three-stage rocket employing liquid hydrogen-oxygen for propellants and having an initial gross weight in the range of 82,000 pounds.[23] A final orbit altitude of 350 miles was recommended, and over-all cost was estimated at $82 million, including sufficient rounds for preliminary testing.

Results of this second RAND study, which was actually a refinement of the *World-Circling Spaceship*, indicated a need for additional research in several vital component areas; certain subsystems had to be further perfected before a realizable satellite system would operate satisfactorily. As noted previously, at no time was there a lack of confidence in available talent or materiels for building air frames or developing rocket engines and guidance systems that would be sufficient to put *something* on orbit. Rather, the areas which needed to be further advanced were those which *would make that something useful* and not simply amount to blasting rocks into orbit. Several of the significant areas which required additional research and development were

[22] Eugene M. Emme, *Aeronautics and Astronautics, 1915-1960*, (Washington, D. C., 1961), pp. 51-52.

[23] A weight reduction of some 147,669 pounds over previous 1946 RAND estimates for a conventional fueled four-stage rocket.

guidance and flight-control, orbital attitude control, ground-space communications techniques and equipment, and dependable auxiliary power sources. In 1947 there was no miniaturized circuitry and no solar energy devices nor other prime internal power sources that would operate for any length of time in free space.

When the second Project RAND study was published in early 1947, the Army Air Force was preparing to reorganize as a separate service under the National Security Act, which became law on July 26, 1947. The National Military Establishment replaced the War Department on September 17, 1947, and the new cabinet post of Secretary of Defense was created. Decisions as to which service would have jurisdiction for development and deployment of long range rockets were postponed by the RDB.[24] None of the three services was immediately authorized to further the development of long range ICBM-type rockets needed to put a satellite into orbit.[25]

As a consequence of severe economies in the Military Research and Development programs directed by the Administration in December 1946, the limited satellite studies in the United States came to a virtual halt. From mid-1947 until mid-1948 only the Navy Bureau of Aeronautics continued satellite research activity. The Air Force discontinued work on the satellite and ICBM programs and placed primary emphasis on strategic bombers and air-breathing ram or pulse-jet guided missiles which operated in the atmosphere and were, therefore, legitimately within Air Force jurisdiction. About the time the Navy satellite studies were terminated due to lack of funds, the Air Force satellite study program recommenced in 1949; in part this was due to advances in guidance and control and the miniaturization of some hardware made by U.S. industry while working on other rocket programs, and in part due to new directions received from the Research and Development Board. In early 1949, RAND was directed to begin extensive studies on the potential military utility of earth satellites, including work on the possible advantages of using such devices for purposes of observation.

The Possibility of Satellites for Aerial Observation

In Europe, at the turn of the century, rockets had been developed specifically for the purpose of tactical aerial surveillance. Work on

[24] The JRDB was reorganized as the Research and Development Board (RDB) under the Department of Defense. Dr. Vannevar Bush was appointed its first chairman.
[25] The U.S. Air Force finally received such authority from the Joint Chiefs of Staff on March 15, 1950.

this advanced concept of applied aerial observation was first described
by A. Bujard in a paper entitled " Rockets in the Service of Photog-
raphy " at a conference in Stuttgart, Germany in 1906. The paper
dealt primarily with the work of a German engineer, Alfred Maul,
who first devised and tested rocket-borne camera devices in 1904.
Maul continued his work, improving the size and reliability of rocket,
camera, and final descent systems:

> The largest model, made in 1912, was equipped with a stabilizing
> gyroscope, reached an altitude of 2600 feet, had a take-off weight
> of 42 kilograms (92½ pounds) and carried a camera with a plate
> size of 200 by 250 millimeters, or about 8 by 10 inches. The
> rocket was ignited electrically from a distance and was reliable,
> but by the time this model was ready it was also possible to aim
> a camera at the ground from an airplane.[26]

Arrival of the airplane as a dependable platform from which aerial
photographs could be taken displaced the development of balloon
and rocket surveillance systems. Although zeppelins and dirigibles
were flown from World War I on, airplanes performed the bulk of
the required surveillance tasks for the various nations. An early mani-
festation of this change in thinking occurred in August 1915, when
the United States Naval Observatory requested the Eastman Kodak
Company to develop a camera capable of taking aerial photographs
from heights of 1,000 to 2,000 yards.

Nevertheless, not all minds were confined to the altitudes particular
to aircraft during the first half of the century. "As early as 1926,
a Leningrad scientific journal carried an article by V. P. Glushko,
now a prominent scientist and military technologist, in which he quoted
an earlier article by H. Oberth, a German (sic) professor, stating
that ' one can observe and photograph inaccessible countries ' by using
a giant mirror mounted on a satellite." [27] Progress in rocket technology
by 1947 brought many earlier ideas to life. For advanced observation
techniques, the pendulum now swung back to the early pre-airplane
observation concepts. This time a satellite would be visualized as an
observation platform.

[26] Willy Ley, *Rockets, Missiles, and Space Travel*, (New York: rev. ed.,
1957), pp. 106-07.
[27] *Soviet Space Programs: Organization, Plans, Goals, and International Implications*, Staff Report, Committee on Aeronautical and Space Sciences, U. S. Senate,
May 31, 1962, p. 56.

Satellite Studies in the United States, 1948-1949

The Air Force/RAND satellite development effort, which began in 1946, progressed through production of type specifications in 1947 and then came to a temporary halt awaiting a Research and Development Board go-ahead on work in those areas requiring expanded and intensified study. During 1947 the Navy studies which had sparked the Air Force satellite effort reached the point of detailed subsystem analysis, particularly in the area of auxiliary power.

In September 1947, the Research and Development Board formally assigned responsibility for coordinating work on the earth satellite programs, scattered among the separate services, to its Committee on Guided Missiles.[28] Shortly thereafter the Committee notified the services that a review of contemporary earth satellite programs would be conducted in early 1948. The Technical Evaluation Group of the Committee on Guided Missiles, under the chairmanship of Clark Millikan, completed a review of the Navy CEFSR and USAF Project RAND satellite programs in March 1948 and released a statement that "neither the Navy nor the USAF has as yet established either a military or a scientific utility commensurate with the presently expected cost of a satellite vehicle. However, the question of utility deserves further study and examination." [29] This was the same story: no support without a military requirement. But this time the decision came from a scientific agency staffed by civilians. Further recommendations were made by the Technical Evaluation Group, "some of which were restrictive or limiting in nature, but which nevertheless encouraged continued efforts along various lines, including continuation of the Project RAND studies of the utility of such a vehicle under joint Navy, USAF sponsorship." [30] At this time Rear Admiral D. V. Gallery attempted to place the Navy as joint sponsor of the Project RAND effort; however, this new proposal for a combined program was refused by the Air Force.

In September 1948, the Committee on Guided Missiles of the Research Development Board " approved recommendations that the Army Hermes Project ' be given the task of providing the National Military Establishment with a continuing analysis of the long-range rocket problem as an expansion of their [study] task on an earth satellite vehicle.' " [31]

[28] *A Chronology of Missile and Astronautic Events*, p. 11.
[29] Hall, *op. cit.*
[30] *Ibid.*
[31] Emme, *op. cit.*, p. 60. According to Dr. Harvey Hall, late in 1948 Army Ordnance formally accepted a directive from the Technical Evaluation Group (of the RDB) *not* to pursue a task on the Earth Satellite Program.

The first public announcement of an American satellite program appeared in the *First Annual Report of the Secretary of Defense,* issued in late 1948. Secretary James Forrestal reported:

> The Earth Satellite Vehicle Program, which was being carried out independently by each military service, was assigned to the Committee on Guided Missiles for coordination. To provide an integrated program with resultant elimination of duplication, the committee recommended that current efforts in this field be limited to studies and component designs; well-defined areas of such research have been allocated to each of the three military departments.[32]

Forrestal's early veiled announcement of the U. S. satellite program caused a great deal of consternation among those working on the satellite project in the United States in 1949 and who were trying to preserve its aspect of secrecy. The ill will engendered by this report was not confined solely to America, however. Within months the Soviet Journal *New Times* made specific reference to the "madman Forrestal's idea of an Earth Satellite" as an "instrument of blackmail." It should be noted, however, that as early as December 1947, *New Times* had "ridiculed the alleged American use of 'Hitlerite ideas' and in particular the 'fantastic' idea of reconnaissance satellites."[33] After this occurrence, *no official reference* in open literature was made to an American satellite effort until November 1954, when the Department of Defense, in a terse two-sentence comment, reported that studies continued to be made in the Earth Satellite Vehicle Program. The statement, approved by Secretary of Defense Charles Wilson, was issued after an earlier press conference statement by the Secretary that he was unaware of an American satellite program.

The Navy Bureau of Aeronautics' studies conducted on the High Altitude Test Vehicle since 1945 had progressed as far as they possibly could go on paper when the Air Force rejected the second proposal for a joint satellite program in mid-1948. Any further effort now had to go into hardware and component parts contracts. A cost analysis and proposal for a program consisting of 12 satellite vehicles (figured on the basis of at least two satellites attaining orbit), set at $150,000,000

---

[32] *First Annual Report of the Secretary of Defense,* (Washington, D. C., 1948), p. 129.

[33] *Soviet Space Programs,* p. 57. Soviet comment on the possible American application of satellites for surveillance purposes appeared again in January 1952, when *Red Star* "attacked Secretary of Defense Forrestal and Dr. Wernher von Braun for having written about the possible military use of satellite vehicles to 'peep in other countries as through a keyhole.'" *Ibid.*

together with a five-year lead-time from go-ahead to first launch, had been turned down by the Research and Development Board in 1948. The total funds spent by the Navy over the three-year period for studies on the single-stage HATV project had come to about $2,000,000. With Research and Development Board restrictions against building any flight vehicles to support a satellite program, and with no funds authorized by the Navy to move into this development area even in clandestine fashion or to pursue further utility studies, the Bureau of Aeronautics was forced to abandon its satellite project.

Still, one last determined attempt to maintain the Navy satellite program was made in late 1948 by Dr. Hall and the members of his organization. At that time an ad hoc subcommittee in the National Advisory Committee for Aeronautics (NACA)[34] was formed to explore and organize methods of obtaining information on the upper atmosphere above 20,000 feet. (The data was needed to provide aircraft firms with information on atmospheric drag and heating effects at these high altitudes for use in the design of advanced jet aircraft.) The idea advanced by this die-hard group of space scientists was based on their three years of study; it consisted of a liquid hydrogen-oxygen High Altitude Test Vehicle reconfigured to a super-performance sounding rocket which would rise to an altitude in excess of 400 miles and thereby, it was hoped, rally financial support for an earth satellite vehicle. The sounding rocket proposal was backed up by a detailed engineering report submitted by the Glenn L. Martin Company under a BuAer contract. Formal acceptance and support for this new rocket was sought not only from the NACA Subcommittee on the Upper Atmosphere, but also from the Research and Development Board, Geophysical Sciences Committee. What were the results?

> No record has ever been found of RDB Geophysical Sciences Committee action. The legal position assumed by BuAer here, in spite of the Technical Evaluation Group (of the RDB) stipulation against flight vehicles in support of the Earth Satellite Vehicle Program, was to the effect that the high altitude sounding rocket could be properly justified under BuAer's long range rocket program rather than by the satellite program. (Although the proposal was accepted by the NACA Subcommittee on the Upper Atmosphere), funds, however, were not forthcoming even for this lesser but significant effort so that this promising program essentially came to an end around the close of 1948.[35]

---

[34] The immediate predecessor of the National Aeronautics and Space Administration (NASA).

[35] Hall, *op. cit.* There is an ironic historical wrinkle to this commentary.

These various occurrences resulted in a deferral of Navy studies of a satellite project until many years later, and no significant satellite project was pursued by the U. S. Army until the Redstone rocket team joined in the proposed Project Orbiter in 1954. The Air Force was the only service which actively continued an earth satellite program from 1949 forward, and then primarily in the form of RAND Corporation studies until a formal Air Force satellite program was authorized in the mid-1950's.

The Satellite as a Political and Psychological Weapon

Among the satellite studies resumed by RAND in 1949 was one on the *utility of satellites*. A study conference, drawn from consultants in both the physical and social sciences, concerned itself specifically with an intensified examination of the satellite as a *political* and *psychological* weapon. The primary aim of this conference [36] was to determine what probable effects the orbiting of a satellite might have upon the ruling hierarchy in the Soviet Union, especially if, through use of photographic or television facilities, it possessed the capabilty of penetrating the shroud of secrecy draped over the Iron Curtain countries.

This particular approach to the utilization of a satellite was determined by: (a) the Research and Development Board directives to continue study of the utility of a satellite—the desirability of achieving certain sociopolitical objectives which might result from orbiting a satellite; and (b) the conclusions of the 1946-1947 RAND studies, i. e., that existing state-of-the-art precluded the use of a satellite as a destructive weapon, but there was the possibility of using the vehicle in a passive military capacity for communications or surveillance purposes.

In setting about the study, personnel assigned to the project first established a guideline of basic satellite characteristics as follows: (1) It would carry a small payload. (2) Its capacity for destruction would be insignificant compared to existing methods. (3) Its orbit

The advanced structures engineering and propulsion system specifications contained in the United States Navy BuAer sounding rocket proposal were several years ahead of equivalent Soviet rocket designs when the project was allowed to die for want of support. At that time the Soviet Union was just beginning high altitude research with large conventional-fueled sounding rockets which culminated in parachute recovery of ejected capsules and animals a short time later, one of the first early steps towards the Russian achievement of an earth satellite vehicle.

[36] Quoted material contained in this section was extracted from RAND Research Memorandum RM-120 (unclassified), unless otherwise noted.

could be chosen to pass over selected areas of the earth. (4) It could not be brought down by present weapons or devices. (5) It could be made visible or non-visible to the naked eye for certain periods of time and at certain intervals. (6) Radio signals or voice messages could be transmitted from the vehicle to listeners equipped with proper receivers on the ground. (7) It could be equipped with photographic and television facilities. (8) Its development in-being would be a costly undertaking.

Having established these guidelines, the conferees categorized and examined the specific functions which a vehicle retaining these characteristics might perform while on orbit:

(1) *The satellite as a spectacle:* The study determined that a satellite might cause initial mystery, consternation, fear, or even panic; but it was deemed unlikely that the impact would be of major significance or of lasting duration.

(2) *The satellite as a demonstration of U.S. technological superiority:* Here the value of a satellite was concluded to be "limited"—that other weapons and devices might register greater impact. As indicative of the growing self-confidence evident in the late 1940s (prior to the announcement of a Soviet A-bomb) the study noted that "the appearance of a satellite would only confirm existing Soviet assumptions concerning the advanced state of long-range missile development in the United States."

(3) *The satellite as a device for communications:* The use of the term "communication" in this context in no way related to present day concepts of a 24-hour stationary communications satellite. Rather, the study visualized communication techniques as most effective for disseminating propaganda. Its value as an attention-getter was minimized.

(4) *The satellite as a surveillance instrument:* The study noted that a most useful avenue of approach would be one of utilizing the satellite in a capacity for weather prediction, as well as for the purpose of military surveillance.

(5) *The satellite as an instrument of political strategy:* Hypotheses advanced about the intrinsic nature of the Soviet regime led the study to conclude that "major intelligence secrets obtained through a visible or non-visible satellite, and then disclosed to the Soviet government, may produce results of a magnitude eclipsing all other possible uses of the vehicle. No other weapon or technique known today offers comparable promise as an instrument for influencing Soviet political behavior."

General conclusions of this RAND study conference placed prime emphasis on the satellite as an "instrument of political strategy," that is, the utility of a satellite probably would reside in its potential as an instrument for the achievement of political/psychological goals if the surveillance capacity of the vehicle were exploited "in a comprehensive, imaginative strategy designed to register maximum impact upon the leaders of the Soviet Union." The satellite would be developed into a surveillance instrument which could penetrate the enforced secrecy behind the iron curtain. Assuming that this approach could be achieved, two possible psychological objectives were considered under separate situations:

(1) If information obtained by satellite observation were systematically conveyed or leaked to key Soviet Officials, suspicion, disruption and possible purges on high levels of the Soviet political and military structure might follow.
(2) If pertinent data were made public and reinforced by dramatic indications that secrecy was no longer possible in the modern world, a major reorientation in Soviet political calculations and plans (e. g., concerning international inspection of atomic energy installations) might follow.

RAND hoped that disclosure of information acquired by a satellite would place Soviet leaders in a position where they would not be able to escape the necessity of revising the basic Marxist-Leninist assumptions and principles (inevitable warfare joined by the USSR) which guided their behavior. The possible reaction in the Soviet hierarchy, in terms of this study, rested upon the recognition of the Politburo's particular vulnerability to "hard facts" and the premium placed upon "realistic adjustments." "If used as an instrument of political power, the satellite can be translated into a hard fact to which realistic adjustment becomes necessary."

Several suggestions were advanced for refining the use of the satellite to achieve the several political/psychological objectives. The suggestions ranged from painting it black (thereby making it invisible), to what appropriate message might be relayed to ground receivers.[37] Debate was even given to the legal complications which might arise from its orbital path over nations considered unfriendly to America.[38]

[37] At a much later date Dr. L. N. Ridenour, a member of this study group, remarked that during a meeting on this topic a young engineer ventured the thought that the message should be "God bless you," whereupon another member immediately countered with "No, it should be, 'This is God, Bless you.'"
[38] This was resolved by noting that a satellite which remains in a North-South orbit can not be accountable for the earth's rotation beneath it which carries every country sweeping by.

At the termination of the study conference specific recommendations were made to the parent RAND Corporation:

(1) The conference urged the RAND Corporation to stress to the Air Force the possible opportunity afforded by the surveillance potential of a satellite vehicle.

(2) RAND was advised to explore in more complete and more systematic detail the assumptions and possibilities advanced for the political/psychological utilization of the vehicle.

(3) On the basis of its deliberations the conference further recommended that the United States, at the highest policy level, be informed of the unique political/psychological opportunities provided by this non-violent instrumentality.

The RAND Corporation, which organized the study conference primarily as an exploratory method for the study of the psychological effects of unconventional military devices, took these conclusions and recommendations under consideration. Implementation of a satellite program based upon conference recommendations was never undertaken. However, emphasis remained attached to a passive surveillance application when RAND began serious component studies and designs for an earth satellite in the following year (1950), after authority to develop long-range booster rockets was initially made in favor of the Air Force by the Department of Defense. These later satellite studies, 1950-1956, are another story.

In Retrospect

The group of consultants who conducted the 1949 Air Force-RAND satellite study had been seeking solutions to existing problems in an effort to deter the possibility of armed conflict with the Soviet Union. The study was concerned solely with research in the realm of plausible sociopolitical reaction to given physical phenomena. The solution was designed to take advantage of certain conditions within a given historical moment. When viewed in terms of current Soviet space accomplishments and the recent revision of Marxist-Leninist principles outlined at the 21st and 22nd Party Congresses, one is inclined to dismiss the conclusions as far-fetched. Given the conditions shortly after the Second World War (i. e., during the Soviet pre-atomic/Stalinist era), a number of these early propositions assume greater significance, especially since several of the psychological propositions were of a "timeless" or universal nature. Had the suggested course of action been implemented, it might well have succeeded. This becomes apparent when one gives thought to *the impact that Sputniks I and II had upon the "ruling hierarchy" in the United States in 1957.* The initial Soviet satellite successes more than fulfilled the over-all political/ psychological expectations of the 1949 RAND study conference—in reverse. It precipitated Congressional investigations into United States missile and satellite programs. Defense Department reorganizations were recommended. Bitter accusations on the "missile gap" were traded among top military and Administration personalities, followed by a number of resignations of key personnel in the military services. Subsequently, the Administration with the Congress created NASA and established new control agencies to "coordinate" national space activities.

With the first Soviet satellite in orbit in 1957, West Berlin's *Tagesspiegel* lamented that the propaganda impact of the event—the evidence it conveyed of Russian superiority in a field of incalculable importance —would be most serious in underdeveloped nations "whose narrow tie to the West has been maintained only by their belief that it represented the peak in technical civilization." In England, Ritchie Calder, science writer for the *New Statesman and Nation,* wrote: "This (Sputnik) is a technological achievement which must shatter forever any illusions about western engineering superiority." And in the United States Bernard Baruch expressed these views in the *New York Herald Tribune:* "America is worried. It should be. We have been set back severely, not only in matters of defense and security, but in the contest for the support and confidence of the peoples throughout the world."

The first satellites, as RAND predicted, did become instruments of political strategy, but not for the United States. The early RAND prediction of probable political/psychological reactions to the first satellites was, of itself, not an exceptional accomplishment. *The true originality and strategic importance of this device, recognized in 1946 by Project RAND and the Navy CEFSR, was never completely understood by the American Government until October 1957.* Even the 1949 RAND study conference ignored the possibility that the USSR might orbit a satellite before the USA. This conviction ran in confluence with a general tendency to disregard Soviet technical accomplishments. As General Medaris, (former head of the U. S. Army Ballistic Missile Agency [ABMA] at Redstone Arsenal), dryly commented:

> During all this time, the Russians were known to be working on rocket development, but it was fashionable to think of them as retarded folk who depended mainly on a few captured German scientists for their achievements, if any. And since the cream of

the German planners had surrendered to the Americans, so the argument ran, there was nothing to worry about.[39]

In 1949, there was, and would continue to remain for a number of years, a genuine failure to realize the tremendous strategic advantage it would give the Russians to be first into space.

[39] Major General J. B. Medaris, *Countdown for Decision*, (New York: 1960), p. 45.

MAJOR U. S.
ROCKET PROGRAMS

"One can resist the invasion of armies, but not the invasion of ideas."

—Victor Hugo

"The present would be full of all possible futures, if the past had not already projected a pattern upon it."

—André Gide

11. *NRL Viking No. 10* being prepared for launching from White Sands Proving Ground, N. M., on May 7, 1954. It equalled world's altitude record of 136 miles, reaching speeds of 4,000-mph. Viking No. 10 collected research data on the upper atmosphere which was flashed to ground stations by radio. (Glenn L. Martin Photo)

13. *Attempted launching of Vanguard Test Vehicle No. 3* (TV-3) December 6, 1957, first flight test of all three live rocket stages. It was the first and last failure of the first-stage rocket and was widely publicized as the U. S. attempt to launch its first I. G. Y. satellite. This photograph remains the general public image of the entire Vanguard program as a " propaganda failure," despite its ultimate scientific and technological contributions. (U. S. Navy) **14.** *Lift-off of NASA's VAN-GUARD II satellite* on February 17, 1959, which made cloud-cover photographs. (NASA)

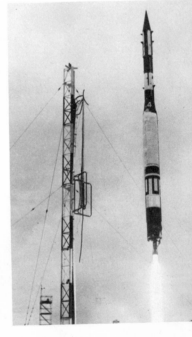

12. *Dr. John P. Hagen,* Director of Project Vanguard, holds a staff meeting at the Naval Research Laboratory. Left to right: Dr. Joseph T. Siry, Head, Theory and Analysis Branch; Daniel G. Mazur, Manager, Vanguard Operations Group, Patrick Air Force Base; James M. Bridger, Head, Vehicle Branch; Cdr. W. E. Berg, Navy Program Officer; Dr. Hagen; J. Paul Walsh, Deputy Project Director; Milton W. Rosen, Technical Director; John T. Mengel, Head, Tracking and Guidance Branch; Dr. Homer E. Newell, Jr., Science Program Coordinator. (NRL)

15. *EXPLORER I.* Final preparation for the night launching of the first U. S. satellite on January 31, 1958. Insert shows closeup of satellite and upper stages atop the Jupiter-C booster. (U. S. Army)

16. *Hermann Oberth (forefront)* with officials of the Army Ballistic Missile Agency at Huntsville, Alabama, in 1956. Left to right: Dr. Ernst Stuhlinger (seated); Major General H. N. Toftoy, Commanding Officer, author of "Project Paperclip"; Dr. Eberhard Rees, Deputy Director, Development Operations Division; and Dr. Wernher von Braun, Director, Development Operations Division. (ABMA Photo)

17. *Mercury-Redstone (MR-3)* with Astronaut Alan B. Shepard (Lt. Comdr., USN) lifts off from Cape Canaveral on May 5, 1961. (NASA Photo) **18.** *Saturn C-1 Space Booster (SA-1)* makes first test flight from Cape Canaveral on October 27, 1962. First test flights of this eight-engine clustered first-stage, generating 1.5 million pounds of thrust, were successful. Saturn development began in 1958 based on Juno V design. (NASA Photo) **19.** *USAF Thor* launch from Vandenberg AFB, California in 1959. (USAF Photo)

20. *General Bernard A. Schriever* is shown here (center) in front of Atlas space booster at Point Arguello, California. On his left is Colonel Joseph J. Cody, Test Wing Commander at Vandenberg AFB, while on his right is Major Patrick B. Mulcaire, Ballistic Missile Division Site Commander. (USAF Photo) 21. *NASA three-stage Delta launches 280-lb. meteorological satellite TIROS II* just before dawn on November 23, 1960. Using Thor first-stage and improved Vanguard upper-stages, the Delta launch vehicle compiled an impressive record of 21 successful satellite launchings out of 22 attempts by 1964. (NASA Photo)

22. *The Secretary and the Chief of Staff of the U. S. Air Force* examine the historic gold-plated capsule of DISCOVERER XIII, first successfully recovered orbital payload, which had made 16 orbits in August 1960. Fifty-star American flag which DISCOVERER XIII carried was later presented to President Eisenhower at the White House. Shown here, left to right, are Colonel Clarence L. Battle, Colonel Charles G. Mathison, Lt. Colonel David Henderson (behind Gen. White), Chief of Staff General Thomas D. White, Secretary of the Air Force Dudley Sharp, Lt. General Bernard A. Schriever, Major General Osmond J. Ritland, and Sergeant Clyde Noble. (USAF Photo)

23. *USAF Atlas-E missile launches* from Cape Canaveral on December 20, 1961. (USAF)

24. *Calibration of Mercury-Atlas (MA-2)* in a horizontal position in preparation for launch early in 1961. (NASA) **25.** *Mercury-Atlas* undergoing a static firing test at Cape Canaveral, Florida. (NASA) →

26. *First flight test of the Titan II* from Cape Canaveral on March 16, 1962. (USAF) 27. *Countdown in the submarine USS George Washington*, for the first successful underseas launching of the Polaris missile on July 20, 1960. Shown (left to right) are Rear Admiral Levering Smith (USN) of the Special Project Office; Captain Norville Ward, Commander of Submarine Squadron 14; Vice Admiral William Raborn, Chief of the Special Project Office; and a member of the crew. (U. S. Navy)

The Redstone, Jupiter, and Juno

WERNHER VON BRAUN

REDSTONE WAS THE first large ballistic missile developed in the United States. From the Redstone came Jupiter, the nation's first intermediate range ballistic missile (IRBM). Redstone and Jupiter compiled a noteworthy list of "firsts" in the early years of free man's effort to explore and understand the newly accessible environment of space.

The measure of their technological success, still largely to be reckoned, is a tribute to the collective dedication and skill of the people who brought Redstone and Jupiter into being. This team of technicians and scientists first served the U. S. Army and then the U. S. civilian space agency. Our first assignment on Alabama soil was in 1950 with the Ordnance Guided Missile Center (OGMC) at Redstone Arsenal, then in charge of the entire Army missile program. While remaining at the same Huntsville facility, our development team became, in turn, the Guided Missile Development Division of the Ordnance Missile Laboratories (GMDD) until 1956, and then the Development Operations Division of the Army Ballistic Missile Agency (ABMA) from 1956 to 1960. In July 1960, this group, many of whom had been active in rocketry since the early 1930's, became the nucleus of the new George C. Marshall Space Flight Center of the National Aeronautics and Space Administration.[1]

The basic Redstone and Jupiter missiles carried names appropriate to their different configurations and missions. The Redstone with modifications became the Jupiter A, Jupiter C, Juno I, and the Mercury-Redstone. Jupiter assumed the name Juno II when three upper stages were added and it became a space booster. Among the contributions of these rocket systems were the following milestones of rocketry and space exploration:[2]

* Dr. von Braun is Director of the NASA Marshall Space Flight Center, Huntsville, Alabama.

[1] President Dwight D. Eisenhower, Executive Order 10793, Jan. 14, 1960; also *Army-NASA Transfer Plan*, Dec. 11, 1959; and David S. Akens, *Historical Origins of the George C. Marshall Space Flight Center*, MHM-1 (Huntsville, 1960).

[2] Ernst Stuhlinger, "Army Activities in Space—A History," *IRE Transactions on Military Electronics*, Vol. MIL-4 (April-July 1960), p. 68; also E. M. Emme, *Aeronautics and Astronautics, 1915-1960* (Washington, 1961). (Ed. Note: It should

- Use of the first U. S. inertial guidance system (Redstone in 1953).
- First successful U. S.-developed large ballistic missile (Redstone in 1953).
- First long-range firing of a U. S. ballistic missile (Jupiter C, on September 20, 1956).
- First successful launch of a U. S. IRBM (Jupiter, on May 31, 1957).
- First recovery intact of a man-made object from space, demonstrating ablative solution of the aerodynamic re-entry heating problem (Jupiter C, on August 8, 1957).
- First Free World earth satellite (EXPLORER I, launched by Juno I on January 31, 1958).
- First recovery of a full-scale IRBM nose cone (Jupiter, on May 17, 1958).
- First deep-space radiation experiment (PIONEER III, launched by Juno II on December 8, 1958).
- First deep-space telemetry success to 400,000 miles (PIONEER IV, launched by Juno II on March 3, 1959).
- First successful U. S. launching of animals into space with successful recovery (Monkeys " Able " and " Baker," by Jupiter on May 28, 1959).
- First American launched in space (Astronaut Alan B. Shepard, Jr., by Mercury-Redstone on May 5, 1961).

The Redstone

The Redstone missile, sometimes called an " offspring " of the V-2, had its origin in the Hermes C project.[3] The Ordnance Guided Missile Center at Redstone Arsenal was asked by the Army Chief of Ordnance in July 1950 to perform a feasibility study on a 500-mile-range rocket weapon. The Korean War had just started.

Late in 1949 the Ordnance Corps had selected Redstone Arsenal, an Army Chemical Corps installation in World War II, as a centralized location for its growing family of battlefield missile programs. Early the next year, the German technical group of about 120 who had

be noted that the V-2 ancestor of the Redstone, with a JPL Wac Corporal as a second stage, achieved a record altitude of 244 miles on Feb. 24, 1949, from White Sands, N. M.)

[3] *Final Report, Project Hermes, V-2 Missile Program,* General Electric Report No. R52 A0510 (September 1952); also Maj. Gen. H. N. Toftoy, " Army Missile Development," *Army Information Digest,* Vol. 11 (December 1956).

helped on the V-2 research launchings at White Sands Proving Ground, transferred with supporting technical personnel to Huntsville, Alabama. The Hermes C-1 study was handed to our team, and the design and development of the new rocket with a 500-mile range was given a very high priority by the Chief of Ordnance in the fall of 1950.

The development plan evolving from our investigation was based on our experience in rocketry and on available hardware. We decided to adapt to our purpose the liquid propulsion system then used in the Navaho test missile—a North American Aviation (NAA) engine. The guidance system, also based on past work, would be an inertial system with a stabilized platform and accelerometers. We favored this method because it was simple, reliable, accurate—and available. And so our missile took form on the drawing board, incorporating some reliable features from the V-2 based on the Hermes study with numerous refinements and new ideas. As design tasks proceeded, the Army redefined the weapon's basic characteristics, established a time schedule, and assigned the project to 1A priority. Plans now called for a surface-to-surface ballistic missile of 200-mile range with high mobility for deployment in the field.

Hardware development progressed through 1951. NAA's Rocket-dyne Division was awarded a contract to modify the promising Navaho engine. A 12-vehicle flight program was approved. OGMC began fabricating components at Huntsville for the first of the test missiles, and the first prototype engine was delivered to us by the contractor in 1952. The Korean War had, of course, increased the urgency of all military development programs. Along with the design changes our new missile lost its Hermes identity. Having no official name, it was variously referred to as "Ursa" and "Major." It was officially christened "Redstone," taken from the name of the Arsenal itself, on April 8, 1952.

Chrysler Corporation received the prime contract to manufacture Redstone research and development (R&D) missiles in June 1953. The same year, our group at Redstone Arsenal, under the command of then Brigadier General H. N. Toftoy, completed fabrication and assembly of the first Redstone missile. On August 20, 1953, the first test Redstone was fired at Cape Canaveral, Florida. There were guidance difficulties, but this brief flight of 8,000 yards was regarded as satisfactory for development purposes. Telemetered data from the test flight assisted us in making the necessary corrections of design weaknesses on succeeding missiles.

The Redstone R&D test flight program extended over the next five years, ending late in 1958. During this period, 37 Redstones were to be flown, testing missile structure, power plant, guidance and control equipment, tracking and telemetry, and other systems of the rocket. Of these 37 test vehicles, 17 were assembled by the Redstone Arsenal team and 20 were manufactured by Chrysler at its own plant. In rocket development, there is no substitute for numerous static firings and closely monitored test flights.

The test program resulted in extensive modification of the missile body and changes in the propulsion, guidance and control, and expulsion systems. The length of the missile was increased by 63 inches, and the body unit was modified from a thick-skinned, cone-cylinder-frustrum shape to a light-weight, cone-frustrum configuration. At the end of the test flight program we considered that we had a thoroughly proven missile ready for early Army tactical use, as well as some special uses for future missions. The Redstone medium-range ballistic missile that evolved from the five-year R&D program was 70 inches in diameter and 69 feet long. This single-stage vehicle was propelled by a rocket engine using liquid oxygen as oxidizer and an alcohol-water mixture as fuel. The power plant, developed by successive improvements through seven engine types from A-1 to A-7, was rated at 75,000 lbs. sea-level thrust, with a burning time of 121 seconds. Missile weight at launch was about 61,000 lbs. Capable of carrying conventional or nuclear warheads accurately to target at supersonic velocity, the Redstone system was mobile and designed for launching in the field under battle conditions.

The inertial guidance and control system, utilizing the ST-80 stabilized platform with guidance computers, permitted the Redstone to follow a pre-planned trajectory independent of outside influences. The flight profile was fed into the missile's program device prior to launch, and signals telemetered back to it activated the guidance system during flight. The missile was controlled during powered flight by aerodynamic tail surfaces and by movable carbon vanes in the engine exhaust jet.[4]

As the first large ballistic missile produced by the U. S. Army, the Redstone was fired in the field for the first time by Army troops during 1958. It was deployed into NATO forces in Europe the same year.[5]

---

[4] Grayson Merrill, *Principles of Guided Missile Design* (Princeton, 1959), p. 512; also F. I. Ordway III and Ronald C. Wakeford, *International Missile and Spacecraft Guide* (New York, 1960), p. 13.

[5] The Redstone was scheduled to be replaced in 1963 by the solid-propellant Pershing missile, also developed at Redstone Arsenal.

Jupiter A and Jupiter C

Two versions of the Redstone evolved during the missile test program and became significant in the early phases of the nation's space program. These were the Jupiter A and the Jupiter C.

The Jupiter A program was inaugurated at Redstone Arsenal late in 1955 in support of the Jupiter IRBM development program, then just beginning at the direction of the Department of Defense. The Jupiter A was a Redstone missile modified to check out components of the Jupiter IRBM. Twenty-five Jupiter A's were fired from Cape Canaveral between September 1955 and June 1958 and were actually a part of the 37-missile Redstone test flight program. Thus while we were increasing the reliability of the basic Redstone rocket we were also developing the Jupiter IRBM.

Far more dramatic was the Jupiter C story. The Jupiter C's first bid for attention came in 1954 when a detailed proposal for orbiting an earth satellite was prepared by our team of rocket engineers and scientists. This proposal, entitled " A Minimum Satellite Vehicle Based Upon Components Available From Missile Development of the Army Ordnance Corps," was submitted to the Department of Defense in the spring of 1955. The document asserted that the Army missile team could launch an earth satellite within a short time using rocket hardware then available. The proposed satellite booster was a Redstone missile with high-speed upper stages consisting of clusters of Loki solid-propellant rocket motors. The Jet Propulsion Laboratory (JPL) of California Institute of Technology and the Office of Naval Research then cooperated with GMDD to formulate our plan into a joint proposal called "Project Orbiter." By decision of the Department of Defense late in 1955, Project Vanguard, proposed by the Naval Research Laboratory, became the nation's approved satellite program. Consequently, Project Orbiter was officially shelved.[6]

We at Huntsville could not scrap the satellite idea, and we did not scrap our satellite-oriented hardware. The staging concept and the work already accomplished became the basis for the Jupiter C (Composite Re-entry Test Vehicle). With this vehicle we solved one of the most challenging problems of the Jupiter IRBM development program—aerodynamic heating of the IRBM warhead upon re-entering the earth's atmosphere. The physics of re-entry heating was a major problem in the development of ballistic missiles.

[6] Maj. Gen. John B. Medaris, " The Explorer Satellites," *Army Information Digest*, Vol. 13 (October 1958), p. 8; also Erik Bergaust, *Reaching for the Stars* (New York, 1961).

Our group was then part of the ABMA, formed at Redstone Arsenal in 1956 to develop the Jupiter IRBM and get the Redstone operational with field Army units. ABMA and JPL worked closely together to develop the Jupiter C for the nose cone re-entry test program. The Jupiter C consisted of a high-performance version of the Redstone

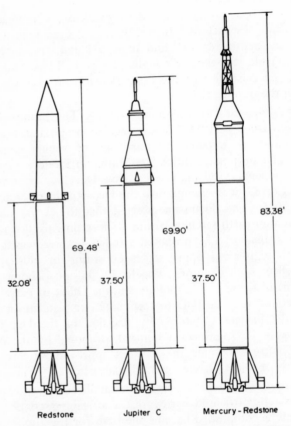

Redstone   Jupiter C   Mercury - Redstone

Fig. 9 Comparative size of Redstone configurations (NASA)

missile as first stage, and two clustered stages of solid-propellant rocket motors developed by JPL as the second and third stages. The solid motors, a scaled version of the Sergeant missile motor, were about four feet long and six inches in diameter. Eleven of the rockets were clustered in a ring to form the second stage, and three identical rockets were fitted inside this ring as the third stage.[7] Each solid motor generated about 1,600 lbs. thrust in space.

The Redstone missile was modified in the Jupiter C to increase the tankage so that it could hold more fuel and oxidizer, and thus extend the engine burning time. The engine itself was modified to burn a more powerful fuel called Hydyne (unsymmetrical dimethylhydrazine and diethylene triamine), boosting the first-stage thrust to 83,000 lbs. Also, the forward section of the Redstone was strengthened to support the launcher of the upper stages, and a spatial-attitude control system was designed to align the instrument section and upper stages precisely with the local horizon at the apex of the trajectory, following separation of the booster.[8]

The upper stages of the Jupiter C vehicle sat in an aluminum tub-like container that rested on a conical projection atop the instrument section. Two electric motors spun the tub. The launcher tub was rotated at high speed prior to launch, and the spin rate was increased in flight, to provide ballistic stability and reduce the effects of thrust dispersion.

The first Jupiter C was launched on September 20, 1956. The three-stage rocket hurled a payload nearly 700 miles high and over 3,000 miles down-range from Cape Canaveral. All stages performed well, and the hybrid rocket established a distance record that stood until the ICBM came along. A second firing, on May 15, 1957, carried a scaled Jupiter IRBM nose cone; the vehicle performed as expected except for a guidance malfunction that carried the nose cone out of the target area and prevented its recovery. Telemetry from the nose cone indicated, however, that it had satisfactorily withstood the heat of re-entry into the earth's atmosphere. A third Jupiter C, launched on August 8, 1957, tested a one-third scale model of a Jupiter IRBM nose cone for re-entry survival. This object was recovered from the Atlantic Ocean by the Navy after a 1200-mile ride more than 600 miles high. This was the first man-made object ever recovered from outer space. This flight also proved the feasibility of the ablative-type nose cone (one whose outer.covering slowly burns away, carrying off excessive

[7] W. H. Pickering, "History of the Cluster System," *From Peenemuende to Outer Space*, edited by Ernst Stuhlinger, F. I. Ordway, J. C. McCall, and G. C. Bucher (Huntsville, 1962), p. 143.
[8] One of the toughest problems we encountered with Explorer was to make this proportional attitude control system linear under vacuum conditions. For elaboration of this problem and its solution, see Wernher von Braun, "Rundown on Jupiter C," *Astronautics*, Vol. 3 (October 1958), pp. 33-34, 83; also G. Robillard, "Explorer Rocket Research Program," *ARS Journal*, Vol. 29 (July 1959), p. 494.

heat and leaving intact the underlying object it shields). This flight fulfilled the mission of the re-entry test program.[9]

While Project Vanguard was the approved U. S. satellite program, we at Huntsville knew that our rocket technology was fully capable of satellite application and could quickly be implemented. All efforts to obtain permission to extend our technology into space were unsuccessful in Washington.

Juno I

Juno I, a four-stage Jupiter C, was destined to launch the first earth satellite of the United States. After Soviet Russia opened the Space Age with great psychological impact by orbiting SPUTNIK I on October 4, 1957, the Department of Defense directed ABMA on November 8, 1957, to go ahead with the launching of a satellite with a Jupiter C as a part of the U. S. participation in the International Geophysical Year (IGY). The Juno I, or satellite-launching, configuration was designed simply by adding a single solid rocket motor as a fourth stage to the Jupiter C, and attaching a scientific payload provided by JPL at its forward end. Eighty-four days after ABMA at last received the go-ahead from Washington, on January 31, 1958, Juno I launched EXPLORER I, an 18-lb. satellite, into orbit. EXPLORER I gained fame as the first U. S. satellite and for orbiting the I. G. Y. experiment which discovered the first of the natural radiation belts of the earth, identified by Dr. James A. Van Allen.[10]

Twice more in 1958 Juno I boosters were successful, orbiting EXPLORER III on March 26 and EXPLORER IV on July 26. Three attempted launchings also failed, with similar payloads. Six of the nine Jupiter C vehicles (including the Juno I's) flown between 1956 and 1958 achieved their missions: three re-entry vehicles and three satellites were launched successfully. The Redstone technology that led to the first U. S. satellite also had another important role in the space effort.

Mercury-Redstone

The National Aeronautics and Space Administration (NASA) was created on October 1, 1958. Within one week NASA approved a

[9] This same Fiberglas coating technique became the standard method of protecting all re-entry objects from heating. See Bill B. Greever, " General Description and Design of the Configuration of the Juno I and Juno II Launching Vehicles," *IRE Transactions on Military Electronics*, Vol. MIL-4 (April-July 1960), p. 70.

[10] Maj. Gen. J. B. Medaris, *Countdown for Decision* (New York, 1960); also James Gavin, *War and Peace in the Space Age* (New York, 1958).

manned satellite program which was shortly to be named Project Mercury. NASA was forced to turn to missile organizations to program its early space missions.

The Army Ordnance Missile Command, ABMA's boss at Redstone Arsenal, offered to supply Redstone and Jupiter missiles to NASA as launch vehicles for the suborbital flights required in the early phases of the manned program. NASA formally requested eight Redstones for the Mercury program. Our people at ABMA also began to assemble two Mercury-Jupiter vehicles, but this work was ended in mid-1959 by the NASA decision to "man-rate" only the "old reliable" Redstone, chosen for suborbital manned space flight because of its demonstrated reliability and flight stability.

In modifying the Redstone for the manned Mercury suborbital mission we lengthened the propellant tank section by six feet, as in the Jupiter C, to permit longer engine burning time. The latest A-7 engine was improved; it would burn alcohol-water, like the standard Redstone, and produce 78,000 lbs. thrust. Modifications were also made to the instrument compartment, and an adapter section was designed for the Mercury spacecraft. A simpler, more reliable control system employing an autopilot was developed. And an abort-sensing system was designed and integrated to assure the greatest possible safety for the human pilot on top of the Redstone. The entire Mercury-Redstone vehicle, equipped with the Mercury spacecraft and launch escape system, was 83 feet long, 70 inches in diameter, and had a total lift-off weight of approximately 66,000 lbs.[11]

During the Mercury-Redstone development period, responsibility for the vehicle passed from ABMA to a NASA Center, activated at Redstone Arsenal on July 1, 1960. Our entire team of civilian technicians transferred "on paper" from Army to civilian control, while physically retaining the same laboratories, shops, and offices where we had worked for the Army. On September 8, 1960, President Eisenhower came to Huntsville to name the George C. Marshall Space Flight Center after the only professional soldier ever to win the Nobel Peace Prize.

The first Mercury-Redstone booster had emerged from assembly in February 1960. In the ensuing months it underwent extensive compatibility tests and checkout with the Mercury spacecraft provided by McDonnell Aircraft Corporation.

The first qualification launch of Mercury-Redstone was attempted at

[11] NASA, Marshall Space Flight Center, Historical Office, *History of the George C. Marshall Space Flight Center, July 1-December 31, 1960* (MHM-2) Vol. 1, pp. 7-9.

Cape Canaveral on November 1, 1960. The vehicle failed to rise from the pad because of faulty ground circuitry.

On December 19, 1960, the first Mercury-Redstone flight vehicle (MR-1A) was launched in a booster-spacecraft test flight. The Redstone carried the capsule to a height of 130 miles and went 235 miles down-range for an entirely successful test.

The next flight (MR-2) occurred on January 31, 1961, testing the Mercury spacecraft's life-support systems. The well-known passenger, a 37-lb. chimpanzee named "Ham," was recovered safely. Because the vehicle deviated from the planned trajectory, another development flight was required before the first manned flight. MR-BD, a final Mercury-Redstone development vehicle, flew on March 24, 1961, to verify booster changes incorporated because of the MR-2 troubles. Recovery of the dummy capsule was not performed, as all objectives of the flight profile were achieved.

On May 5, 1961, the first American flew in space. MR-3, with Lt. Comdr. Alan Shepard, Jr. (USN) as passenger-pilot in the FREEDOM 7 capsule, was a complete mission success. Astronaut Shepard was recovered from the ocean 302 miles down-range after a 15-minute suborbital flight to an altitude of 115 miles. It was a significant milestone for the U. S. manned space flight program. It was also a satisfying accomplishment for our dedicated team at Huntsville, because our rocket was the first man-rated U. S. space booster.

Astronaut Virgil I. Grissom's (Captain, USAF) successful MR-4 flight on July 21, 1961, was virtually a carbon copy of Shepard's flight. The loss of Grissom's LIBERTY BELL 7 capsule, which sank in the Atlantic after his safe egress, did little to mar the mission's success. NASA therefore cancelled a scheduled third manned flight and the Mercury-Redstone program ended in the summer of 1961, its objectives fully achieved. The next step in the U. S. manned space flight program would be orbital flight with a more powerful vehicle, the Mercury-Atlas.[12]

Jupiter

Groundwork for the Jupiter IRBM was laid in late 1955 when the Department of Defense decided that the Army would develop a 1500-mile-range missile—a logical extension of the Redstone program. The Jupiter IRBM project was assigned to our group at Huntsville, and

[12] NASA, Marshall Space Flight Center, Historical Office, *History of the George C. Marshall Space Flight Center, July 1-December 31, 1960* (MHM-2), Vol. 1, pp. 11-14; *January 1-June 30, 1961* (MHM-3), Vol. 1, pp. 7-19; and *July 1-December 31, 1961* (MHM-4), Vol. 1, pp. 8-19.

ABMA was activated on February 1, 1956, under the command of Maj. Gen. John B. Medaris, to carry the work forward on a crash basis. The Navy was a work partner when the development began, since the missile was to be designed for launching from both land and sea. Early in the program the Navy withdrew and started developing a solid-propellant IRBM, the Polaris.

A rapid buildup of personnel and facilities occurred at Redstone Arsenal in 1956 as the crucial Jupiter development advanced. Accomplishments of the Redstone program made work on the new missile less difficult, although far from easy. Our people resolved development problems steadily through 1956 and 1957. Thirty-seven Redstone missiles, as we mentioned, were used to test components, subsystems, and systems of the Jupiter IRBM during its development period. Meanwhile, operational control of the new weapon was assigned to the Air Force after roles and missions were defined in the Department of Defense. We delivered the first Jupiter to the Air Force in August 1958, and some 60 were deployed overseas as part of the NATO force structure until they were retired in 1963.

Experiments conducted and discoveries made in the course of the Jupiter IRBM development program proved useful in the nation's space effort. Following the Jupiter C nose cone re-entry tests of 1957, which verified the ablation principle of heat protection, we constructed a full-scale nose cone for tests with the Jupiter missile. Flight and re-entry of this body in May 1958, and of a similar one in July 1958, reaffirmed the results of the earlier tests. Both Jupiter nose cones were recovered, although an earlier one was lost. The most significant Jupiter space flight, however, came on May 28, 1959, when two primates ("Able" and "Baker"), riding in a capsule aboard a nose cone, survived the flight in good health in spite of re-entry temperatures of approximately 5,000 degrees Fahrenheit. This experiment demonstrated to scientists that living creatures could pass through outer space and be brought safely back to earth.[13]

The single-stage Jupiter IRBM was 60 feet long and 105 inches in diameter. Its three major assemblies were the thrust unit, the aft unit with instrument group, and the nose cone. The primary propulsion system was the NAA S-3D engine, which used liquid oxygen as oxidizer and kerosene as fuel. This main engine, rated at 150,000 lbs. thrust, was mounted on gimbals to permit pitch and yaw movement. Roll control was obtained by deflecting exhaust gases from the turbine and swivelling the turbine exhaust nozzle. A vernier thrust system

[13] Ernst Stuhlinger, "Army Activities in Space—A History," *IRE Transactions on Military Electronics*, Vol. MIL-4 (April-July 1960), p. 66.

provided fine control of cut-off velocity. Spatial attitude was controlled by eight jet nozzles spaced equally around the missile body. The delta-minimum inertial guidance and control system, based on that of the Redstone, employed the ST-90 stabilized platform. The Jupiter's mobile ground support equipment also was patterned on that of Redstone.

Juno II

While Juno I came directly from the Redstone, Juno II was based on the Jupiter IRBM. The Juno II was, therefore, a modified Jupiter IRBM, but with the upper staging and payload sections of the Juno I. Closely related to the Juno I because they both used the same high-speed top stages, the Juno II was designed as a launch vehicle for lunar probes in response to a request of March 1958 by the Advanced Research Projects Agency (ARPA) following the two Explorer successes with Juno I.

In the conversion of Jupiter to Juno II, the missile's nose cone, vernier motor, spin rockets, and all items of non-essential equipment were removed to save weight. The tank section was lengthened three feet to extend the burning time of the power plant. The upper stages and launcher were mounted like Juno I's, so they could be spun at high speed for flight stability. A Juno II innovation was a shroud covering the upper-stage cluster assembly. This shroud was necessary to protect the payload and upper stages from aerodynamic heating during ascent and to provide support for an angle-of-attack meter. It was jettisoned in flight prior to ignition of the upper-stage rocket motors.

Although the Juno II was not an optimum vehicle, it provided a quick and economical way to launch a payload over three times as heavy as that lifted by its Redstone predecessor, the Juno I. And like many other things in this early era of space achievements, it was available for minimum expenditure of time and money.[14]

Ten Juno II vehicles were used in space research from 1958 through the end of the program in 1961. There were two phases of the Juno II space program: deep space probes (PIONEERS III and IV) and the so-called heavy earth satellite program (EXPLORERS VII, VIII, and XI). Of the ten Juno II space missions, four were complete successes, one was a partial success, and five missions failed for a variety of reasons.

PIONEER III, the first U. S. lunar probe, was a 13-lb. payload sent

[14] Bill B. Greever, " General Description and Design of the Configuration of the Juno I and Juno II Launching Vehicles," *IRE Transactions on Military Electronics*, Vol. MIL-4 (April-July 1960), pp. 71 ff.

63,500 miles into space on December 6, 1958. This probe fell short of the moon because of premature cut-off of the first-stage engine. But it was adjudged a qualified success because of its deep space penetration and its cosmic radiation discoveries, confirming the EXPLORER I data on the Van Allen radiation belts.

PIONEER IV traveled past the moon and entered a solar orbit after launch on March 3, 1959.

Explorer earth satellites carrying more sophisticated space science experiments and weighing about 90 lbs. were orbited by Juno II on October 13, 1959, November 3, 1960, and April 27, 1961, to end Juno II's space adventures. EXPLORER VII provided significant data on magnetic fields, magnetic storms, solar flare activity, and radiation belts; EXPLORER VIII carried eight experiments and transmitted information on electron density and temperature, positive-ion mass and density, and micrometeorite distribution; and EXPLORER XI returned valuable data on gamma rays.

Juno III-V

The successes of Junos I and II were projected to several other Juno configurations at Redstone Arsenal in the 1956-58 period. While the Juno III and Juno IV concepts never reached the hardware stage, the design and study of Juno V led directly to the giant Saturn.

Juno III studies began in 1956. These considered a vehicle based on the standard Jupiter booster, with a 500-600-lb. orbital payload capability. The upper stages were to consist of solid rockets somewhat larger than the scaled Sergeants of the earlier Junos, and the second-stage cluster would have had 12 motors instead of 11. The heavier cluster presented design problems, so the proposal was abandoned in the hope that a more sophisticated and more economical vehicle could be developed.

The Juno IV concept resulted from an ARPA request in 1958 for an advanced satellite carrier vehicle with a 500-lb.-payload orbital capability. JPL joined our ABMA team in submitting consolidated proposals for the vehicle. Several configurations were studied. The Jupiter missile was again considered as the booster, and there were varied second- and third-stage suggestions. None ever got off the drawing board, and the Department of Defense discontinued the study the same year it began.

Birth of Saturn

A multi-stage rocket with a large, clustered-engine first stage was envisioned by our designers at ABMA in 1957. Juno V was the tentative name of the proposed vehicle, which would generate 1.5 million lbs. thrust and would be capable of lifting multi-ton payloads into earth orbit or on deep space missions. We submitted this ABMA concept to the Department of Defense under the title, "Proposal for a National Integrated Missile and Space Vehicle Development Program."

In August 1958, ARPA, which directed the military space program, gave formal approval by authorizing initial planning on a space booster of this magnitude. With this go-ahead, ABMA began design work on a missile and space booster that could be built from a maximum of proven components with the least possible expenditure of time, money, and effort. Thus, Juno V was, in fact, an infant Saturn.

For the first-stage propulsion system we investigated several possibilities before deciding to simplify and improve the Jupiter-Thor (S-3D) power plant. This engine we uprated in thrust, renamed the H-1, and adapted to operate independently in a cluster of eight.[15] Tankage consisted of a 105-inch Jupiter IRBM tank in the center surrounded by eight 70-inch Redstone tanks, to contain the kerosene fuel and liquid oxygen oxidizer. Many Redstone and Jupiter components could be adapted and used in the new vehicle, and most of the hardware could be built with existing tools, using established fabrication procedures. Among Jupiter system components converted to Saturn use was the ST-90 stabilized platform, that could be employed in the early flight program.

And so, by 1959 the Saturn program was picking up speed as we moved toward selection of upper staging, resolution of a multitude of development problems, the provision of facilities, and the realization that this new giant would soon follow Redstone and Jupiter into space.

*   *   *

The Redstone and Jupiter missile systems were born and grew to technological maturity in the decade of the 1950's. These now primitive rockets were nonetheless technological stepping stones to some of the advanced space launch vehicles of today—especially the Saturn family of lunar mission boosters. Along the way, while bolstering the nation's defense posture in their primary role as weapons, Redstone and Jupiter also made worthwhile intermediate contributions to the United States space program and to our growing knowledge of the universe.

[15] David S. Akens, *Historical Origins of the George C. Marshall Space Flight Center*, MHM-1 (Huntsville, 1960), pp. 58-60; NASA MSFC, *Saturn Illustrated Chronology, April 1957-November 1962* (Huntsville, 1963); and Oswald Lange, "Development of the Saturn Space Vehicle," *From Peenemuende to Outer Space* (Huntsville, 1962), p. 5.

Rocket technology of the two previous decades was brought into focus at Redstone Arsenal during these eventful years under direction of the Army. Now, this work continues in the 1960's under the aegis of the National Aeronautics and Space Administration. The Saturn I

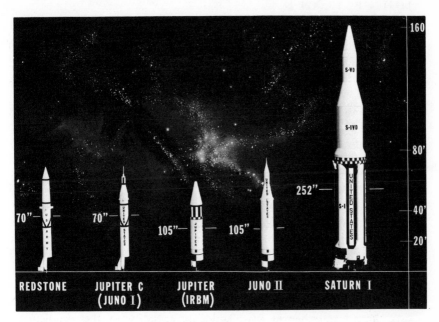

Fig. 10   Evolution of the Saturn booster (NASA)

vehicle, principal offspring of the Redstone and Jupiter, is well launched on a development program that has already seen 7 successful test flights in 7 attempts. As the vastly more powerful, more complex Saturn V takes form with still more advanced technology, we are hopeful for a history of accomplishment even more eventful.

The Viking and the Vanguard

GREAT CONFUSION still reigns among the general public in regard to Project Vanguard, the first United States earth satellite program created as a contribution to the International Geophysical Year (I. G. Y.). Vanguard was fated to become a so-called " propaganda failure " in what was to unfold in the popular press as a " space race." [1] Vanguard's scientific and technological accomplishments, overshadowed by the psychological impact of the Soviet Sputnik, deserve recognition beyond the space science community; inevitably they will receive full historical analysis. This paper only briefly examines how Project Vanguard came about, its role in the evolution of rocket technology, and the application of missile-derived rocketry to basic scientific purpose.

At the end of World War II, a combination of circumstances led to a fortunate breakthrough in science which remarkably influenced our understanding of the universe and which led us into the engineering feats that became a central feature of the space exploration program. These circumstances, in 1946-1947, were the existence of surplus and captured military rockets and a few teams of highly specialized scientists, joined together in war, suddenly faced with the problem of getting back into basic scientific endeavors. One such group was at the U. S. Naval Research Laboratory (NRL).

* Professor of Radio Astronomy at Pennsylvania State University, Dr. Hagen became Director of Project Vanguard in 1955, the first U. S. scientific earth satellite program. He joined the Naval Research Laboratory in 1935, subsequently receiving a Presidential Certificate for his work on radar and associated projects during World War II. He headed NRL's Radio Physics Research Group when it was formed in 1950. Transferring to the National Aeronautics and Space Administration with Project Vanguard in October 1958, Dr. Hagen was made Director of NASA's Office of the United Nations Conference in 1960 and, later, Assistant Director of NASA's Office of Plans and Program Evaluation, before joining the Ionospheric Laboratory at Penn State in 1962.

This article is based on Dr. Hagen's paper given at the program on " The History of Rocket Technology " at the meeting of the Society for the History of Technology co-sponsored by Section L (History and Philosophy of Science) and Section M (Engineering) of the American Association for the Advancement of Science on December 28, 1962, in Philadelphia.

[1] Alistair Cooke, " The Story that Got out of Hand," *Manchester Guardian*, December 8, 1957.

In January 1946 the U. S. Army announced that a V-2 firing program to acquire experience with large liquid-fuel rockets would begin at White Sands, New Mexico. Government agencies and universities were invited to consider using these technological spoils of war for high-altitude sounding research and experimentation. Thus was born the informal Upper Atmospheric Research Panel with representatives from the Army Signal Corps, the Applied Physics Laboratory (APL) of Johns Hopkins, the Army Air Forces, the Naval Research Laboratory, and Princeton, Harvard, California Institute of Technology, and Michigan. Coordinated sounding rocket research began, with the firing of the first V-2 in June 1946; the last of 63 was fired at White Sands in September 1952.[2]

V-2 sounding rockets provided pioneering atmospheric soundings to about 100 miles. The magnetic and high-energy particle radiation found at these altitudes but absorbed at lower levels was measured. The work was scientifically promising, but the supply of war-surplus V-2's began to run out, so that the design and construction of new and U. S.-made sounding rockets became necessary.

The first of these, as Aerobee, was initiated by the Applied Physics Lab and could reach a maximum altitude of 80 miles with a small payload. It was the beginning of a series of Aerobee rockets. The second of these large sounding rockets was the Viking rocket, designed by the Naval Research Laboratory and the Martin Company of Baltimore.[3] The Viking could project a much heavier payload to a height of 150 miles. Both these rockets were highly successful, and by their use the knowledge of the atmosphere was extended to 150 miles altitude. The usefulness to meteorology of photographing the earth's cloud cover from these heights was demonstrated, and surprising new information about the sun and cosmic rays was gained.

Thoughts of earth satellites and of vehicles which could reach the moon and the nearby planets were obviously alive among those designing, building, and using these rockets. In those days, such thoughts were quite "heady," for the nation had not yet become accustomed to, nor did it recognize the value of, expending hugh sums for scientific research and technological development in areas other than those with purely military implications. Those who voiced thoughts about satellites in NRL and elsewhere were thinking about projecting scientific experimentation and not merely launching a projectile into orbit by

[2] Cf. Homer E. Newell, *Sounding Rockets* (New York, 1961); Robert Jastrow, ed., *The Exploration of Space* (New York, 1960).

[3] See the well-written, informal history by Milton W. Rosen, *The Viking Rocket Story* (New York, 1955).

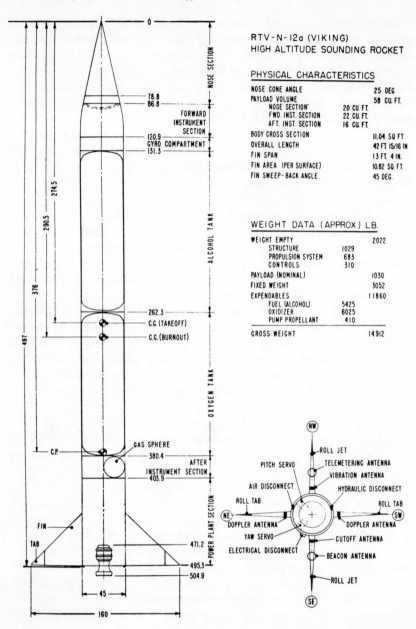

RTV-N-12a (VIKING)
HIGH ALTITUDE SOUNDING ROCKET

PHYSICAL CHARACTERISTICS

NOSE CONE ANGLE		25 DEG
PAYLOAD VOLUME		58 CU. FT.
NOSE SECTION	20 CU. FT.	
FWD. INST. SECTION	22 CU. FT.	
AFT. INST. SECTION	16 CU. FT.	
BODY CROSS SECTION		11.04 SQ FT.
OVERALL LENGTH		42 FT. 15/16 IN.
FIN SPAN		13 FT. 4 IN.
FIN AREA (PER SURFACE)		10.82 SQ. FT.
FIN SWEEP-BACK ANGLE		45 DEG.

WEIGHT DATA (APPROX) LB.

WEIGHT EMPTY		2022
STRUCTURE	1029	
PROPULSION SYSTEM	683	
CONTROLS	310	
PAYLOAD (NOMINAL)		1030
FIXED WEIGHT		3052
EXPENDABLES		11860
FUEL (ALCOHOL)	5425	
OXIDIZER	6025	
PUMP PROPELLANT	410	
GROSS WEIGHT		14912

Fig. 11. Outline drawing of NRL Viking high-altitude sounding rocket (NRL)

rocketry. Happily, however, missile-related research did require NRL and Martin to study the problem of designing a multi-stage rocket vehicle which would propel a nose cone to such a high altitude that it would re-enter the earth's atmosphere at an extremely high velocity. A full design of such a test vehicle was completed which was based on the Viking as a first stage and Aerobee as a second stage. It was clear that, with some refinements and with the addition of a third stage, satellite velocities could be obtained.[4] This NRL feasibility study of 1954-55 was to become the genesis of the Vanguard rocket.

Concurrently, scientific societies interested in geophysics and radio propagation began seriously to consider the values to science of experiments done from earth satellites. The Third International Polar Year was proposed, which, in turn, was expanded in scope to become the now-famous International Geophysical Year at the time of the expected peak of sunspot activity in 1957-58. This latter notion was quickly picked up in international scientific circles during 1954. Summer meetings in Europe of the two international bodies dealing with radio propagation and geophysics, the International Scientific Radio Union (URSI) and the International Union of Geodesy and Geophysics (IUGG), resulted in resolutions calling for the launching of an artificial earth satellite during the I. G. Y. As is well known, both the United States and the U. S. S. R. picked up this notion.[5]

Origin of the U. S. Satellite Program

On July 29, 1955, the White House announced that the United States would launch "small, unmanned, earth-circling satellites as a part of the U. S. participation in the I. G. Y." This announcement was the product of coordinated efforts within the National Science Foundation (NSF), the National Academy of Sciences (NAS), and the Department of Defense (DOD). The announcement stated that the Department of Defense would launch a satellite at some date during the I. G. Y., which was to end in December 1958, the NAS would determine the scientific experiments to be orbited, and the NSF would

---

[4] In order for a body to stay in orbit about the earth (i. e., become a satellite), it must attain a velocity of about 25,000 ft. per second and must be at at least an altitude of a hundred miles above the surface of the earth to avoid serious atmospheric drag.

[5] On the I. G. Y. as a whole, see the National Academy of Sciences, *I. G. Y. Bulletin* (Monthly), June 1957-1962. Also see Hugh L. Dryden, "IGY: Man's Most Ambitious Study of His Environment," *National Geographic* (February 1956), pp. 285-98; Margaret O. Hyde, *Exploring Earth and Space: I.G.Y.* (New York, 1958); Walter Sullivan, *Assault on the Unknown: I. G. Y.* (New York, 1961).

provide the necessary funding.[6] As it turned out the NSF provided but a small fraction of the funds, the major portion coming from the Department of Defense.

To determine the means for launching the U. S. satellite an advisory group was established in the Department of Defense. Called the Committee on Special Capabilities, this group under the chairmanship of Dr. Homer J. Stewart examined proposals submitted by the military services. Its review first indicated that: (1) the United States had no ready intercontinental ballistic missile; and (2) it had, at that time, no tested intermediate range ballistic missile. Any program to launch a satellite, then, must be based on something other than a military missile program.

Three satellite launching proposals were presented to the Stewart Committee: First, a proposal based on the Atlas missile, then a top priority military program but not yet a ready vehicle; second, a proposal based on the Redstone missile with a cluster of solid upper stages; and third, the NRL proposal based on the Viking as the first stage, the Aerobee as the second, and a still to be designed solid-fuel third stage. The Redstone proposal was limited in that the mass-ratio of the Redstone was low as then designed, so only a small mass could be placed in orbit. The NRL proposal, on the other hand, introduced a new vehicle having a high mass-ratio, relying upon gimballed engines for control, and having growth potential; further, our proposal assumed that the development of the Viking-based vehicle would in no way interfere or detract from the urgent military development of ballistic missiles.

After lengthy deliberation and some reconsideration, the DOD Committee on Special Capabilities recommended the proposed NRL approach in August 1955. It was not a unanimous recommendation. The DOD Policy Council endorsed this recommendation, and a tri-service program under Navy managership and DOD monitorship was designated "Project Vanguard." The objectives of Project Vanguard were: to develop and procure a satellite-launching vehicle; to place at least one satellite in orbit during the I. G. Y.; to accomplish one scientific experiment; and to track its flight to demonstrate that the satellite had actually attained orbit.

The NRL proposal, now approved and called Project Vanguard, was as follows: The first stage rocket was to be based on the Viking,

[6] In October 1958, the International Council of Scientific Unions, meeting in Washington, approved extension of the I. G. Y. through December 1959, under the name of the Committee on Space Research (COSPAR). The NAS became the U. S. adhering body to COSPAR.

having all of the basic features of this proven vehicle but with a larger engine based on the General Electric engine left over from the Army's Hermes project. The second stage was to be an improved Aerobee vehicle, although it was not decided, in the beginning, whether to pressure or to pump feed the fuel. However, the propellants were to be storable and were indicated as dimethylhydrazine and nitric acid. The third stage was planned as a solid-fuel stage. In optimizing the design of the entire vehicle it turned out that the third stage would weigh about 500 lbs., which meant that the third stage would be, when built, a real advance in solid-fuel rocket technology for that time. On top of this three-stage vehicle it was planned to place a nose cone which would weigh 20 lbs., including the scientific experiment.[7]

Project Vanguard began on September 9, 1955. On this date, the Department of Defense wrote a letter to the Secretary of the Navy authorizing the Navy to proceed with the NRL proposal. This is a date to remember, because just two years, six months, and eight days later (March 17, 1958) the first successful Vanguard satellite was launched. The letter from the Secretary of Defense stated clearly that what was needed was *a* satellite (i. e., one) during the I. G. Y. which was to end in December 1958, and that the Vanguard program was in no way to interfere with the on-going military missile programs. This basic directive was subsequently to be forgotten in the post-Sputnik turmoil.

Organizing the Project

The Secretary of the Navy passed responsibility for Vanguard down the chain, culminating with a letter directive to the Naval Research Laboratory. The responsibility for carrying Vanguard within the Navy rested with the Office of Naval Research (ONR), NRL's parent organization. At the inception of the project the director of ONR was Adm. Frederick R. Furth (a former director of NRL); later Adm. Rawson Bennet became director of ONR and guided the project through its most difficult period and through the completion of the project and its transfer into NASA after the I. G. Y. At NRL, the Director, Captain S. Tucker, and the Civilian Director of Research Dr. E. O. Hulburt, decided that this project was of such importance

---

[7] John P. Hagen, "The Exploration of Outer Space With an Earth Satellite," *Proc. IRE*, Vol. 44 (1956), p. 744; M. W. Rosen, "Placing the Satellite in its Orbit," *Proc. IRE*, Vol. 44 (1956), p. 749; D. G. Mazur, "Telemetering and Propagation Problems of Placing the Earth Satellite in its Orbit," *Proc. IRE*, Vol. 44 (1956), p. 752; John T. Mengel, "Tracking the Earth Satellite, and Data Transmission, by Radio," *Proc. IRE*, Vol. 44 (1956), p. 755.

and scope that it should not be handled by one of the regular divisions of NRL. They formed a special group to carry the responsibility for Project Vanguard within the Navy. This group, which it was my honor to lead, quickly put into process a letter of intent with the Martin Company.

During this time, there was long discussion with Martin over systems responsibility. The Martin Company, as with other aircraft companies at that time, felt that the contractor should have overall systems responsibility for vehicles. Our position was that the government could not slough off its responsibility and that overall systems responsibility for the Vanguard vehicle was therefore to be retained by Project management. This practice was later to be more generally instituted in missile and space system procurement.

After our letter of intent had been given to Martin, the unfortunate fact came to light that the original Viking engineering team in the Martin Company had been broken up. Unknown to the Navy, Martin had received a prime contract from the Air Force to develop the second-generation ICBM called Titan. Some of the leading Viking engineers were placed on the much larger Titan program. Thus, while Vanguard was not to interfere with the high-priority military missile programs, we were dealt a hard blow right at the start. This was a disappointment, indeed a shock, as we had cleared our intentions with the DOD before letting our letter of intent. But it was felt, after review, that the experience of the Vanguard group and the remnants of the Viking team in Martin assigned to Vanguard could go ahead with the design of the basic vehicle. In hindsight, things could have been much easier for the Vanguard group if the original Viking team of Martin had remained intact.

In a letter to the Navy Department, in the spring of 1956, the Vanguard group clarified its definition of what Project Vanguard really was—a complete system for space exploration. In addition to the basic rocket technology involved, we had to place a reliable scientific experiment into an orbit and not only prove that it was in orbit, but gather data from the satellite via telemetry. This had never been done before.

While teams within the Vanguard project were busy getting the vehicle development underway, the National Academy of Sciences established a Technical Panel, with Richard W. Porter as chairman, under its I. G. Y. committee. This panel was to select the experiments to be launched by the U. S. earth satellite program. Holding many meetings, the Technical Panel for the Earth Satellite Program discussed the possible experiments that should or could be performed. Vanguard, through a NRL representative, Homer E. Newell, and others, worked very closely with the NAS Technical Panel. The one thing that the Vanguard group insisted upon was that any experiment selected must have very high reliability of performance; hence an experiment could not be flown without a thorough testing program during which the experiment would be subjected to all the environmental factors expected in space.

At this time, the I. G. Y. Committee, thinking in terms of a better measurement of the upper air densities, requested the Vanguard group to make the satellite spherical in shape; in fact, a 30-inch sphere was requested. It had been our original plan to orbit a simple nose-cone. After discussion we agreed that we could change our design and launch a 20-inch sphere. This, however, actually required a re-design of the Vanguard vehicle in the second stage, for it now had to have a larger diameter. At the same time, it was also determined that the guidance system for injecting the satellite into orbit would weigh much more than originally planned. Thus in the fall of 1955, a re-design of the entire Vanguard vehicle was undertaken with these two factors in mind. We had frequent meetings with the DOD Committee on Special Capabilities, to whom detailed reports on work progress and design modifications were submitted.

The organization of the program became as follows: the Martin Company was the systems contractor and would build the first stage and take responsibility for the assembly of the completed vehicle. The General Electric Company would build the first stage engine, the pumps, and all of the auxiliary apparatus necessary for its operation. The Aerojet-General Company was assigned responsibility for the second stage except for the guidance, which was the responsibility of the Minneapolis Honeywell Company although the guidance package was installed in the upper part of the second stage.

For the third stage, we instituted parallel contracts with the Grand Central Rocket Company and the Allegheny Ballistics Laboratory. This was done inasmuch as the third stage represented the most forward technological step in the whole of the Vanguard rocket and was the only major new component design in the entire vehicle. This stage had to weigh about 500 pounds. Grand Central Rocket Company proposed a metal case for the rocket while the Allegheny Ballistics Laboratory, a subsidiary of the Navy operated by the Hercules Powder Company, proposed a novel Fiberglass casing. The latter had advantages in weight and performance but was more chancey. However, it was considered wise to start both of these approaches to be certain that one would come through as a successful vehicle. The other major contractor was the Bendix Corporation. Their contract was for the construction and installation of the tracking devices which were developed under the name "Minitrack," a system still in use today.

By March 1956, the re-design of the Vanguard vehicle was completed, and a full schedule containing six test vehicles and seven satellite-launching vehicles was prepared. The first two test vehicles were left-over Viking rockets; the first (TV-O) was simply a Viking with new telemetry and tracking devices to develop launching operations at Cape Canaveral. The second test vehicle (TV-1) was a Viking first stage with the new solid third stage which would test out the ignition at altitude, the nozzle, spin stabilization, and the total thrust of his new third stage. The third test vehicle (TV-2) was the first vehicle to use the Vanguard (enlarged Viking) first stage, with dummy second and third stages.

The first three-stage test vehicle was TV-3, the first stage having been tested in TV-2, the third stage in TV-1, and the second stage receiving its first test. "TV-3 back-up" was simply a vehicle planned in case of difficulty with TV-3. The TV-4 test vehicle would be minus the special telemetry required for vehicle development and would begin to resemble the actual satellite launching vehicle, while TV-5 would be the final launching vehicle and indeed resemble the satellite-launching vehicles to come. It would also contain a 20-inch sphere. Following these six test vehicles, seven satellite-launching vehicles (SLV's) were each planned to orbit a 20-inch sphere and I. G. Y. payload. This, then, was our plan.[8]

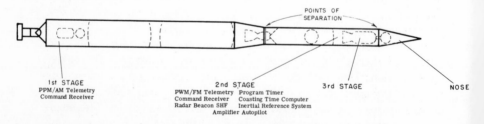

Fig. 12 Outline of Vanguard satellite-launching rocket (NRL)

[8] For listing of test and satellite launch vehicles, see Kurt Stehling, *Project Vanguard* (New York, 1962), pp. 269-81.

Launching and Tracking Systems

In the fall of 1955, having established the initial specifications for the launching vehicle, we now cast about for a place from which to launch the first U. S. space vehicle. Several choices presented themselves. First was White Sands, New Mexico, where we had done all our early testing of the Viking and Aerobee rockets. White Sands was quickly ruled out because of the danger to populated areas of falling stages of the satellite-launching vehicle. It had been well established from practice with V-2's and Vikings that a vertical rocket probe could be sent high into the atmosphere with some assurance that its empty tanks and spent engines would fall to the earth within the test range. For a satellite-launching vehicle, however, the discarded first stage would land some few hundred miles away from the launch site, and the empty second stage something on the order of a 1000 to 1500 miles away. It was, therefore, out of the question to use a launch site in the central part of the United States, such as White Sands.

The most logical site was Cape Canaveral, Florida, then just being expanded for the launching of large liquid-fuel ballistic missiles. It was attractive because a satellite would be launched toward the east in order to take advantage of the rotation of the earth; this eastward launching would then mean that the casings of the spent rockets would fall into the Atlantic. At the same time, Roosevelt Roads in the Carribean, where the Navy had a station, was also considered, having also an over-water advantage. For many reasons, most of them financial, Cape Canaveral was selected as the launching site for Vanguard.

It was first assumed that existing facilities at the Cape would be made available for launching Vanguard. A visit to the Cape and a survey revealed that the most probable location would be to share the facilities used by the Army missile program in launching the Redstone. Vanguard made this proposal, and we were turned down abruptly by the Army on the basis that any interference with the Redstone program would be harmful to the U. S. ballistic missile program. Their argument was bolstered only by the fact that the Jupiter-C missile, then being worked on, was being used to study nose-cone re-entry. After this turn-down by the Army, we returned to Washington. After discussions with the Department of Defense it was decided that we could build our own launching complex, using money found in the Emergency Fund of the Secretary of Defense. We started a full-fledged program of building a block-house and a launching pad suitable for our purposes as well as for the future use of a missile program such as the Air Force Thor. Building such a complex was an eighteen-month program. By the fall of 1955, it was still possible to complete this complex and yet launch the test vehicles and the satellites within the time-span of the I.G.Y.

It was also determined that Cape Canaveral was not equipped to handle a satellite launching operation because additional down-range stations would be required. Ballistic missiles were one-stage rockets; guidance was employed only during the time of burning of the rocket engines (the first minute or two of flight), after which the missile was on its own. In a multi-stage satellite-launching vehicle, Vanguard needed control during first stage burning; then we were required to follow the vehicle and control it during the burning of the second stage, which might take place a few hundred miles down-range; and finally, control again during the third stage burning, which would be as much as 1000 miles from the launching site. We set about to install the necessary equipment.

First, on the islands of Grand Turk, Mayaguana, and Antigua, Mini-track radio-tracking devices were installed. At Cape Canaveral and on the Island of Grand Bahama we installed powerful FPS-16 radars. These were to track the satellite-launching vehicle during the early parts of the flight and to predict the impact of the burned-out stages. They determined the apogee of the trajectory and whether the ignition of the last stage was initiated at the proper time or whether the Control Center would have to ignite the third stage manually. At that time there were only two FPS-16 radars in existence. One was pre-empted for Vanguard. The use of FPS-16 radars made it possible for us to go forward with the design of the launching vehicle with no large transponder in the Vanguard itself, thus saving weight and design complications. It proved, however, to be a major task to modify and re-design the FPS-16 for our purpose.

Initially our work at the Cape was in an old unused building, Hangar "C." In these early days, we designed the largest hanger "S" (now used in the Mercury program) along with the block-house and the pad. We moved into hanger "S" in 1956. We also found that there was no gantry crane available at the cape. Vanguard had to disassemble the Viking gantry at White Sands, transport it to Florida, and reassemble it. Starting from scratch, Project Vanguard had to build and install most of the necessary equipment to develop Cape Canaveral from a mere missile to a satellite launching facility in order to carry out our mission. It is sometimes shocking to remind persons that the entire NRL Vanguard in-house management staff consisted of only 15 persons, while the total Vanguard team consisted of 180 persons, including clerical help, technical, and shop personnel.

Radio and Optical Tracking

Tracking a satellite, once in orbit, also called for original systems design. In the Vanguard group, we defined ways and means of tracking the satellite, proving that it was in orbit, and determining the actual orbit. Tracking was under the direction of John T. Mengel. It was decided to use the Minitrack system initially developed by NRL as a guidance system with different radio frequencies at White Sands. The Vanguard-designed Minitrack system called for a frequency of 108 mc/s with an antenna separation of about 500 feet. Vanguard satellites would require a beacon transmitter to operate with Minitrack (108 mc/s). At first we planned to have four Minitrack stations in the southern part of the U. S., but it became clear that we should be prepared to track the satellite no matter how the orbit went. Thus, a series of stations on a north-south line were laid out. The antenna patterns of each station set about 500 or 600 miles apart would provide an overlap of fan beams at a height of 100 to 200 miles; we could thus build a radio fence to locate and track the satellite. By placing the northerly station just outside of Washington, D. C. (Blossom Point, Md.) and extending the chain of stations southward through the U. S., Central and South America to Santiago, Chile, our requirements would be served. By September, 1957, seven of these stations were operational. We also established stations in Woomera, Australia, and Pretoria, South Africa. Our prototype station, used in the development of all stations, was sited at the Naval Laboratory at San Diego, California. This later became one of our most important stations in the Minitrack set-up—the San Diego station gave us the first reliable indication that any satellite was actually in orbit around the earth.

The Vanguard group was aided in setting up the world-wide Minitrack stations by the Army. Arrangements with the foreign countries were under the direction of Captain W. Berg of the U. S. Navy, who was assigned to the Vanguard team and did a fine job of arranging for an international cooperative effort in tracking which carried over into NASA. Vanguard recognized the importance of participation in the tracking effort by nationals of the countries in which the many Minitrack stations were located and arranged for teams from these countries to share in operating the stations. Many of the foreign nationals were brought to NRL where they took an intensive training course in the principles of radio tracking and where they were able to obtain operating experience at the prototype station at Blossom Point, Maryland.

In addition to the tracking function, the Minitrack stations had antennas and receivers set up to read out the data transmitted by the scientific satellites (i.e., ground telemetry stations). These functions were extremely important in the later stages of the Vanguard program and are being used to the present day.

To back up the radio tracking, a system of optical tracking stations were established and managed by the Smithsonian Astrophysical Laboratory in Cambridge, Mass. This optical network was laid out on an east-west basis, with several stations distributed around the world within 20 or 30 degrees of the equator.

Orbit Computations

To complete the tracking picture, it was necessary to solve the difficult problem of computing the orbits of close-in satellites. A small committee of four people, Drs. J. W. Siry, G. M. Clemence, R. L. Duncombe, and P. Herget, was assigned for the computation of orbits. They did an excellent job, not only in planning orbital computation but in programming the work for the large computers necessary to carry out this kind of work. Computation was given over to the IBM 709 computer, which was established in a specially built Project Vanguard Computing Center in downtown Washington.

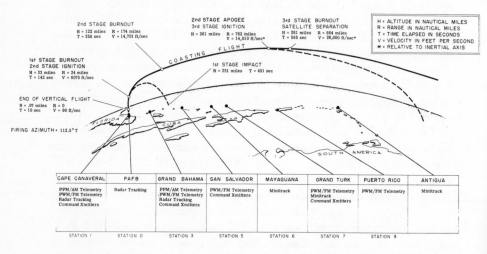

Fig. 13   Trajectory data and electronic ground station location (NRL)

Tying all these things together was a communications network. A control center was established at NRL at Anacostia, from which tele-type connections were made to the Cape and all the tracking stations as well as the Vanguard Computing Center in Washington. Thus, from one location the whole of the progress in the tracking and data acquisition could be monitored and controlled.

Vanguard Progress

Once all the planning and initial implementation had been completed came the difficult period of solving the myriad problems which inevitably arose. One of the major problems as Vanguard proceeded was the amount of funding. It was a continuous effort, the great one as far as my time and energy was concerned, to raise adequate funds to complete the project. The total cost of all of Project Vanguard was $110,000,000. In this amount there are no hidden costs; every conceivable item that could be charged to Project Vanguard showed in this $110,000,000. This included the design and construction of the launching vehicle and the support of all the scientific work that went into the design and construction of the experiments. It also covered all of the radio tracking, the establishment of overseas sites, and the construction of extensive facilities at Cape Canaveral and its down-range stations. At the time, it seemed a rather large figure. In retrospect, when one compares the cost of other missile and follow-on space programs, it does not appear excessive. Not a small amount of this money was left over and appeared in the first budgets of the National Aeronautics and Space Administration after October 1958.

It must be pointed out that there was no Congressional appropriation for Project Vanguard, except for the initial I. G. Y. appropriation to the NSF. This was a basic reason why its funding was a difficult problem. Every cent that was expended came out of the DOD Secretary's Emergency Fund. Nearing the very last stages of Vanguard after the launching of Sputnik, Congress did authorize the Secretary of Defense to re-program within the Defense budget to find what additional monies were needed for the completion of Vanguard. There were also official utterances about "priorities" and "industry speed-ups" in the program; these did not occur.

By the spring of 1957, things had moved quite far along. We had launched TV-O successfully and with it had tested our facilities at Cape Canaveral and down-range. In the spring we successfully launched TV-1, the second stage (actually, the final Vanguard third stage); this flight established that the spin-stabilization of the upper stage was successful (gyroscopic effect kept trajectory straight) and the engine nozzle was adequate. Third, we demonstrated for the first time that a stage of this size could be successfully ignited in the vacuum of the upper atmosphere. We were ready to move along.

By July 1957, due to the success of TV-1 and the third stage design we scrapped our plans for flying nose cones on our test vehicles, switching to small six-inch spheres to test the total thrust and provide a thorough operational test of our down-range tracking stations. This decision was made in July of 1957, an important date to bear in mind. By September we had TV-2, the first vehicle using a Vanguard first stage installed at Cape Canaveral. The launch crew had much difficulty checking out this vehicle during hangar tests. Many parts had to be cleaned or replaced before it was ready for the launch pad. TV-2 was on the launch stand when the International I. G. Y. Organization met for one of its periodic sessions in Washington. It was here announced on October 4, 1957, that the Soviet Union had successfully launched an earth satellite. This event caused a great deal of turmoil and concern within the United States. But TV-2 was successfully launched on October 23, 1957, carrying a 4,000-lb payload to an altitude of 109 miles and 335 miles down range.

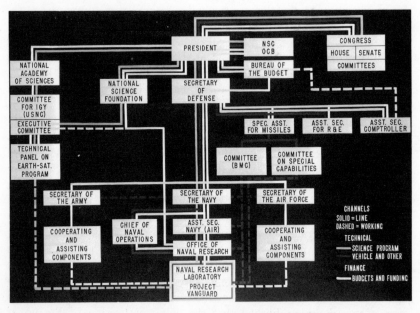

Fig. 14 Chart of Project Vanguard Policy and Working Channels (NRL). This chart was prepared by the Project Vanguard Staff, November 27, 1957, for submittal to the "Inquiry Into Satellite and Missile Programs," Hearings before the Preparedness Investigating Subcommittee of the Senate Committee on Armed Services, Lyndon B. Johnson, Chairman. Approval for presentation to the Subcommittee was not granted.

After Sputnik

Much pressure was then exerted to speed up, if possible, our program. Mr. William M. Holaday, responsible for guided missiles in the Office of the Secretary of Defense, and I, in October 1957, prepared a summary of the status of Project Vanguard. With this in hand, we briefed President Eisenhower, giving him a very factual report of our standing and telling him that we had planned in December to launch the first full-fledged test vehicle in the Vanguard program, emphasizing it was only a test which had a very remote bonus— a satellite. This was TV-3, the first attempted launching of a complete Vanguard vehicle with all three live stages, as well as the first flight of the second stage. Dependent upon the outcome of the TV-3 flight, we pointed out in this White House conference, Project Vanguard would have more assurance as to what our chances of success in future launchings might be.

Shortly after our briefing of the President, the White House Press Secretary, James C. Hagerty, released a statement on October 11, 1957, which blandly said that Project Vanguard will launch a U. S. satellite in the near future. In other words, our first live three-stage launching was billed as a satellite launching success in advance and committed us to a public deadline with an untried vehicle. This White House announcement came as a rude shock to all of us in the Navy as well as the Department of Defense. It was not possible, however, to effect a correction or clarification of the statement released by Hagerty, for the news media had "gone overboard" with the notion that our first complete test vehicle was intended to launch the first Vanguard satellite. In the final analysis, then as now, this was an unfortunate event; because of it, Vanguard as well as U. S. prestige suffered greatly and unnecessarily. On December 6, 1957, the launch of TV-3 was attempted. The Vanguard first stage engine had its first and last failure in the entire program. Yet it did occur; the vehicle failed to launch and fell back on the stand to blow up in a spectacular pyrotechnic display. Although we had three successful test launches in a row, the failure of TV-3 was heard around the world.

After the emotional flurry was over, we repaired the stand and proceeded with our planned test series of launchings. In our book, these were yet test vehicles and not true satellite-launching vehicles. On March 17, 1958, test vehicle TV-4 successfully launched its six-inch sphere into satellite orbit. This became VANGUARD I. Including the burned-out third stage rocket casing which went into orbit, a total weight of about 55 lb. was placed into orbit. This launching occurred two years, six months and eight days after the initiation of the program from scratch. Vanguard started with virtually nothing in 1955, completed vehicle design in March 1956, and had a fully successful flight two years later. One can challenge any other new rocket program in the United States to demonstrate a completely successful launching within such a short time.

In the six-inch VANGUARD I satellite were two radio transmitters. One was operated by batteries within the sphere, the other by six solar-cells (the first to be used in space) located on the outside of the sphere. The internal batteries became exhausted, as planned, within the first several weeks. But the solar-cells kept functioning, so that, over five years after launching, the satellite is still radiating transmissions.

The life-time of VANGUARD I in orbit will be long, inasmuch as the vehicle operated extremely well in inserting the satellite into an orbit at a height of 400 miles above the surface of the earth with excess velocity so that its apogee was about 2500 to 2600 miles. Thus VANGUARD I was placed far above the denser part of the atmosphere where density drag would not seriously affect the orbit.

After the launching of VANGUARD I, Project Vanguard went on through the remaining satellite launchings. VANGUARD II (SLV-4), launched on February 17, 1959, was the first satellite designed to photograph the cloud cover of the earth and was a forerunner of the famous Tiros weather satellites. VANGUARD III (SLV-7), launched on September 18, 1959, used the more powerful Allegheny Ballistics third stage. This allowed us to orbit a sphere which was 20 inches in diameter but weighed 50 pounds, so that a total of 75 pounds was placed into orbit with VANGUARD III.

Summary

The achievements of the Vanguard program help place it into historical perspective.[9] First, in VANGUARD I, the first use was made of solar-cells for powering a space vehicle. First measurements of the density of the atmosphere at 400 miles altitude discovered that the atmosphere was three times more dense than had been projected from our earlier sounding rocket work. Another first achievement of VANGUARD I was to demonstrate the damping effect of the earth's magnetic field upon the rotation of the satellite in orbit.

By careful observation of the stable and precise VANGUARD I orbit it was possible to determine that the oblateness of the earth was something less than earlier established. Prolonged orbital observations

[9] See excellent summary in John Lear, " The Moon that Refused to be Eclipsed," *Saturday Review* (March 5, 1960), pp. 45-48.

of VANGUARD I over longer periods of time brought out a further refinement on knowledge of the shape of the earth—that is that the earth is somewhat pear-shaped with a peak at the North Pole and a flattening at the South Pole. These deviations, of course, were very small. But in terms of the gravitational field of the earth they were extremely significant. These orbital deviations of VANGUARD I likewise pointed out that in order for this oblateness and the pear-shape to exist, at least to the extent indicated by VANGUARD, the mantle under the earth's surface must be a hard crust and not a plastic as earlier thought. Among the other scientific achievements of VANGUARD I was the documentation that there was a 27-day variation in the earth's outer atmosphere. This achievement was shared with some of the other early satellites such as SPUTNIKS I and II.

VANGUARD I had two other achievements which came somewhat later. It was demonstrated that there was a lunar-solar perturbation of the orbit and then, of more importance, a perturbation of the orbit due to the pressure of solar radiation. This was not a large factor in the case of VANGUARD I, for its area to mass ratio was relatively small. But it made possible for us to predict accurately that there would be a large effect on the 100-foot diameter ECHO I balloon-satellite [10] launched on August 12, 1960, as its area to mass ratio was very large. VANGUARD II, although it had the unfortunate collision with its third stage causing it to spin excessively, established the feasibility of the principles upon which weather satellites could be designed. VANGUARD III, coming later, did a worthy job of mapping the earth's outer magnetic field and counting micrometeorite impacts. Not only did Project Vanguard itself produce solid scientific achievements, but is must also be looked upon as the development of a complete system for space research, serving as a model for later scientific satellite programs.

Technologically, the Vanguard vehicle was used in the design of many later vehicles. There are now more Vanguard-originated rocket cases and pieces in orbit around the earth than of any other satellite program. A few technological descendents of Vanguard are the NASA Scout vehicle which uses the Vanguard third stage, the Air Force Thor and Atlas series of Able vehicles on which Vanguard second and third stages were placed, and, finally, the Delta launch vehicle of NASA. This latter space booster is a three-stage vehicle using a Thor first stage and improved Vanguard second and third stages. The Delta booster turned out to be the most successful vehicle that NASA has flown, with 15 successes in 16 attempts as of April 1963.

[10] Passive communications satellite made of aluminized Mylar plastic.

Among other contributions of Vanguard was the use of gimballed motors to steer the flight of a vehicle. Vanguard also developed the high mass ratio solid rocket as its third stage, which is useful in military missiles as well as the Scout, and it first developed fiberglass cases for solid rockets. Out of Vanguard came the Minitrack system and the network now used by the United States for all earth satellite tracking. From this came the Active Minitrack which was further developed by the Navy and now goes under the code name of SPASUR, an excellent space surveillance system. Besides pioneering the use of solar-cells, Vanguard also made technical advances through the use of solid state devices and printed circuits toward miniaturizing the volume and weight of complex electronic systems need to carry out scientific missions. The I. G. Y. experiment of Dr. James A. Van Allen (State University of Iowa), which discovered the radiation belts of the earth on EXPLORER I launched by the Army, was originally designed and developed for launching on Vanguard.

One point which should not be overlooked is that Vanguard pioneered in the development of highly reliable payload systems. The methods developed to insure a high degree of reliability have been carried over into the NASA Goddard Space Flight Center and show up in the excellent space science record achieved by NASA payloads.

In hindsight, Vanguard also pioneered a system of rapid reduction of data from space satellites. But perhaps the greatest achievement of Project Vanguard, one most evident to those have witnessed this early history of space flight, was the development of a group of dedicated and talented scientists and engineers who came to understand thoroughly, perhaps the hard way, the overall complexities of the space programs. This team was assimilated into the National Aeronautics and Space Administration and became the human core of the Goddard Space Flight Center at Greenbelt, Maryland. It seems no exaggeration for me to state that Project Vanguard, with its scientific orientation, its worldwide tracking facilities, and its technological contributions to rocketry and space operations, served well as a foundation for the distinguished space science programs which were to become manifest under NASA.

Perhaps historians are more concerned about success or failure of a novel venture when all the facts are revealed. On Vanguard, perhaps my colleague, Milton W. Rosen, commented best in this vein when he said:

> Why, then, the question of success or failure? It is because political significance and wide publicity have taken Vanguard and

like endeavors out of the realm of scientific investigation and placed them into the arena of public exploits. In this arena, there is no payoff for near misses, good tries, or worthwhile experiments. Nor is anyone satisfied by the quotation of long odds. A horse that does not finish might just as well have been scratched.[11]

As basic scientific research stemming from the capabilities offered by rocket progress is increasingly projected into the public arena, perhaps the full story of Project Vanguard offers perspective and guidance. This paper is far from a complete story. Nevertheless on the fifth anniversary of the launching of VANGUARD I on March 17, 1963, it was still transmitting and was the only satellite launched before 1959 still transmitting in orbit. VANGUARD I had made 19,700 orbits and is now estimated to have an orbital lifetime of more than 2,000 years.

[11] "What Have We Learned from Vanguard?" *Astronautics*, Vol. 4 (April 1959), pp. 106-11.

The Atlas, Thor, Titan, and Minuteman

ROBERT L. PERRY

ALTHOUGH AN intercontinental ballistic missile (ICBM) was among the several basic new weapons urgently recommended during the first postwar analysis of United States military needs, several factors combined to delay the start of actual development until 1954. Perhaps the chief of these was a compound of complacency and self delusion arising from the popular notion that possession of the atomic bomb and the means of its delivery conferred near invincibility on the United States, the only victorious power to emerge unscarred from World War II. That attitude was complicated by the conviction, expressed by some of the nation's most respected scientists and echoed by some of its most prominent military spokesmen, that the V-2 rocket missile was inherently an inaccurate, range-limited weapon, prohibitively expensive, and of slight military effectiveness, which Germany would have done well to forego in favor of improved "conventional" weapons—such as jet aircraft.

General of the Armies Henry H. Arnold, certainly the most farsighted of all World War II allied leaders, was the first important military spokesman to endorse the need for an ICBM. For his pains he was subjected to the derision of leading civilian scientists, most of whom seemed content that "logical" extensions of existing weapons should remain the objectives of "realistic" military planning. Few believed that a genuine need for an ICBM would develop within the predictable future. Two or three decades hence would be time enough.[1] By 1947 it was a precept of American folklore that the only

* Historian of the USAF Space Systems Division (Los Angeles, Calif.), Mr. Perry has been associated with Air Force research and development as a civilian historian since the early 1950's and was formerly Chief Historian of the Wright Air Development Center (Dayton, Ohio).

Author's Note: Portions of this article are based on USAF historical files. Although it has been reviewed by the Air Force to insure that it does not contain classified information, it reflects the judgments of the author and is not to be construed as carrying any official sanction of the Department of the Air Force.

[1] Vannevar Bush, *Modern Arms and Free Men* (New York, 1949), was probably the best known spokesman for the viewpoint that a long range ballistic missile was not worth developing.

possible opponent of the United States, the Soviet Union, was incapable of developing an advanced technology and was in a near comatose condition as a result of war damage.

To have undertaken a serious ballistic-missile program in the immediate postwar years would have required a very substantial investment in dollars and skilled manpower. Neither was among the resources of the military services before 1950. Additionally, it appeared logical to develop improved jet aircraft, moderate-range aerodynamic missiles, and lighter nuclear warheads before attempting such visionary devices as intercontinental rocket missiles or satellites. Faced with the hostile skepticism of respected scientific authority, the services discreetly shelved their plans for ballistic missiles and concentrated attention on less demanding programs—though in light of the times they perhaps were demanding enough.

Origins of the Atlas Program

In 1950, after the detonation of the first Russian nuclear weapon had somewhat deflated national egotism, the Air Force re-established its ballistic missile program but severely limited the dollar investment and conditioned schedules on a probable 15-year effort. Experience of the previous five years seemed to indicate that no radically new weapon could be developed and deployed in less than a decade. None of the aerodynamic missiles on which work had begun in 1945 had matched expectations; significant technical difficulties combined with rapidly changing requirements had negated much of the apparent progress of the late 1940's. In 1950 the manned bomber seemed the only certain pre-1965 strategic weapon, with the aerodynamic missile its leading competitor.

Indifferently funded and considered much less promising than contemporary programs involving air-breathing missiles, the ICBM project remained a pedestrian effort for the first four years after its 1950 re-activation. Unable to sponsor high-risk—and high payoff—programs in the contemporary atmosphere of technical and fiscal conservatism, the Air Force planned the sequential creation of successively more complex and efficient ballistic rockets until—in a vaguely defined future—a service-ready weapon could be gradually phased into the inventory in the fashion of an improved bomber or one of the aerodynamic missiles then "approaching readiness."

Three circumstances combined during 1953 to force a change in that situation. First, the United States acquired reliable information that the Soviet Union was well along in the development of a long-range rocket weapon. Second, there was a breakthrough in nuclear physics, and the feasibility of relatively lightweight thermonuclear weapons was established. Finally, a generation of scientists and military planners more concerned about the danger of losing a new war than with preserving the tactics of the past war edged into the policy councils of the defense establishment.

In February 1954, a special Air Force Strategic Missiles Evaluation Committee headed by Professor John von Neumann concluded that an effective ICBM could be developed and deployed early enough to counter the pending Soviet threat *if* exceptional talents, adequate funds, and new management techniques suited to the urgency of the situation were authorized. The committee specifically recommended that existing requirements for huge five-engine rocket missiles be overhauled to correspond to the new realities, that existing ICBM schedules be drastically reoriented, and that a special development-management group be created, supported adequately in funds and priorities, and given authority to realign, expand, and accelerate the ICBM program. Only by these means, the committee maintained, could a militarily useful ballistic missile be had within a reasonable span of time.[2]

Thus was defined the "what" of the task. *How* it was to be done could be stated only in the most general terms. Technology was, at best, rather uncertain. Operational objectives could be but loosely identified. The proposed management approach pre-emptorily departed from contemporary procedures. Knowledge concerning the probable cost and military effectiveness of the end product was non-existent—although widely variant estimates were readily come by.

Trevor Gardner, assistant to the Secretary of the Air Force, was the principal sponsor of the von Neumann Committee and its findings. Armed with the committee report, he pushed through approval for the creation of a special management agency with specific responsibility and authority for the ICBM project. Its military element was the Western Development Division (WDD, later the Air Force Ballistic Missile Division) of the Air Research and Development Command—supported by a Special Aircraft Project Office of the Air Materiel Command. The former was charged with research and development functions and the latter with procurement and production responsibilities. Each was manned with hand-picked personnel of the highest

---

[2] Background information on the travail of the ballistic missile program in the period 1945-1954 was developed during a series of congressional hearings from 1957 to 1961. See particularly *Hearings Before The Preparedness Investigating Subcommittee of the Committee on Armed Services, U. S. Senate*, 85th Cong., 1st and 2nd Sess. ("Johnson Committee"), Nov. 1957 and Jan. 1958; H. R. No. 1121, 86th Cong., 1st Sess., Sept. 1959; H. R. No. 324, 87th Cong., 1st Sess, May 1961.

proven competence. The Ramo-Wooldridge Corporation, under contract to the Air Force, provided systems engineering and technical direction services.[3]

The first responsibility of that combination was to establish a weapon configuration—a comose task that had been attempted at intervals over the previous eight years with scant success. The available ingredients included a series of unproven booster rockets developed for the Navaho missile program and an airframe design projected for the 1950-concept Atlas ICBM program. The guidance system then contemplated was unacceptably intricate and inherently unreliable. There was no proof that new premises of warhead re-entry were applicable to an actual weapon. Only the most limited information was available on such crucial items as high-rate-of-flow fuel and oxygen pumps, vibration effects, and the feasibility of igniting a rocket engine at altitude.

Each of these considerations profoundly influenced the course and pace of early development. Progress toward a militarily effective weapon that could be made available relatively soon was dependent on evoking a controlled revolution in technology. The inherent difficulty of program management was compounded by a need to invent, develop, prove, and incorporate new technology in a total system without compromising the operational objective—to get a deployable ICBM at the earliest possible date.

The uncertainty of rocket ignition at altitude principally occasioned the " one-and-one-half-stage " configuration of the Atlas weapon, with everything burning at lift-off. Choice of a three-engine design in place of the earlier five-engine proposal forced drastic weight limitations to compensate for the lessened total thrust. The promise of a light nuclear warhead—not yet a reality because warhead technology too was in adolescence—validated the selection of the "lightweight" missile design. Of necessity, a thin-skin, pressurized airframe with integral fuel and oxidizer tanks became the accepted configuration.

As insurance that no single critical element would fail in development and paralyze the entire program, the Air Force contracted for alternative approaches to each of the major subsystems. Subsequently, with a fair degree of confidence that the refined Atlas design was sound, it became possible to program the backup subsystems as a more sophisticated missile: Titan. The Titan differed from Atlas in having a monocoque airframe, a different engine, a more advanced

[3] See particularly *Hearings Before the Military Operations Subcommittee, Committee on Government Operations*, House of Representatives, 86th Cong., 2nd Sess., May 1960.

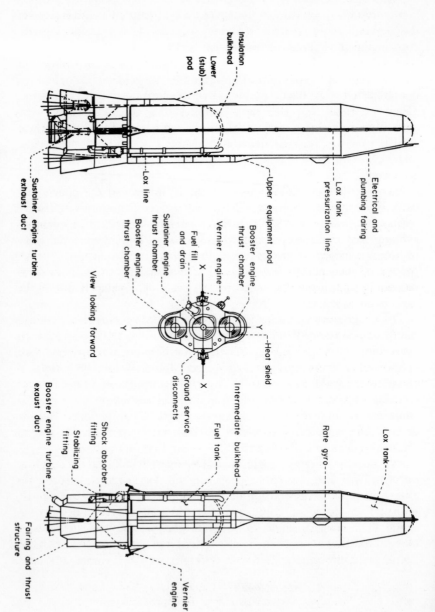

Fig. 15   Three-view drawing of basic Atlas configuration (USAF)

Insulation bulkhead

Lower (stub) pod

Sustainer engine turbine exhaust duct

Lox line

Upper equipment pod

Booster engine thrust chamber

Vernier engine

Fuel fill and drain

Sustainer engine thrust chamber

Booster engine thrust chamber

View looking forward

Ground service disconnects

Heat shield

Intermediate bulkhead

Fuel tank

Booster engine turbine exhaust duct

Shock absorber fitting

Stabilizing fitting

Vernier engine

Fairing and thrust structure

Electrical and plumbing fairing

Lox tank pressurization line

Lox tank

Rate gyro

Lox tank

guidance subsystem, and in being a true two-stage missile. As it evolved, it was specifically engineered for launch from underground, hardened silos, thus representing a considerable advance over the early "soft" Atlas.

For practical purposes, each of the principal Titan subsystems was compatible with the basic Atlas design. Had it become essential at some point during early development, either the Rocketdyne engine of the Atlas or the Aerojet design for Titan could have been transposed to the other. Guidance was similarly managed; indeed, the all-inertial guidance system initially developed as an alternative in the Titan program eventually found its place in the Atlas F, contributing substantially to the task of adapting that improved missile to housing in silo emplacements.

New Management Concepts and Practices

Although such innovations could conceivably have emerged from a program conducted along "classical" lines, their rapid acceptance and their quick translation into approved program objectives marked a significant departure from traditional management concepts. Consolidation of systems engineering and technical direction functions under Ramo-Wooldridge rather than under a "single prime contractor," as had been the habit of the immediate past, was one contributor. A unique military structure that found the WDD commander immediately responsive to Pentagon guidance but which assigned him unprecedented authority for program management was another. The personality of the program's military director, General Bernard A. Schriever, was without question one of the chief determinants. He was thoroughly convinced that in the ballistic missile effort lay the future security of the nation, and he succeeded in communicating both his convictions and his fervor to the military and civilian members of the ICBM team.[4]

That team, a tightly knit group of extremely competent specialists at the beginning, and still a relatively small community when the first Atlas became operational, conceived and applied to the ballistic missile

[4] K. F. Gantz (Lt. Col., USAF), *The United States Air Force Report on the Ballistic Missile* (New York, 1958); address by Maj. Gen. B. A. Schriever, Cmdr., AFBMD, Buffalo, N. Y., June 1 1958; remarks by Col. Otto Glasser, Asst. D/Cmdr. AFBMD, to Air Force Assn., Chicago, Ill., May 21 1958; address by Schriever before Frontiers of Science Foundation, Oklahoma City, Okla., 1 May 1958; Simon Ramo, "The ICBM Program—Its Relation to Past and Future Developments," paper for American Rocket Soc., June 1 1957.

effort a management technique subsequently dubbed "concurrency." [5] Although variously interpreted, concurrency essentially implied the simultaneous completion of all necessary actions to produce and deploy a weapon system. In a program characterized by remarkably short lead times from conception to deployment, most decisions had to be made well in advance of the receipt of test-authenticated data basic to the decisions themselves. Industrial facilities had to be planned and built for both test and production, military construction programs begun, and operational bases designed and started before initial flight testing of the weapon itself.

The effective application of concurrency required three preconditions. Authority and responsibility had to be consolidated in one agency, else management control would be neither quick reacting nor responsible. Unusually great technical competence was essential to insure and maintain high management confidence in the validity of technical decisions; decisions involving the expenditure of huge sums of money and commitments to technical courses not easily reversed frequently had to be based on technical considerations only partially proved in test. Funding and programming decisions outside the authority of the program director had to be both timely and firm. In the ICBM program, creation of the WDD complex in Los Angeles satisfied the first two of these conditions, while the approval of special management channels to expedite the decision-making process was designed to satisfy the third.

Performance and availability were the controlling factors in most program decisions, but sound financial management remained an essential of the program. Indeed, the task of maintaining an effective deterrent force in being while a revolutionary new weapon was being developed and deployed dictated the imposition of stringent cost controls.

The concept of a weapon system approach was scarcely new in 1954, when WDD was first formed. Schriever himself had been instrumental in its creation and was one of the first to appreciate that as originally

[5] The germ of the concurrency thesis was contained in a special staff study, "Combat Ready Aircraft," prepared by (then) Col. B. A. Schriever for the Air Staff in 1950 and given limited service circulation in 1951. There is perhaps no better example of the influence of management theory on the course of a weapon development. With allowances for the change in circumstances between 1950 and 1955, the Schriever thesis of the former year was selectively applied to the problem of developing a ballistic *weapon*. Maj. Gen. O. J. Ritland (Cmdr., AFBMD), "Concurrency," *Air University Quarterly Review*, XII (Winter-Spring 1960-61), updates the thesis in a resume of its particular application to the missile effort of the Air Force; H. R.1121, Sept. 1959, is also most enlightening.

conceived and applied it had limitations. To the ICBM effort he applied a refined system technique—the "program package" concept— designed to insure that all major factors in the ballistic missile effort were treated in terms of their complex interrelationships and not in isolation. Concurrency, particularly as it applied to the simultaneous development and deployment of a revolutionary new weapon, and the package program, vital to management efficiency, were principal ingredients of ICBM development.

The Air Force ballistic missile effort contemplated not merely the production of vehicles before research and development was complete—that had been attempted several times with varying degrees of success—but simultaneous work in basic and applied research, vehicle design, component design, test facility design and construction, component and system testing, the creation of production facilities, and the design, proof, and test of launch site facilities without which the missile would be impotent. All of these considerations had to be taken into account in the assembly of an operational plan and in scheduling the availability of an operational weapon.

Overlaid on this complex of interacting factors were several influential considerations that could not be controlled by program managers but which intimately affected their efforts. Concepts of missile deployment and knowledge of thermonuclear blast effects changed enormously while the program was in its early stages. The pressure of national policy that required the maintenance of a balanced force—both ICBM's and more conventional weapons—was constantly felt. The pace of production and deployment, and to a lesser extent development, was conditioned by a budget equation built around the state of the domestic economy, the inter-service distribution of funds, fluctuations in the temperature of the "cold war," and constantly changing estimates of the relative cost and effectiveness of individual weapon systems. This mix of budgetary, force structure, technological, cost effectiveness, and national policy factors exerted fluctuating pressure on ICBM evolution.

Additionally, the assignment rapidly outgrew its original framework. When General Schriever, his small military staff, and the core of the Ramo-Wooldridge Corporation joined forces in Los Angeles in July 1954, they were charged with recommending an expanded program and —ultimately—with providing an operational Atlas at the earliest possible time. The general configuration of the Atlas had been settled by early 1955, by which time the mode of operation was also well established. In May 1955 the back-up projects from the Atlas program were blended into a second intercontinental missile design, Titan, deliberately incorporating some advanced features forbidden for Atlas because of their greater sophistication and longer lead time. By October 1955 the obvious relationship between space vehicles and the only large boosters being developed in the United States impelled assignment of the initial Air Force satellite development to the Western Development Division. One month later, Air Force headquarters directed accelerated development of the Thor intermediate range ballistic missile (IRBM) and assigned that responsibility to the Schriever team.

By late 1955, the original task of devising, developing and deploying a single ICBM had been compounded by the addition of responsibility for a second ICBM, an IRBM, and an Atlas-boosted satellite system. Although Titan was more deliberately paced than its ICBM predecessor, Thor was deliberately designed as a maximum risk program with the objective of demonstrating flight potential at the earliest possible date. Only three and one-half years were provided for the transition from conception to operation.

Finally, in mid-December 1955 the Western Development Division was charged with responsibility for creating an "initial operational capability" for the intercontinental missile at the earliest possible date. The assignment made the Los Angeles group responsible for deploying the weapon on launch sites and manning the sites against the contingency of an emergency requirement for operational launches. Assignment to a research and development agency of responsibilities traditional in an operating military command was a most exceptional expansion of mission.[6]

In 18 months, a relatively confined if technically demanding assignment was constantly expanded until it encompassed diverse weapon systems and associated management responsibilities of unprecedented consequence. Quite apart from thoroughly complicating the technical development problem, the resultant managerial task presented greater difficulties than had been faced by any other weapons acquisition team ever assembled. Thus the *management of technology* became the pacing element in the Air Force ballistic missile program. Moreover—as had not been true of any earlier missile program—technology involved not merely the creation of a single high-performance engine and related components in an airframe, but the development of a family of compatible engines, guidance subsystems, test and launch site facilities, airframes, and a multitude of associated devices.[7]

---

[6] Johnson Committee Hearings, Nov. 1957, testimony and statements by J. H. Doolittle (Lt. Gen., USAF, Ret.), Lt. Gen. D. L. Putt (DCS/Dev., USAF), and Maj. Gen. B. A. Schriever (Cmdr., AFBMD).

[7] Ritland, *loc. cit.*

Difficulties and Successes

The pace of technological progress in basic rocketry constituted one of the most remarkable elements in the creation of an effective ballistic missile. Not until December 1954 was the three-engine configuration of the Atlas approved, and then it involved a rocket design which had been authorized but ten months earlier. The Thor project, assigned in December 1955, embodied the earliest possible employment of engines earlier intended for the Atlas. The complete missile was tested on a launch pad in January 1957. Almost precisely 13 months had elapsed since the Thor contract had been signed. The first Atlas test occurred on 11 June 1957—exactly 30 months after the airframe contractor had been advised of vehicle configuration approval. A completely successful full range flight for the Thor followed in September 1957; for the Atlas—after the solution of a succession of extremely difficult engine and guidance problems—it came in November 1958. One month later, on 16 December 1958, a Strategic Air Command crew launched a Thor from the operational training site at Vandenberg Air Force Base, marking transition of the missile to initial military readiness. On 18 December, from a launch site on the other side of the continent, the Air Force put an entire Atlas into orbit (Project Score) and from it radioed a Christmas message from the President of the United States to the people of the world. The first Titan booster, carrying a dummy second stage, successfully completed a launch from the Atlantic Missile Range on 6 February 1959—the third of the Air Force ballistic missiles to pass into flight test status. Twenty-two days later a Thor-Agena combination boosted the first Air Force satellite into orbit (DISCOVERER I).

Each such achievement marked a triumph over technological obstacles of considerable difficulty. The basic Atlas propulsion system, for instance, had a design start in the Navaho missile program. But for the ballistic missile effort, a different fuel was used and a substantial increase in thrust was necessary. The first booster engines scheduled for flight test were to be rated at 135,000 lbs.—a figure that was readily attainable on the test stand but which proved more elusive once the engine was interconnected to plumbing and propellant tanks compatible with the actual missile. For the operational engine, a thrust increase of 25 per cent was needed. The first test stand firing, in June 1956, was conducted on schedule largely because research and component test activities were pushed through concurrently. In the case of the turbopump, the process of carrying over a device designed for another application had produced a marginal component which ultimately had to be significantly modified. Combustion instability, a characteristic of virtually all rocket engine development programs, was dangerously troublesome during tests of the Atlas sustainer engine. The sustainer initially refused to conform to design expectations for thrust and specific impulse. While the total system design continued, and while program managers kept pushing toward the operational

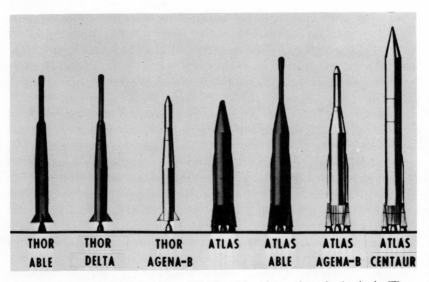

Fig. 16   Thor and Atlas Boosters (USAF). Not shown here is the basic Thor IRBM, various Atlas ICBM series, and the Mercury-Atlas. The Thor-Delta with Thor first-stage and Vanguard-derived upper stages compiled an impressive launching record for NASA, including the Tiros weather satellites, Explorers, ARIEL I, SYNCOM, and other satellites. Atlas-Agena B launch vehicles boosted the NASA Ranger lunar probes as well as MARINER II which made the historic fly-by the planet Venus in December 1962. Both the Thor and the Atlas have booster numerous Department of Defense satellites. On October 27, 1963, the first successful liquid-hydrogen Centaur (Atlas first-stage) was launched.

deployment goal, the original engine was substantially refined to emerge as the MA-2 version used in the D-series Atlas missiles. Even before the problems of the MA-2 version had been solved, a vastly improved MA-3 version progressed from drawing board to test stand; representing a major redesign of the original, the MA-3 became the power plant of improved E and F-model Atlas ICBM's. The principal change in later models was the provision of an individual turbopump for each booster chamber, but the number of pneumatically operated valves was also sharply reduced and a hypergolic start system replaced the original squib igniter.

Many of the difficulties of Atlas engine development were common to—and in some instances first experienced in—the Thor program. The most troublesome, of course, was the turbopump disorder which ultimately led to redesign and alteration of the installed units. Competent engineering would eventually have eliminated the defect whatever the course of technical management, but in this instance the concerted actions of the engine contractor, the airframe contractor, the static and flight test specialists, and the management group centered in Los Angeles provided for an intensive program of research and component development without suspension of the critical flight test schedule. Through 1958, 30 Thor missiles were flight tested. Of this number, only three experienced turbopump difficulties. The last of these, on 17 August 1958, was also the last instance of that trouble; during the following 15 months, 85 flight tests involving both Thor and Atlas missiles saw no recurrence of the original difficulty.

Acceptance of a high risk flight program and continuation of the flight program during the period of turbopump trouble permitted verification of the compatibility of the airframe, engine, and control system; verification of guidance subsystem performance; verification of the design of operational launch equipment; verification of the missile nosecone separation process; and demonstration of the full-range potential of the missile system. High confidence in the validity of the technical process and in the adequacy of research and test engineering was the chief factor in the decision to adhere to test schedules even though it was apparent that a vital component was in difficulty. The fact that the Thor attained an initial operational capability three and one half years after program inception, and the intercontinental Atlas less than five years after program inception, provided the eventual validation of that management approach.[8]

Insofar as the liquid-fuel rocket engine was the keystone of the Air Force ballistic missile program, that service early recognized that the basic problem was not *what* could be done, but how rapidly. The essential rocket-engine technology had been created in the Navaho program and enough had been done by 1954 to demonstrate its basic soundness. It was clear, however, that the translation of experimental technology into operational weapons would require considerably more

[8] See particularly, H. R. 1121, Sep. 1959, pp. 101-109, and Rpt. of Comptroller General of the United States to the Congress, "Review of Administrative Management of the Ballistic Missile Program of the Department of the Air Force," May 1960.

than a refinement of engine components and their attachment to a cylinder containing fuel cells, guidance electronics, and a payload. The program goal was not a rocket—not even a rocket that could be mass produced. It was a weapon that could be deployed and used.

In that circumstance lay the basic difference between the Air Force ballistic missile effort and contemporary developments of other large rocket vehicles. From the day that Trevor Gardner secured approval of the accelerated Atlas program to the time the first missiles were turned over to operational commands, the only meaningful objective was a militarily useful weapon. Inherent in that approach was the concept that any weapon delivered to field forces had to be reliable, readily producible, and usefully employable if the occasion arose.

Such an outlook had implications for much more than the original Atlas, Thor, and Titan programs. Reliability of operation was one of the prime goals of standardization in the missile production program. It proved enormously significant when the United States space effort was first permitted to breathe freely in the aftermath of Sputniks I and II. The rocket engines, guidance systems, airframes, and related components which together constituted the Thor and Atlas D missile systems proved superbly qualified to serve as space boosters. At the end of the first five years of the space age they represented 90 percent of all the first stages used in the successful American satellites and space probes. Indeed, between June 1961 and July 1963, precisely half of all the space projects attempted by any nation were boosted by the Thor alone, either in its original configuration or under its NASA name: Delta. Of the 134 space launches officially attempted during that period, 12 used Scout solid-fuel rockets, 27 were Soviet projects, while 28 employed the Atlas and 67 the Thor (including 15 using the Delta nomenclature). Of the 200 Thors launched in the six years before June 30, 1963, 166 were completely successful. As a space booster, the Thor-Agena or Thor-Delta configuration was 98 percent successful.[9]

In the meantime, while the Thor and Atlas missiles moved into large scale production and began deployment to operational squadrons, vaulting technology was harshly altering the shape of the total program. Three circumstances were chiefly responsible: renewed recognition of the need for "hardened" launch sites that would offer reasonable protection against an enemy first strike; progress toward the long-term goal of developing storable propellants, so that a liquid-fuel missile need not be exposed to the extra hazards of last minute fueling or, alternately, to difficulties inherent in the use of liquid oxygen as a

---

[9] *Space Log*, July 1963; *New York Times*, Western Ed., July 3, 1963.

principal propellant; and the refinement of single-grain solid rockets substantially larger than anything conceived before Sputnik.

The first two of these factors, "hard siting" requirements and the recognized need for non-cryogenic propellants, led to creation of Titan II, a very substantially improved version of the original Titan ICBM. Apart from reducing missile-reaction time by the many minutes needed to fuel each missile, the adoption of non-cryogenic propellants eliminated one of the most troublesome items of missile technology— high-rate-of-flow propellant loading equipment. Seizing the opportunity provided by incorporation of such a radical change, the Air Force also programmed for Titan II such innovations as in-silo launch from very hard sites, all-inertial guidance, and a substantially more powerful second stage.

Much of the basic research essential to in-silo firing, to the operational use of non-cryogenic propellants, and to adoption of a sufficiently accurate all-inertial guidance system had been undertaken well in advance of the May 1960 contract for development and production of Titan II. Nevertheless, the complete success of the first test missile during its 16 March 1962 firing was something new to missile testing; for the first time a missile completely satisfied its range and accuracy specifications during its initial trial. (Prototype firings which extended from June 1961 into January 1962 had included five complete and two partial successes in seven attempts, in itself something of a record.)

Minuteman

A still more radical innovation in large rockets—and in ICBM technology—was the improbably rapid development of the solid-fuel ICBM, Minuteman. That event was, in its early stages, the consequence of a near-fanatic determination on the part of one dedicated officer, Colonel Edward N. Hall. Colonel Hall had first been exposed to the problem of mixing and casting relatively large (for the time) solid rockets in the immediate post-war years, between 1945 and 1948. He was intermittently involved with solid-rocket technology at intervals over the next several years until, in 1955, he became associated with the ICBM effort. By that time, independent research had provided a solution to one difficulty which for the previous decade had kept rocket engineers from successfully assembling and firing a large solid-fuel rocket; a reliable igniter, compatible with large-scale rocket castings, was first successfully tested in 1955.

The key to casting large grains was a technique of dispersing an oxygen-rich compound such as ammonium perchlorate in a polymeric

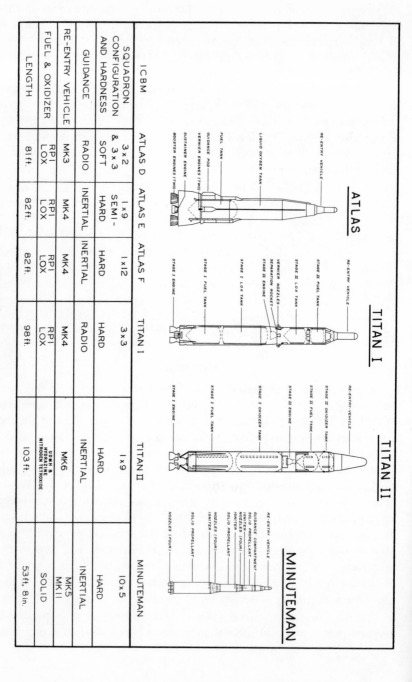

I.C.B.M	ATLAS D	ATLAS E	ATLAS F	TITAN I	TITAN II	MINUTEMAN
SQUADRON CONFIGURATION AND HARDNESS	3×2 & 3×3 — SOFT	1×9 — SEMI-HARD	1×12 — HARD	3×3 — HARD	1×9 — HARD	10×5 — HARD
GUIDANCE	RADIO	INERTIAL	INERTIAL	RADIO	INERTIAL	INERTIAL
RE-ENTRY VEHICLE	MK3	MK4	MK4	MK4	MK6	MK5 MKII
FUEL & OXIDIZER	RP1 LOX	RP1 LOX	RP1 LOX	RP1 LOX	UDMH & HYDRAZINE NITROGEN TETROXIDE	SOLID
LENGTH	81ft	82ft	82ft	98ft	103 ft	53ft, 8in.

Fig. 17 ICBM comparisons (USAF chart).

organic binder that acted as a fuel. Sound igniter design and a reasonable fund of experience in JATO rockets were other resources available in 1955, but still there seemed no realistic prospect of developing a solid-fuel ICBM.

Before proceeding with accelerated development of the Atlas, Thor, and Titan, General Schriever in the fall of 1955 had assembled a small group of experts to appraise carefully the status of the solid-fuel rocket technology. Colonel Hall, then in charge of General Schriever's propulsion section, directed the inquiry. Its product was the conclusion that the difficulty of commanding precise thrust termination, the uncertainty of structural integrity in grain-to-case bonding (particularly under conditions of extreme heat and high accelerations), and the slight prospect of obtaining uniform solid-propellant mixtures over a period of several months would prevent any near-term application of solid rockets to ICBM uses. (There was little serious Air Force consideration of clustering solid rockets, even as upper stages, because of the generally unsatisfactory experience with such "bundles"—which tended toward highly erratic performance.)

For the next two years, through the end of 1957, the Air Force sponsored a vigorous program of applied research and engineering development aimed toward the evolution of a high-thrust single-grain solid-fuel rocket. The difficulty of obtaining high specific impulse, the nonavailability of thrust-control devices (either for thrust termination or for vector control), and the lack of high-strength lightweight engine cases presented major obstacles. But by late 1957 the program had resulted in the development of solid-fuel engines weighing as much as 25,000 pounds, in the perfection of strip-winding techniques for cases, and in solutions to problems of nozzle cooling and nozzle gimballing.

It would be an oversimplification to say that the real effect of the SPUTNIK panic on the ballistic-missile program was to stimulate production of missile systems then in advanced development. But in some significant respects such was the case. Under the concept of concurrency, development, production, and deployment were concomitant. But for practical purposes they were confined to missile systems which in most respects had been technically defined somewhat earlier. And the lessons of those earlier choices were by 1957 becoming fully apparent.

Indeed, in the atmosphere of extreme penny-pinching that preceded the SPUTNIK-prompted program expansion, it seemed highly probable that production of the Atlas, Thor, and Titan might be limited deliberately because of the prospectively great cost of those systems.

Before SPUTNIK, therefore, considerable interest was expressed in the feasibility of defining and then developing a solid-fuel ICBM which could be built and deployed for substantially less money than any of the liquid-fuel missiles. The desire, or its expression, happily coincided with technological advances in solid-fuel rocketry which made such a prospect feasible from an engineering standpoint. Funding difficulties, however, caused attention to be diverted, momentarily, to the possibility of combining a solid-fuel upper stage with the first stage of the Titan as an alternative to a third major ICBM development program.

In September 1957 the entire issue was entrusted to a special working group, again headed by Colonel Hall, which concentrated its attention on a solid-fuel missile proposal referred to as "Weapon System Q." Acting as an embryonic project office, the group shortly began to advocate development of an "idealized" solid-fuel missile, a second-generation system differing from Atlas, Thor, and Titan in being specifically designed for low-cost, high-rate production; slow obsolescence; and quick reaction combined with maximum survivability in the face of an ICBM assault on the continental United States.

Policy, strategy, fiscal, and technological considerations pointed to the same course; when the Soviet Sputniks prompted massive acceleration of United States missile and space programs in the early winter of 1957-1958, one of the major decisions was to approve development of a new solid-fuel ICBM system—shortly dubbed Minuteman.

All of the lessons of missile development drawn from experience in the Atlas, Thor, and Titan programs were applied to Minuteman. In particular, the concurrency thesis found a full application which, in many respects, made Minuteman the first major system completely subject to that approach.

Its importance could be judged by the fact that a production decision was made several months in advance of the availablility of the first missile, and that work on the first operational site actually began before guidance-system design was final and before there was experimental proof that thrust-vector control could be maintained by gimballing the rocket nozzles. Irreversible decisions on site configuration had been literally cast into concrete—on launch sites—well before the first test flight of a Minuteman missile system, on February 1, 1961. Indeed, decisions basic to the character of the United States stategic force structure were predicated on the confident assumption that the Minuteman program would satisfy its objectives.

The key indication came on February 1, 1961, when for the first time a complete missile with all systems operating had an unqualified success on its initial test. Contractors for Minuteman's three stages, guidance system, and system integration had not been selected until July 1958 and the decision to sponsor a complete system development had not been taken until September of that year. The complete process of system development, from program inception through first full-scale test success, had taken a fraction more than three years.[10]

Minuteman represented more than merely an unusually successful missile-system development. It was, in several respects, the culmination of a revolution in technology, in systems management, and in military strategy. In being a solid-fuel ICBM, as in several other respects, Minuteman was markedly different from its predecessors. Although it seemed most closely related to Polaris, and stemmed from the same base of research and technology, Minuteman was the inevitable culmination of a development process that had its origin in the Atlas acceleration decision of 1954.

General Schriever made this clear in pointing out that the Air Force ballistic missile program had demonstrated "the need to base new programs solidly on the knowledge gained in current programs and to consider objectively all the technological approaches that may be able to satisfy an operational requirement." He noted that the process had to be continuing, and "not without regard for programs under development." He concluded that "such an approach does not eliminate the element of risk—but it does greatly minimize the risk involved." [11]

From Missiles to Space

Theorists—and historians—might argue the virtues and disabilities of concurrency, of emphasizing weaponry rather than rocketry alone, and of insistence on an orderly—if sometimes disturbingly rapid—sequence of technology. Pragmatism, however, was on the side of the Air Force. The United States strategic missile force was made up of Atlas, Titan, Minuteman, and Polaris weapons, while for practical purposes the national space program still was entirely dependent on boosters taken directly from the Atlas and Thor programs.

Whether the "standard vehicle" approach was the cause or the consequence of Air Force booster program requirements was a question that might exercise the ingenuity of historians in years to come. In effect, however, the fiscal pressures which surrounded rocket and

[10] Sources of information on Minuteman include: "Minuteman Propulsion," prepared by Col. L. F. Ayres for IAS mtg March 10-11 1960; H. H. Martin, "Our New Generation of Rockets," *Saturday Evening Post*, Oct. 1 1960; A. G. Haley, *Rocketry and Space Exploration* (Princeton, Van Nostrand, 1958); *Missiles and Rockets*, various, particularly June 6, 1960, October 17, 1960.

[11] Gen. B. A. Schriever (Cmdr. AFSC), "Achievement of Technological Superiority: in *NATO's Fifteen Nations*, Dec. 1962-Jan. 1963.

missile development served to compel attention to the least costly means of performing given assignments. When the assignment itself bulked so large that it dominated a scene, the development of a specific vehicle could result. In other instances, however, the need to adapt what was available, at reasonable cost, overrode abstractions. The fact that payloads were most often tailored to available vehicles could not be denied; of the major space goals in the 1960's which could not be satisfied by Atlas, Thor, or Titan, only the lunar expedition carried sufficient weight to justify an independent vehicle development effort. Adaptation or modification generally served. The Thor and Atlas were prominent examples. Another was the Agena upper stage developed from the original (1954) military space program of the Air Force; by 1963, more than 100 Agenas had been launched into space. Able and Able Star upper stages derived from the Vanguard program, with antecedents stemming back to Aerobee probe rockets of the early 1950's, represented another instance.

By 1962 it was becoming apparent that technology would support larger and more sophisticated space boosters and that the requirements of the national space program would justify development of at least one basic new vehicle.

But again, as in the earlier instance of the Atlas and Thor, a new program based on a foundation of established—if not entirely proven—technology seemed the best approach. Titan III, a "workhorse" booster composed of an improved Titan II core, advanced upper stages, and "strap-on" solid rockets, completely satisfied the formula defined by General Schriever. It took advantage of the most advanced concepts of solid-fuel rocketry that had grown from the Minuteman and Polaris efforts, built on a framework that included the most advanced aspects of the largest and most powerful liquid-fuel rocket missile actually available to the United States, and yet represented a very substantial step into the technological future.

Taken individually, none of the advances incorporated in the Titan III program seemed remarkably radical, yet their product was a vehicle with a total thrust in excess of 2,500,000 pounds. (The Titan IIIA core had a thrust of 430,000 pounds, the second stage 100,000 pounds, the transtage 16,000, and the IIIC solid-fuel motors 1,000,000 pounds each.) The original goal of the Atlas program, rather less than a decade earlier, had been a highly optimistic 135,000 pounds of thrust from a single engine.[12]

[12] Titan III development is discussed in: *Aviation Week*, May 21, 1962 and Feb. 25, 1963; *Missiles and Rockets*, April 30, 1962 and May 14, 1962; and in substantial numbers of newspapers and magazine articles elsewhere.

Notwithstanding the evidences of departure from established channels of development and of radical innovation under the pressure of military requirements or the thirst for international prestige, the Air Force ballistic missile and booster programs retained both technological and organizational continuity, and coherence, through their first eight years. And the accomplishments were not inconsiderable; everything based on Atlas, Thor, Titan, or Minuteman, or on related technological developments, stemmed essentially from contracts let early in 1955 and from a program that did not receive substantial financial support for three years after that.

BIBLIOGRAPHICAL NOTE: In addition to the specific sources noted earlier, information on several aspects of the missile and space effort may be obtained from the following, chiefly popular-approach, books:

J. L. Chapman, *Atlas: The Story of A Missile*, (N. Y. Harper and Bros., 1960).

Julian Hartt, *Mighty Thor*, N. Y. (N. Y. Duell, Sloan, and Pierce), 1961.

Willy Ley, *Rockets, Missiles, and Space Travel*, (N. Y. Viking, 1961).

Roy Neal, *Ace in the Hole, The Story of the Minuteman Missile*, (N. Y. Doubleday, 1962).

The Polaris

WYNDHAM D. MILES*

AT 12:39 ON THE afternoon of July 20, 1960, thirty miles off the coast of Florida, a tall, bottle-shaped Polaris missile leaped out of the ocean, erupted flame from its base, and rocketed upward. Higher and higher it climbed, smaller and smaller it appeared, until it faded into the heavens, leaving behind a tenuous trail of white smoke and vapor. At this spot where the missile had emerged the ocean was empty. It was as though the object had popped magically from the deep. But below the surface a submarine, *George Washington*, hovered silently. Within the vessel a happy crowd of officers, seamen, and civilian scientists congratulated each other on the first undersea launch of a ballistic missile.

The Fleet Ballistic Missile System (FBM), as the Polaris, launch submarine, and supporting units were called, had been born more than four years before the historic flight off Cape Canaveral. In September 1955 the Killian Committee recommended that the military forces develop an intermediate range ballistic missile (IRBM) with a range of 1500 nautical miles. The National Security Council endorsed this recommendation, and President Eisenhower approved it and passed it on to Department of Defense. As a result, Secretary of Defense Charles E. Wilson initiated two IRBM programs: one was the development by Air Force of a land-based missile, IRBM-1, which does not concern us here, while the other was the joint development by Army and Navy of a missile, IRBM-2, that could be launched on land or on sea and also serve as an alternative to the Air Force IRBM. The Army and Navy divided their task so that the Army would develop the missile and land-launch system, the Navy the sea-launch system.

Secretary Wilson designated a special system of management to speed development. The line of authority started with the Office of The Secretary of Defense Ballistic Missile Committee, concerned with ICBMs and IRBMs, passed down to the Joint Army Navy Ballistic

* Historian of the National Institutes of Health (Bethesda, Maryland), Dr. Miles was a civilian historian with the Army Chemical Corps (1953-60), the National Archives (1960-61), and the U. S. Navy (1961-62). A regular contributor to historical and technical journals, he is co-author of a volume with Leo P. Brophy and Rexmond C. Cochrane, *The Chemical Warfare Service: From Laboratory to Field* (1959).

Missile Committee (JANBMC), branched to Army's Ballistic Missile Agency (ABMA) and Navy's Special Projects Office (SP). Major General John B. Medaris commanded ABMA, Redstone Arsenal, Alabama; Rear Admiral William Raborn headed SP, Washington, D. C.

Jupiter

In the closing months of 1955, Redstone Arsenal's Guided Missile Development Division drew up preliminary plans for the IRBM. Designers had two factors as a base for their calculations. First, they knew the estimated weight of the warhead of the desired yield that would be available when the rocket finally reached the production stage in 1958-60. Second, the only rocket engine of the necessary size available was the North American Aviation engine of 150,000 lbs. thrust. Starting with this information, designers conceived a missile 65 foot high and 95 inches in diameter. Navy was concerned about the height of the missile (roughly six stories) because of the difficulties that would arise in handling and launching such a monster at sea. In February 1956, DOD, Navy and Army agreed on the following characteristics: length—58 feet; diameter—105 inches; range—1500 nautical miles.

Jupiter, as the missile was named on March 12, 1956, was a descendant of Army's Redstone. ABMA carried out considerable development and fired a number of test vehicles. Vehicles composed of a Redstone lower stage and solid fuel upper stages, used to test and develop nose cones, were known as Jupiter C. Redstone missiles carrying Jupiter test components were called Jupiter A.

Fleet Ballistic Missile System (FBM)

While the Army was developing Jupiter, the Navy was designing the sea launch system. The Navy had begun experiments with long range missiles near the end of World War II. One line of development had proceeded through aerodynamic air-breathing missiles: Regulus and Triton. Another line had proceeded through a large high-altitude rocket: Viking. On September 6, 1947, aircraft carrier *Midway* launched a V-2 rocket. On May 11, 1950, *U. S. S. Norton Sound* launched a Viking to a then-record altitude of 106 miles. The Navy had studied the relative merits of surface ships and submarines as missile platforms, and it had outlined the strategic and tactical concepts for a FBM system.

In planning Jupiter launch ships, SP considered submarines and surface vessels.[1] Submarines would have had greater strategic value, but

[1] SP, as I use it, is the team of Navy people and contractors of the Special

subs capable of carrying Jupiter would have been monsters. SP, therefore, concentrated on surface ships, leaving submarines for the future.

Launching a missile at sea from a surface ship would be more difficult than launching on land. Waves and swells would rock a ship,
making it hard to stabilize a missile exactly vertical. Moreover, the
ship's motion would make it difficult to determine the azimuth of the
missile (this would have to be done precisely or the missile would not
fly accurately to its target). Flexure of the ship's hull would also
increase difficulties in determining the azimuth. A missile ship would
have to have a navigation system that could calculate, even in worst
weather, the ship's exact position on the surface of the ocean so that
missiles would be directed on an accurate flight toward the target. The
ship would need a complicated electrical system for readying, aiming,
and launching the missile. It would have to have apparatus for producing liquid oxygen and insulated tanks for storing it. Special ele-
vators would be needed to raise the missile from the hull to the deck and
keep it erect. Stabilizing fins would be needed to steady the ship. To
investigate and solve these problems, the Navy planned three experimental ships; one for development of navigation equipment, one as an
experimental launch ship, and one as a prototype combat ship.

Solid Fuel Jupiter

While SP-ABMA were moving rapidly to develop the Jupiter
system, SP was simultaneously investigating solid fuels. The Navy
would have preferred a solid fuel rocket over a liquid fuel because
solid fuels would simplify logistics, handling, storage, design, and
safety. Admiral Raborn had asked JANBMC at its first meeting,
November 1955, for permission to investigate solids. After months of
persuasion, to show that SP would not duplicate other solid fuel work
and that Navy had much to gain from solid fuels, Raborn received
DOD's consent to see if a solid fuel missile was feasible.

The Navy had begun its first solid propellant rocket development
at Naval Powder Factory, 1942, which led to firing of rockets from
naval aircraft in 1943. Navy laboratories and contractors thereafter

Projects Office who designed, developed, and produced the FBM system. I do not
refer to people by name in this short article because too many people were
involved (thousands of industrial, governmental, and academic scientists and
engineers; thousands of contractors, stretching to the fourth tier and beyond).
Furthermore, it is just about impossible in a large, modern project like Polaris
to find individuals who deserve sole credit for an idea or invention. The actors
were groups of intelligent, competent, industrious people.

worked with composite propellants (1942), extruded double base propellants (1945), and internal burning grain rockets (1945). Under the
Navy, Alleghany Ballistics Laboratory had initiated work in 1945 on
cast double base propellant systems that led to the first large (approximately 3400 lbs.) solid propellant rocket for Bumblebee. In 1946 work
began on polymerizable composite propellants, in 1949 "Platonic" cast
double base propellants were discovered, and in 1955 increased burning rates had led to the use of end-burning grains.

SP had its contractors draw up plans for a two-stage missile (commonly called "solid fuel Jupiter"), consisting of a ring of six solid
fuel rockets (first stage), surrounding a single solid fuel rocket (second
stage). Jetavators and jet vanes would steer the missile. Propellant, of
ammonium and potassium perchlorate suspended in a polyurethane
matrix, would be cast in the motor cases. In action, the ring of six
motors would ignite simultaneously and carry the missile on the first
lap of its journey. At the proper time the inner motor would ignite
and pull away.

End of the Army-Navy Partnership

At this point in time, ABMA was developing liquid fuel Jupiter, SP
was developing a sea launch system, and SP was also developing, as a
long shot, a large solid fuel missile. But off to the side events were
occurring that were to cause cancellation of the Army-Navy project
and to start Navy toward a small solid fuel missile.

From June to September 1956, the Committee on Undersea Warfare
of the National Academy of Sciences-National Research Council met
at Woods Hole, Mass. In a discussion Edward Teller, University of
California, gently criticized the Navy for thinking in terms of a ballistic missile which would be operational in 1963, but tying it to a 1956
nuclear technology. Teller felt that a warhead much lighter than
Jupiter's warhead could be readied by 1963.

This view was extremely important to the Navy. Teller's estimates,
if agreed to by laboratories involved with the warhead, would allow
Navy to plan a much smaller, lighter missile than Jupiter. A smaller
missile could lead to the use of submarine launch ships and of solid
fuel motors.

Admiral Raborn sent officers to obtain independent estimates of the
weight and yield of a warhead that would be expected in a few years
under aggressive development. Experts did not agree in their predictions, but they gave Raborn figures that encouraged him to try for a
small missile. SP called the small missile Polaris.

A number of Naval officers favored immediate cancellation of

Jupiter. Others believed that SP should start on Polaris but continue with Jupiter. Differences of opinion stemmed from the circumstance that solid fuel technology was behind liquid. Among arguments against solid fuel rockets were these: the guidance system was far from perfect, whereas the guidance system for liquid fuel rockets was fairly well developed; the steering of solid fuel rockets had not been demonstrated, whereas the steering of liquid fuel rockets had been well proved; control of burning, needed for ballistic flight accuracy, had not been demonstrated in solid fuel rockets, but was well in hand with liquid; there were developmental problems in solid fuel missile design, whereas the liquid fuel rocket was well along.

While SP debated, it had Lockheed draw preliminary plans for a small solid fuel missile. There were four basic plans, each for a missile weighing 31,000 lbs. with an expected range of 1500 miles, but differing in dimensions.

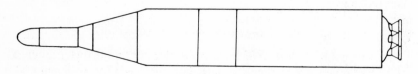

Fig. 18 Polaris (USN)

By autumn Raborn had decided that SP should drop liquid fuel Jupiter, concentrate on solid fuel Jupiter and on Polaris. Soon he took a step further, decided to drop solid fuel Jupiter. Rear Admiral John E. Clark, Navy member of JANBMC, asked Brigadier General John P. Daley, Army member, if Army wanted to develop Polaris. Daley replied that Army had reached its capacity in IRBM development and would continue with liquid fuel Jupiter.

The Chief of Naval Operations and Secretary of the Navy went along with Raborn's decision. The Secretary of the Navy asked DOD for permission to drop Jupiter and concentrate on Polaris. Wilson agreed and on December 8, 1956, divorced Navy from Army in IRBM development.

Polaris

In its revised program, Navy chose the nuclear-powered submarine as the missile ship. Submarine and missile were to be ready for trial in 1963, for the fleet by 1965. The Navy still planned to test surface ships as carriers, but subs came first.

SP had to develop Polaris, the submarine, and ancillary equipment simultaneously to meet the deadline. In order to do this, SP needed "envelopes" of the major systems involved.

To illustrate the concept of an envelope, it might be stated that the height, diameter, and weight of a Polaris missile is 28 feet, 60 inches, and 15 tons. These figures give the overall outline without going into detail about the parts inside the missile. The envelope of Polaris comprised the length, diameter, weight, center of gravity, environment (temperature, humidity, etc.), points where the missile would be supported in the tube, points of access to the inside of the missile, power requirements, and cabling requirements. Knowing these things, submarine builders, launch-tube designers, and other units could go ahead without having an actual Polaris.

The submarine envelope included the number of missiles a submarine would carry, the method of launch, the method of aligning missiles before launch, surveillance, count-down sequence, testing, servicing, power requirements, space requirements, and other things. With these points established, submarine builders could go ahead.

Envelopes were needed in each major area — missile, submarine, launching, navigation, fire control, re-entry body, and so on. Admiral Raborn called together a number of government, industrial, and academic scientists into a Steering Task Group to establish envelopes. This STG worked like beavers, January through March 1957, assembling and studying data. Finally it settled on the envelope of the submarine, the launch system, the missile, and other components.

Acceleration

During the spring and summer of 1957, Admiral Raborn and his officers studied the possibility of accelerating development of the FBM system. Acceleration was a complicated matter. SP and its contractors had estimated the earliest dates by which the warhead, missile, guidance mechanism, submarine, navigation system, fire control system, communications system, and other components would be ready for assembly into the FBM system. Complicated research, development, and production schedules had been drawn up. SP could not simply squeeze the schedule and produce the system sooner.

In the autumn, events occurred that forced acceleration. On October 4, the Soviet Union rocketed SPUTNIK I into orbit. Public and government opinion favored a speed-up of American missile development.

SP figured that under certain conditions development might be quickened. The government would have to allow overtime, the Navy and DOD would have to eliminate all administrative bottlenecks, SP would have to stimulate patriotism of every worker, contractors would have to fire test vehicles more frequently, contractors would have to leap-frog some steps in development, DOD would have to accept temporarily missiles with a 1200 nautical (1380 statute) mile range instead of 1500 nautical miles (1740 statute), and some things would have to be deferred or delayed. By such means, SP could have three submarines ready by September 1961, with the first ready for sea duty with "emergency missiles" by February 1962.

SP drew up alternate sets of plans based on the above philosophy. While DOD was studying these, Russia sent up another satellite (November 3). SP's planners pushed harder. On December 9, Secretary Wilson told SP to accelerate. Once acceleration had been ordered, SP took short cuts, some of them engineering gambles.

SP took a nuclear submarine on the ways at New London, cut it in half, and built in a Polaris midsection. *George Washington*, as the ship was called, was launched on June 9, 1959.

SP had been considering the inclusion in the submarine of a "quench" system that would drown accidental fires in rocket motors. There was a difference of opinion regarding the need or practicability of such a quench system, but under acceleration there was simply no time to develop the system and it was dropped.

Acceleration forced SP to cancel a series (FTV-2) of test vehicles. This series had come along more slowly than planned; explosions at Aerojet's propellant plant had further slowed the work, and engineers felt that they would have less chance of meeting an accelerated schedule if they continued the series. SP decided to cancel remaining tests and obtain data by adding a few vehicles elsewhere.

The test program had to be speeded. Test vehicles had to be fired more frequently, which meant that missiles had to be checked out more rapidly, and this in turn meant that more facilities had to be erected quickly at Cape Canaveral.

The speed-up did not alter Navy's ultimate goal. So far as the missile was concerned, it might be said that acceleration brought about the early production of a development model of Polaris. The team, once it started, increased the pace and had the first two Polaris submarines deployed before the end of 1960.

Problems in Development

In this short article it is impossible to go into all the areas of the FBM system. Some of the subsystems are self evident by mentioning some basic problems.

Polaris submarines were to stay submerged for weeks at a time. The

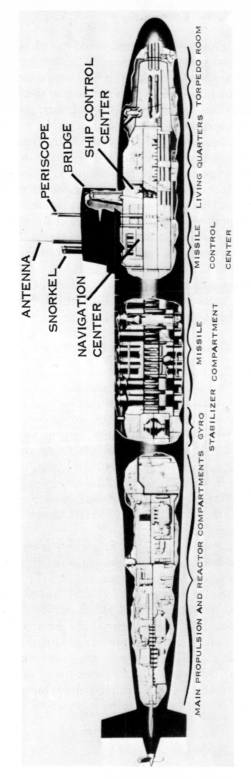

Fig. 19 Typical Polaris Fleet Ballistic Missile Submarine (USN)

most precise navigation system in the world had to be designed so that a ship could tell its exact position any time of the day or night without coming to the surface and exposing itself. Air purification equipment, to purify air constantly, had to be developed so that a ship would not have to surface. Intellectual, physiological, and psychological needs of the men, cut off from the world for weeks, had to be kept in mind.

A method of communicating from the United States to submarines, a method as reliable as humanly possible, had to be devised. There had to be developed a fire control system composed of a complex group of computers and electronics capable of giving precise rapid directions to the missile. A vast training system had to be established to educate the men in the operation of the complex FBM system, and to have the men ready by the time the ships and missiles were ready. Nuclear-powered, Polaris submarines had to be built faster than ships had ever been built before in peacetime. A method had to be devised to allow SP to keep track of development and production in hundreds of places scattered over the United States (the method, called PERT, is an important new management tool and has been adopted by many large industrial firms).

Development of the Launch System

Immediately after the Steering Task Group in March 1957 fixed the missile envelope and the method of launching (vertical launch from a tube within the submarine), SP had to determine if the launch scheme for ejecting a missile from a tube by compressed air or gas was practical. Engineers decided on a simple demonstration. They rigged a tube, "Pea-Shooter," on a wharf at San Francisco Navy Yard, inserted a redwood log the size of a Polaris missile, released a blast of compressed air into the base of the tube, and watched the log come flying out. The launch concept had been proven feasible, although much work lay ahead before a satisfactory launch system would be ready for a submarine.

At the beginning of the program SP viewed as its primary goal the launching of Polaris missiles from submarines on the surface. Strategic advantages of underwater launch were so great that a new goal, submerged launch, quickly obscured the old. SP had to prove the practicality of underwater launch as quickly as development allowed; the date depended upon the speed with which preliminary development of the launch system and missile proceeded. SP did this in 1958 by submerging a full-size launch tube in the water near San Clemente Island, California. By March 23 a full-scale model of Polaris had been lowered into the tube. An engineer pushed the button and the model came bursting through the surface in a geyser of spray. "Pop-up,"

as the test facility was called, had demonstrated the feasibility of underwater launch.

Of the many techniques that could be visualized for launching missiles from submerged submarines, SP divided the several that were
worth investigation into two types, wet and dry. In the dry launch
the missile would be enclosed in a shell. This shell would surround the
missile in its upward flight through the water, then open at the surface
like the skin peeling off a banana and let the missile blast away. In the
wet launch the bare missile would be shot from the submarine.

Advantages of the dry launch were these: a shell would protect the
missile; engineers could shape the shell to make it hydrodynamically
stable and insure that the missile would rise straight up. There were,
of course, a number of disadvantages, not the least of which was greater
complexity.

An advantage of the wet launch was its simplicity. But engineers
could not tell, without time-consuming model tests, if an expelled
hydrodynamically unstable missile would rise vertically, without swerv-
ing or turning turtle. Furthermore, water pressure might crush a bare
missile. Also, the front of a bare missile might be stove in when it
rammed against the ocean as the missile shot from the launch tube.

There were, in addition, several schemes for expelling the missile
from a submarine. It could be done by compressed air, by a small
rocket fastened to the base of the missile, by the missile's buoyancy, or
even by a balloon which would pull the missile to the surface. SP
rapidly narrowed the choice to compressed air or gas. Gas could be
generated by a slow burning powder. A gas generator would weigh
less, take up less space, and be less complex than a compressed air
system. But development of a gas generator system posed more
problems than a compressed air system.

SP eliminated some launch and ejection ideas by tests on scale models.
At the end of 1957, acceleration forced SP to make certain decisions.
It decided to concentrate on wet launch from a diaphragm covered
tube, but to continue dry launch for a time in case wet launch failed.
It also decided to concentrate on a compressed air ejection system but
to continue with gas on a small scale.

Many other things besides launch and ejection methods had to be
investigated. SP had to decide on the launch depth, to study underwater currents that might throw a missile off course, to study wave-
induced motion of the water at various depths, to find a tough material
to cover the end of the launch tube so that water would not pour in
when the hatch opened, to find a method of puncturing this material
at the instant the missile rose, to find the best way to support the

missile in the tube so as not to crush it, to protect the missile from shock of depth charge explosion, and so on.

The Missile

After the parameters had been settled, SP and contractors had to draw up definite plans and time-tables for development and construction. These plans had to show the order in which components would have to be developed and the dates upon which they would have to be ready for assembly into subsystems and systems.

On April 2, approximately 80 men from SP and contractors met at Palo Alto, California, to coordinate plans and time-tables for the missile. Out of this meeting came a development schedule based on estimates of the time it would take to develop major parts. The men also scheduled experimental flights that would be needed.

For development of the missile, five test vehicles were to be used. Vehicle A would be used in development of thrust termination, B in development of re-entry body, C in development of jetavators and of thrust termination, D for final re-entry body tests. Information from these test vehicles would flow into vehicle E, which would have characteristics of Polaris. Engineers planned more than 30 flight tests, continuing into the autumn of 1958 (they changed the number of flights several times during development, as they learned more about the missile).

In addition, the men drew up an overall schedule. The date in 1958 when the first Polaris would be able to fly, was dictated by the time it would take to develop the rocket motor. The date when the first guided Polaris would be ready to fly, November 1959, was set by the time it would take M. I. T. and G. E. to ready the guidance mechanism (it would be delivered in July, but needed four months to eliminate " bugs " and ready the missile). This overall schedule and the flight test schedule were modified at the end of 1957 when SP accelerated.

Among the many problems in development was the perfecting of a steering device. Liquid fuel missiles are steered by swiveling the engine. This cannot be done with a solid fuel missile. Willie Fieldler invented the jetavator, a device that moves into the jet stream, pushes the stream to one side and causes the missile to turn.

Another problem cropped up in the plant where the rubbery propellant was mixed. Explosions occurred in 1957, and the contractor had to improve the mixing process.

Considerable work had to be done on the propellant itself in order to make certain it would cure properly after being cast into the motor cases. If cracks developed in the propellant, it would burn too fast and the motor would explode.

The first flight of a full-scale Polaris test vehicle, AX-1, came on September 24, 1958, at Cape Canaveral. It blasted off properly, but instead of arcing out to sea it headed straight up. At 40,000 feet the safety officer blew it apart. A small, inexpensive programmer had failed to tell the missile to turn.

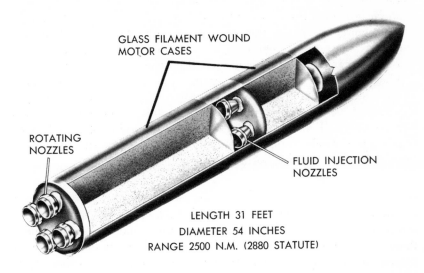

GLASS FILAMENT WOUND
MOTOR CASES

ROTATING
NOZZLES

FLUID INJECTION
NOZZLES

LENGTH 31 FEET
DIAMETER 54 INCHES
RANGE 2500 N.M. (2880 STATUTE)

Fig. 20   Polaris A-3 Missile. Advanced A-3 has a designed range of 2,500 nautical miles as compared to 1,200 n. m. for the A1 and 1,500 n. m. for the A-2 (USN)

Two weeks later AX-2 broke apart and burned on the pad. On December 30, AX-3 took off well but had to be destroyed a minute later. Analysis show that heat from the burning propellant was destroying the aft end of the missile. On January 19, 1959, AX-4 and, on February 27, AX-5 behaved erratically after take-off and had to be destroyed.

The first five test vehicles failed, but before they did so they sent back data that guided engineers to improvements. On April 20, AX-6 blasted off, curved out to sea perfectly, separated properly, and dropped its nose in the Atlantic 300 miles off shore.

Early test vehicles were guided by automatic pilots. On July 15, AX-11 carried aloft the first inertial guidance system. A jetavator broke off, but AX-11 stayed in the sky long enough to prove the guidance.

The above vehicles took off from pads. But Polaris was to leave from a tube, and this had to be tested. On August 14, AX-13 blasted out of a tube, a duplicate of a submarine tube, at Canaveral. On the 27th, the firing was duplicated at sea from test ship *Observation Island*.

A new series of test vehicles, A1X, in which were incorporated all improvements stemming from flights of series AX, began in September. With this series, SP was almost at its goal.

So far it had not been proven that Polaris, after ejection under water, would ignite above the surface and go. On April 14, "Pop-up" launched a test missile carrying a small charge of propellant. The missile burst from the ocean and ignited perfectly.

There remained a test of the entire system. This was first done above water on March 29 when *Observation Island* launched a missile that landed 900 miles down range. On July 20 it was done under water when *George Washington* launched its first Polaris. SP still had to improve the missile, complete work in certain areas, push production, but the FBM system was born.

*   *   *

The full history of Polaris remains to be written. Research and development continues in solid fuels, materials, guidance, communications, and every other subsystem. Hand-in-hand with research is production, management, military strategy, and national policy. Furthermore, Polaris is only a part of solid fuel technology, which includes Scout, Minuteman, Pershing, and other rockets. Years will elapse before the complete story can be put together, but in the meantime there is much for historians to work on.

BIBLIOGRAPHICAL NOTE

For more than a year I enjoyed the privilege of being historian in Navy's Special Projects Office, reading documents, talking with SP's engineers, scientists, and administrators; and taping interviews with Admiral Raborn, his deputies, staff, branch heads, section heads, and consultants. Most of the pertinent research and development information on Polaris is still classified and therefore unavailable to the public, but there are scores of published documents which the historian may find useful, and of which the following is a selection:

Progress of Atlas and Polaris Missiles. Hearings before the Committee on Science and Astronautics, 86th Congress, 1st Session, July 28 and 29, 1959.

Review of the Space Program. Hearings before the Committee on Science and Astronautics, 86th Congress, 2nd Session, January 20 . . . February 5, 1960, Part 2, pages 548-657.

Naval Reactor Program and Polaris Missile System. Hearing before the Joint Committee on Atomic Energy, 86th Congress, 2nd Session, on Review of Progress in the Naval Reactor Program and Developments in the Polaris Missile Submarine System, April 9, 1960.

Rear Admiral William F. Raborn, Jr., "The Navy's New Partnership in Weapons," *Sperryscope* 14, No. 16, (1958), pp. 6-9.

Ed Rees, *The Seas and The Subs* (New York, 1961).

Shirley Thomas, *Men of Space* (Philadelphia, 1961), Vol. III, pp. 138-61, has a sketch of Raborn, an outline of the Polaris project, and a short bibliography.

James Barr and William Howard, *Polaris* (New York, 1960).

Trajectory, vol. 1, No. 1 (Winter 1960-61). The entire issue of this magazine, issued by Lockheed Aircraft Corporation, is devoted to Polaris.

F B M Fact Sheet. This pamphlet may be obtained from U. S. Navy, Special Projects Office, Washington 25, D. C. It is revised periodically, the latest (1 February 1963) issue running to 19 pages.

MANNED FLIGHT

"I confess that in 1901 I said to my brother Orville that man would not fly for fifty years. Two years later we ourselves made flights. This demonstration of my impotence as a prophet gave me such a shock that ever since I have distrusted myself and avoided all predictions . . ."

—*Wilbur Wright, before the Aero Club of France,*
November 5, 1908

"If there is any twentieth-century aspiration which corresponds to that of the nineteenth century for conquest of the air, it is perhaps that of the conquest of space with the early goal, travel to the moon. Like the concepts of flight during the nineteenth century, these concepts of space travel are the results of attempts of imaginative men to apply the technology of their day to the problems of interplanetary travel. It may well be that success will await a still broader basis of experience in science and technology, experiment and more experiment, and unanticipated scientific developments."

—*Hugh L. Dryden, Director of N.A.C.A., " The*
Next Fifty Years," Aero Digest (July 1953)

28. *USAF-NACA - Rocket-Powered X-1 Research Airplane.* This was the airplane which first exceeded the speed of sound on October 14, 1947, with Capt. Charles E. Yeager (USAF) as pilot, at Muroc, California. It was built by Bell Aircraft Co. (Bell Photo)

29. *Launching of a Polaris (A-2)* from the submerged nuclear-powered submarine, *USS Alexander Hamilton*, off Cape Canaveral on August 23, 1963. The *Hamilton* was the twelfth Fleet Ballistic Missile (FBM) submarine to undergo systems testing at Cape Kennedy. (U. S. Navy)

30. *Rocket and jet research aircraft* of the National Advisory Committee for Aeronautics (NACA) at Edwards AFB, California, in 1956. Flying regularly at transonic and supersonic speeds, the research airplanes explored new areas used in the design of military and civil aircraft. In the center is the Douglas X-3; at lower left, the Bell X-1A flown late in 1953 at a record 1,650-mph or 2.5 times the speed of sound. Continuing clockwise from the X-1A are the Douglas D-558-1 "Skystreak"; Convair XF-92A; Bell X-5 with variable sweepback wings; Douglas D-558-11 "Skyrocket," first piloted airplane to fly at twice the speed of sound; and the Northrup X-4. NACA, U. S. Air Force, U. S. Navy, and the aircraft industry joined to design, build, and fly these and other advanced airplanes in the high-speed flight research program which led to the X-15 and manned space flight. This program with rocket-powered aircraft began in 1944. (NASA Photo)

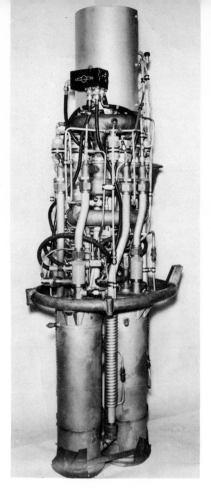

31. *Reaction Motors XLR-11 rocket engine* which powered the X-1, the first supersonic airplane. (Reaction Motors Photo) **32.** *Historic final meeting of the National Advisory Committee for Aeronautics*, Washington, D. C., August 21, 1958, closing forty-three years of service to " the scientific study of the problems of flight, with a view to their practical solution." This so-called " Main Committee " of NACA coordinated overall problems facing the science of flight, which in turn was advised by technical committees with representatives of government, industry, and universities, and was served by the laboratories of NACA. With the passage of the National Aeronautics and Space Act of 1958 by the Congress in July, the personnel and laboratories of NACA became the organizational nucleus of the National Aeronautics and Space Administration which began functioning on October 1, 1958.

Shown here (left to right) are: James T. Pyle, F. A. A. Administrator; Dr. Hugh L. Dryden, Director of NACA; Preston R. Bassett; Under Secretary of Commerce Louis S. Rothschild; Secretary Leonard Carmichael of the Smithsonian Institution; Dr. James H. Doolittle, Chairman of NACA; Dr. John F. Victory, Executive Secretary, NACA; Dr. Francis W. Reichelderfer, Chief, U. S. Weather Bureau; Dr. Frederick C. Crawford, Thompson Products; Maj. General Marvin C. Demler, USAF (attended for Lt. Gen. Roscoe C. Wilson, Deputy Chief of Staff, Development, USAF); General Thomas D. White, Chief of Staff, USAF; Assistant Secretary of Defense (R & E) Paul D. Foote; Vice Admiral Robert B. Pirie, Deputy Chief of Staff of Naval Operations (Air); Rear Admiral Wellington T. Hines, U. S. Navy Bureau of Aeronautics; Charles J. McCarthy, Chance Vought; and J. W. Crowley, Associate Director for Research, NACA. (USAF Photo)

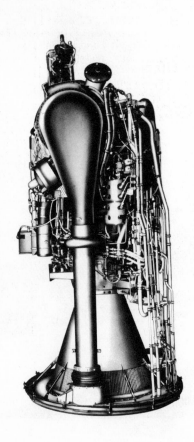

33. *The rocket-powered X-15 research airplane* landing after launch from a B-52 "mother aircraft," a rocket-powered research flight, and a glide to a landing on a dry lake bed near Edwards AFB, California. The X-15 was designed from its beginning in 1952 to fly to speeds of 4,000 mph. and at altitudes between 50 and 100 miles. (NASA Photo) **34.** *Reaction Motors XLR-99 rocket engine* which powered the NASA-USAF-USN X-15 research airplane to record altitudes and speeds. (Reaction Motors Photo)

35. *X-15 Awards Ceremony in NASA Headquarters* on July 18, 1962, when NASA Outstanding Leadership Awards and Distinguished Services Awards were presented by Vice President Lyndon B. Johnson, Chairman of the National Aeronautics and Space Council. Shown (left to right) are Major Robert M. White (USAF), Hartley A. Soulé (X-15 Project Manager), NASA Administrator James E. Webb, Vice President Johnson, Paul F. Bikle (Director of NASA Flight Research Center), Joseph A. Walker (NASA), and Commander Forrest Petersen (USN). Test pilots White, Walker, and Petersen had earlier in the day, along with A. Scott Crossfield, received the Robert J. Collier Trophy from President Kennedy at the White House. (NASA Photo)

36. *The Mercury Astronauts.* First official photo of the seven engineer-test pilots selected for the first U. S. manned space-flight program in their Mercury space suits. Front row (left to right), Walter M. Schirra, Jr. (Lt. Comdr. USN), Donald K. Slayton (Capt. USAF), John H. Glenn, Jr. (Lt. Col. USMC), and M. Scott Carpenter (Lt. USN). Back row (left to right), Alan B. Shepard, Jr. (Lt. Comdr. USN), Virgil I. Grissom (Capt. USAF), and Leroy G. Cooper, Jr. (Capt. USAF). (NASA)

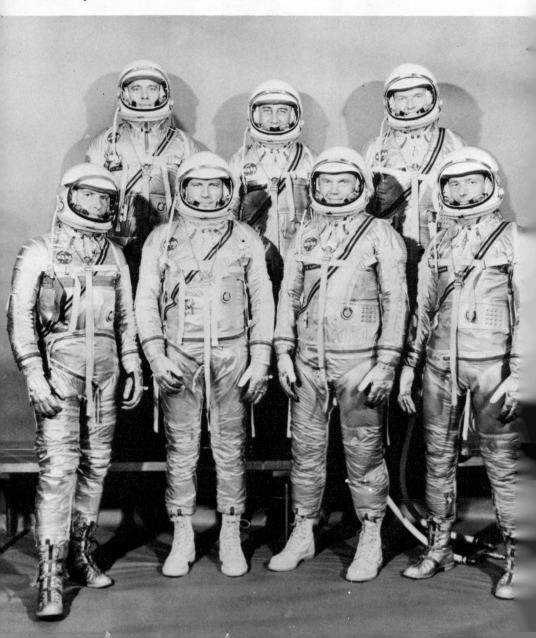

38. *Project Mercury Launch Vehicle Little Joe.* (NASA)

37. *Mercury Spacecraft* with Escape Tower. (NASA)

39. *Project Mercury Launch Vehicles* Redstone (left) and Atlas (right). (NASA)

90. *Before the mockup of a Lunar Excursion Module (LEM)* the late President John F. Kennedy speaks briefly to NASA personnel at the Manned Spacecraft Center at Houston, Texas, on September 12, 1962. To the right are Vice President Lyndon B. Johnson and Dr. Robert R. Gilruth, Director of the MSC. President Kennedy and party were on a tour of space installations which included visits to Cape Canaveral, the Marshall Space Flight Center, and the McDonnell Aircraft Corp. Previous to his visit to MSC, President Kennedy had made a major address at Rice University on U. S. space policy in which he said this nation intends "to become the world's leading spacefaring nation. . . .

"We choose to go to the moon . . . in this decade and do the other things, not because they are easy, but because they are hard. . . .

"It is for these reasons that I regard the decision last year to shift our efforts in space from low to high gear as among the most important decisions that will be made during my incumbency in the office of the Presidency." (NASA Photo)

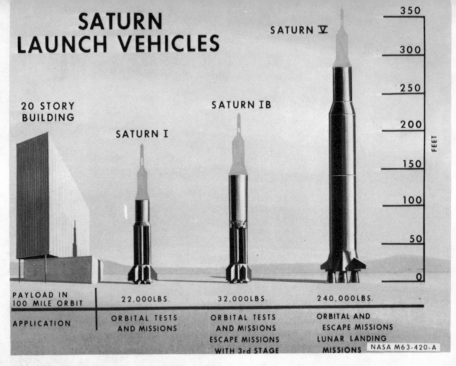

SATURN LAUNCH VEHICLES

20 STORY
BUILDING

SATURN I

SATURN IB

SATURN V

				FEET
				350
				300
				250
				200
				150
				100
				50
				0

PAYLOAD IN 100 MILE ORBIT	22,000LBS.	32,000LBS.	240,000LBS.
APPLICATION	ORBITAL TESTS AND MISSIONS	ORBITAL TESTS AND MISSIONS ESCAPE MISSIONS WITH 3rd STAGE	ORBITAL AND ESCAPE MISSIONS LUNAR LANDING MISSIONS

NASA M63-420-A

41. *Saturn Launch Vehicles. (NASA)*

42. *Bell rocket-belt Pilots* Robert F. Courter, Jr. (left) and Peter Kedzierski, over the Bell Aerosystems plant in Niagara Falls, New York. (Bell) 43. *Peter Kedzierski*, Bell Aerosystems rocket-belt pilot, in flight over the U. S. pavilion at the Paris Air Show in the summer of 1963. (Bell)

The Rocket Research Airplanes

KENNETH S. KLEINKNECHT *

WORLD WAR II brought an end to the development of the airplane as had been conceived by Orville and Wilbur Wright. War-stimulated propulsion advances in the form of turbojet and rocket engines brought manned flight beyond the speed of sound within man's reach. Continued development of rocket-powered airplanes for aerodynamic research led the technology of manned flight to the threshold of space at altitudes above atmospheric densities providing lift to airfoils.

The rocket-powered aircraft of the X-series of research airplanes, conceived and developed under the aegis of the United States National Advisory Committee for Aeronautics (NACA, later to become the National Aeronautics and Space Administration, NASA) and the military services provides the theme of this article.[1] The historic

* Kenneth S. Kleinknecht is Deputy Manager, Gemini Program and was formerly Manager, Mercury Project, Manned Spacecraft Center, National Aeronautics and Space Administration, Houston, Texas. He joined the NACA Lewis Propulsion Laboratory in 1942, transferring to the NACA High-Speed Flight Station, Edwards, California, in 1951, where he was associated with the design and operations of all of this Country's research-airplane programs and participated in the NACA evaluation of the X-20 Dyna Soar. Shortly after Project Mercury began in 1958, Kleinknecht joined the NASA Space Task Group at Langley Field, Virginia, which was redesignated the NASA Manned Spacecraft Center in November, 1961, and moved to Houston. Kleinknecht has authored or co-authored numerous technical papers and received the NASA Medal for Outstanding Leadership from the late President John F. Kennedy for his managerial and technical role in Project Mercury.

In the preparation of this article, the author is indebted to the following for assistance: Messrs. Charles V. Eppley, Historian, U. S. Air Force Flight Test Center, Edwards Air Force Base, California; Hubert M. Drake, Chief, Advanced Planning, NASA Flight Research Center, Edwards, California; and James M. Grimwood, Historian, NASA Manned Spacecraft Center, Houston, Texas. It has proved impossible to include proper credit to all of the civilian and military persons whose dedicated effort made possible the overall success of the rocket-research airplane story. The full history yet remains to be documented and written. See author's note, p. 211.

[1] This article concerns itself only with the United States' NACA/NASA, Army, Air Force, or Navy rocket-powered research aircraft of the X-series of experimental aircraft. For discussion of the role of the NACA in carrying forward basic aeronautical research of military and civil utility, see Jerome C. Hunsaker, "Forty Years of Aeronautical Research," *NACA Annual Report for 1955* (Washington: 1956); George W. Gray, *Frontiers of Flight* (New York: 1948); Arthur J. Levine, *U. S. Aeronautical Research Policy, 1915-1958* (New York: Columbia Univ. Dissertation, 1963).

significance of the X-1, the D-558-II, the X-2, and the X-15 are today airborne in supersonic military aircraft as well as future Mach 3.0 * aircraft such as the RS-70 and the supersonic transport. Additionally, the contributions of these X-series rocket-powered aircraft in the fields of aerodynamics, structures, and pilotage were indispensable for manned space flight applications, particularly in Project Mercury.

Fig. 21. RESEARCH AIRCRAFT AND ROCKET ENGINE CHARACTERISTICS

AIRPLANE	X-1 NO. 1	X-1A X-1B	X-1E	D-558-II	X-2	X-15
Rocket Engine	RMI* XLR-11	RMI* XLR-11	RMI* XLR-11	RMI* LR-8	Curtiss- Wright XLR-25	RMI* XLR-99
Number of Thrust Chambers	4	4	4	4	2	1
Rated Sea Level Thrust, Pounds	6,000	6,000	6,000	6,000	15,000	50,000
Specific Impulse, Seconds	190	190	190	190	185	230
Duration at Maximum Thrust, Seconds	150	250	225	180	165	85
Weight, Pounds						
Full	12,400	16,500	16,000	15,800	26,000	34,300
Empty	7,300	7,600	8,000	9,400	12,200	13,900
Approximate Maximum Mach Number	1.4	2.5	2.2	2.0	3.0	6.1

* Reaction Motors, Incorporated (later, in May 1958, to become Reaction Motors Division of the Thiokol Chemical Corporation).

From the establishment of the NACA in 1915 to the beginning of World War II, attainable altitudes of aircraft had increased by several thousands of feet while speeds approached 400 miles per hour. Meanwhile, serious study had already begun in Germany on rocket-propulsion force as a means of aircraft locomotion. Because the Treaty of Versailles prohibited military aviation, Germany, led by Professor-

* Mach number: A number expressing the ratio of the speed of a body or of a point on a body with respect to the surrounding air or other fluid, or the speed of a flow, to the speed of sound in the medium; the speed represented by this number. Thus, a Mach number of 1.0 indicates a speed equal to the speed of sound, 0.5 a speed one-half the speed of sound, 5.0 a speed five times the speed of sound, etc. In the standard atmosphere at sea level, sonic speed is approximately 1,100 feet per second or 760 miles per hour.

General Karl Becker, began to undertake basic research to determine military applications of rocket propulsion.[2] In 1928, Max Valier became one of the first individuals to experiment with a liquid-propellant rocket motor, which he used to drive a small racing car. Rocket-powered winged flight was demonstrated in its first primitive form with glider flights in Germany in the late 1920's. On June 11, 1928, Friedrich Stamer, of Germany, achieved a flight of one mile in a tailless Lippisch glider after a launch assisted with an elastic rope and a 44-pound thrust rocket, with another rocket being fired once airborne. In August, 1929, a Junkers 33 seaplane made a solid-propellant rocket-assisted takeoff at Dessau, Germany, and later, Fritz von Opel flew his Sander RAK. 1 glider almost two miles from Frankfort-am-Main, Germany, with 16 rockets of 50 pounds thrust each.[3] Later, in 1935, Hellmuth Walter and Wernher von Braun worked on liquid-propellant rocket engines for aircraft application. The next year von Braun mounted his 650-pound-thrust engine to a small aircraft, designated the "Junkers Junior," for the first airplane ground test using a propulsion system of this type. Prior to World War II, the Germans undertook several liquid-propellant airplane projects, Heinkel 112 (the first airplane with a rocket motor in its tail) and Heinkel 176 (the first rocket fighter plane), but, with the outbreak of hostilities, major rocket-research efforts with aircraft became a victim to research on ballistic missiles.[4]

America had not been completely derelict in looking past the conventional propeller-driven airplane toward new development. As early as 1922, Edgar Buckingham of the U. S. Bureau of Standards made a theoretical analysis of jet propulsion (NACA Report No. 159, "Jet Propulsion for Aircraft"). However, little was done in the field because of the astronomically high fuel-consumption rates, weight, and complexity of the conceivable flyable equipment. In the late 1930's, the NACA's Langley Aeronautical Laboratory once again engaged in some preliminary investigation of inducted jet propulsion, but the conclusions were similar to those drawn earlier. At this time, however, there was a decisive change in the aeronautical climate. As World War II approached for the U. S., the advances of foreign powers in jet propulsion, particularly by Nazi Germany and England, brought about the

[2] See Dornberger, pp. 29-34.
[3] E. M. Emme, *Aeronautics and Astronautics, 1915-1960* (Washington, D. C.: NASA, 1961), p. 24; *Anon.*, "Thirty-Five Years of Winged Rocket Flight," *The Thiokol Magazine*, Vol. II (1963), pp. 10-15.
[4] "Thirty-Five Years of Winged Rocket Flight," pp. 10-11; Walter Dornberger, *V-2* (New York 1955), pp. 124-126.

realization that the United States was falling considerably behind in the propulsion field, although maintaining leadership in basic research, aerodynamics, reciprocating engines, and civil transports.

After the outbreak of the World War II, but prior to Pearl Harbor, the first serious American research efforts radically to advance airplane-propulsion technology were made in March of 1941. Dr. William F. Durand, former Chairman and a member of NACA (1915-33) was called out of retirement to head a special NACA committee on jet propulsion. Some two years before, a special investigating committee headed by Charles A. Lindbergh had criticized the lack of an American engine-research facility, which resulted in the establishment of a NACA propulsion-research laboratory in Cleveland, Ohio.[5] As it turned out, these efforts were belated as had been the creation of the NACA itself in 1915 for World War I.[6]

In late 1941, General Henry H. Arnold, Chief of the Army Air Forces and a member of the NACA, was able to secure a Whittle jet engine from the plant of Gloster Aircraft Company, Limited, in England. The General Electric Company was assigned the task of producing a jet engine and the Bell Aircraft Corporation to build an airframe. The result was the P-59 " Airacomet," flown on October 1, 1942. The P-59 only attained a maximum speed of 404 miles per hour, a figure that conventional planes were then pressing. General Arnold remarked that its " legs weren't long enough " to reach a target successfully because of high fuel consumption, and that engineering efforts best be focused upon improvement of military airplanes already in production or final design. The exigencies of war, for the NACA the job of "cleaning up" conventional aircraft, thus delayed much basic and specialized research. This eventually led to an urgent requirement for the rocket-research airplanes. Historically, America fortunately did not suffer because of this practical decision, despite the fact that the Germans demonstrated advanced technology in their jet-powered Me 262 and rocket-propelled Me 163B just before the end of the war. The Germans were too late; their jet and rocket airplanes were superior in the air, but the decision of the war in the air had already been irretrievably obtained by conventional Allied Air Power.[7]

[5] Designated the Lewis Propulsion Laboratory in 1948 in honor of Dr. George W. Lewis.

[6] Hunsaker, "Forty Years of Aeronautical Research," pp. 262-264; Gray, *Frontiers*, pp. 277-279. Not one aircraft of American design and manufacture reached combat in World War I.

[7] Gray, *Frontiers*, pp. 278-280; William Bridgeman and Jacqueline Hazard, *The Lonely Sky* (New York: 1955), pp. 10-13; E. M. Emme, *Hitler's Blitzbomber* (Air University: 1951); Mano Ziegler, *Rocket Fighter* (New York: 1963).

German jet and rocket aircraft thus suffered the same fate as the V-2 ballistic missile.

OPERATIONAL PORTENTS AND RESULTING ACTIONS

During the war years, the engineering workload at the NACA laboratories had been exceedingly heavy. Between the end of 1941 and 1944, design studies and tests were conducted on 115 types of military aircraft. At one time, July of 1944, there were 78 different types of aircraft simultaneously under investigation. Application of NACA research produced dramatic results in the war zones: vertical dive bombing, improved wing designs, improved engine-cooling methods, and improved high-lift devices, to list a few. Aside from their practical value in combat speed and manuever, these improvements also served as portents that conventional propeller-driven aircraft were approaching their operational performance limits. Propeller tips had been at the sonic barrier for years. At the fringes of transonic speed * in level flight, aircraft controls began to "freeze," extreme buffeting was prevalent and, in many instances, airplanes went completely out of control, broke into pieces or went into terminal dives.[8] Once again the frontier of flight technology demanded the initiation of a new and specialized basic research; the airplane was technologically ready to leave one plateau of development and proceed to a higher level.

Continuing operational reports of American combat pilots who tangled with or observed German jets prompted John Stack of the NACA Langley Laboratory and Robert J. Woods of Bell Aircraft to press for a research-airplane program in 1943. Before the end of the year, the Navy Bureau of Aeronautics, the Army Air Forces, and NACA personnel held a conference at the NACA Headquarters in Washington, D. C.; they explored the idea of special research airplanes to investigate the transonic-speed region. Early the next year, General Arnold and Dr. George W. Lewis added their support. The United States had gained general air superiority in the war zones, but the apparent technical achievements of the German jet and rocket aircraft were a stimulus for some urgency.

Jet propulsion and rocket propulsion obviously presented new avenues for piercing the sonic barrier of flight. Comparing their diminutive size with the amount of thrust produced, rocket power-plants offered an attractive mode. For example, the German Me 163B

[8] Hunsaker, "Forty Years of Aeronautical Research," p. 267; Gray, *Frontiers*, p. 87; Bridgeman and Hazard, *Lonely Sky*, p. 11.
* Transonic: A regime when air flow is mixed, part subsonic and part supersonic.

airplane, with a rocket engine weighing only 220 pounds, was able to generate 3,800 pounds of thrust, and could climb to 40,000 feet in 2½ minutes. The rocket engine of a V-2 was comparable to the weight of a large reciprocating engine, but the thrust was equal to ten or twelve conventional reciprocating engines. In addition, the rocket engine, carrying its own chemical oxidizer, did not rely upon the atmosphere as did the conventional and jet-propulsion motors. The major drawback was that the rocket engine required from ten to twenty times as much fuel as the turbojet engine.

Performance of rocket-powered missiles was spectacular. In the case of the V-2, the missile was propelled to a range of 168 miles and to a height of 68 miles, even though the normal operating time of the engine was measured in seconds. With the exception of experimental jet-assisted takeoff (JATO) tests, such as those by California Institute of Technology and Captain Homer A. Boushey with an Ercoupe in 1941, rocket-airplane experimentation in America was almost nonexistent. In addition, very little had been gained from subsonic wind-tunnel experimentation; there was a frustrating choking effect generated as speeds approached that of sound.[9] Thus, at the outset of the rocket-research airplane program in the United States, many unknowns existed.

In 1944, Congress appropriated funds for the research aircraft program and designated the NACA, the Navy, and the Army Air Force as cooperating members. The Army Air Force and the Navy funded the program and the NACA provided the technical supervision. A selected contractor would build and test-fly the airplane initially; then the Army Air Force and NACA would jointly perform the flight research, the Army Air Force to ascertain and evaluate possible military application and NACA to conduct highly instrumented and detailed flight research, reporting its accrued data to the aircraft industry as a whole.[10] Thus began the two decades of dedicated cooperation between the military services and NACA/NASA in advancing the technology of flight.

As to a possible design concept for the research airplanes, NACA engineers believed that, if airplanes could be built strong enough to survive buffeting and all anticipated loads and that if rocket propulsion was utilized to provide high thrust at high altitudes where drag was

[9] Gray, *Frontiers*, pp. 303-305; "Thirty-Five Years of Winged Rocket Flight" p. 3; Walter T. Bonney, "The Research Airplane," *Pegasus* (June, 1952), p. 2. See Malina, pp. 55-57.

[10] Charles V. Eppley, *The Rocket Research Aircraft Program, 1946-1962* (Edwards Air Force Base, California: U. S. Air Force Flight Test Center, 1963), p. 2.

low, then transonic speeds could be attained in level flight. This was not, however, the general belief of the aeronautical community; they surmised that any flight beyond the sound barrier would be restricted to missiles.[11] From the standpoint of a prospective contractor then, there was an element of risk involved. What company would stamp its name on an airplane that might smash itself and the pilot to smithereens on the first flight?[12] The first rocket-powered research airplane in the United States was the X-1.

The X-1 Series

The original concept of the X-1 design resulted from a conference in March of 1944 held at NACA's Langley Laboratory and attended by the Army Air Force, Navy, and NACA personnel. NACA proposed that a jet-propelled transonic research airplane be developed. Discussions continued and by the end of the year, the Army Air Force indicated a strong preference for rocket engines. In February 1945, Bell Aircraft was awarded the contract to construct three transonic-flight research airplanes powered by liquid-rocket engines. The program was first designated Project MX-653, then XS-1, and, finally X-1.

The original X-1 powerplant was designed and built by Reaction Motors, Incorporated (later to become Reaction Motors Division of the Thiokol Chemical Corporation) of Rockaway, New Jersey, under Army Air Force contract. Designated the XLR-11, the engine produced 6,000 pounds of thrust at sea level from four separate regeneratively cooled chambers (1,500-pound thrust each). Its propellants were liquid oxygen and a mixture of 75 percent ethyl alcohol and 25 percent distilled water. The propellants were pressure-fed to the rocket chambers by nitrogen because difficulties were experienced with development of a turbine-propellant pump. Although not throttleable, the four chambers, or rockets, could be ignited either in series or simultaneously, thus allowing operation with thrust increments of 1,500 pounds. Another feature of the XLR-11 engine was that it could be shut down and be restarted in flight. The X-1 carried more than 5,000

[11] The sound barrier was first broken by a ballistic missile, the V-2, on October 3, 1942. For a discussion of the flight, see Dornberger, *V-2* (New York: 1955), pp. 3-17.

[12] Hartley A. Soulé and Walter C. Williams, "NACA Use of Special Airplanes for Research," presented at the Society of Automotive Engineers Meeting, New York, New York, April 12-14, 1954; NASA Langley Research Center Staff Study, "Conception and Research Background of the X-15 Project," June, 1962, p. 3; Bonney, "Research Airplane," p. 2.

pounds of fuel, enough for 150-seconds' burning time. The X-1's fuselage was designed to reach a terminal velocity of 1,700 miles per hour and an altitude of 80,000 feet. When engine-turbopump development did not progress as fast as had been anticipated, the alternate system using nitrogen pressure to supply engine propellants reduced the predicted speed to about 1,000 miles per hour.[13]

Concurrent with the development of the X-1 and as a second approach to attain the transonic ranges of speed, a contract was awarded by the Navy Bureau of Aeronautics to the Douglas Aircraft Company, Inc., to initiate and design the D-558-I, an aircraft powered by a turbojet of some 4,000 pounds of rated thrust at sea level, as compared with the 6,000–pound thrust rocket of the X-1. This dual development program, X-1 and D-558-I, provided a greater assurance of success in the conduct of transonic research and supplied a jet-powered research companion to the rocket-powered X-1, which was expected to be somewhat less reliable. The X-1 was to be air-dropped by a modified B-29 airplane for flight, while the D-558-I took off from the ground. Since the latter was capable of Mach 0.84 speeds in level flight and approximately Mach 0.99 in dives, it was also capable of performing research at transonic speeds as was the X-1. In a sense, the D-558-I, was actually a backup research airplane for the X-1.[14]

Meanwhile, other means of performing research at transonic speeds were under investigation and development. In 1945, at NACA Langley's Pilotless Aircraft Research Station on Wallops Island off the coast of Virginia, tests using rocket-lofted models were initiated. A NACA Langley study of the wind-tunnel choking effect, headed by John Stack, was in progress, eventually leading to the development of the slotted-throat or ventilated transonic tunnel. Similarly, at NACA Langley, a B-29 was also used to drop heavy, streamlined bodies which would exceed Mach 1.0 in free fall. During this transonic descent, a telemeter receiver, a radar unit, and a telescope were trained on the falling body to determine what was happening while it passed through the transonic region. This bomb-drop work was carried out under the direction of Robert R. Gilruth who also developed a procedure of transonic study known as "wing flow." Using this method, a

[13] Walter T. Bonney, "High Speed Research Airplane," *Scientific American*, Vol. 189 (October, 1953), pp. 36-41; Bonney, "Research Airplane," pp. 4-5. At the outset, the X-1 was not planned necessarily to be a rocket airplane. Designers had a free choice of powerplant, provided performance met preliminary specifications. There was, however, one criterion: The plane's appearance was to be as close as possible to a conventional airplane. Also see Willy Ley, *Rockets, Missiles, and Space Travel* (New York: 1957), p. 422.

[14] Gray, *Frontiers*, p. 356; Bonney, "Research Airplane," p. 5.

model of an airfoil was mounted on the upper part of a wing to protrude into the accelerated airstream. The resultant drag and lift could be measured through the Mach 1.0 speed range.[15]

By the fall of 1945, it had become apparent to NACA and the Army Air Force project offices that the propulsion-system development for the X-1 was behind the development of the airframe. Bell Aircraft, at the suggestion of Robert M. Stanley, conceived the "mother"-plane carrying mode, typical of many of the research-rocket airplane programs. According to the plan, the bomb bay of a B-29 would be

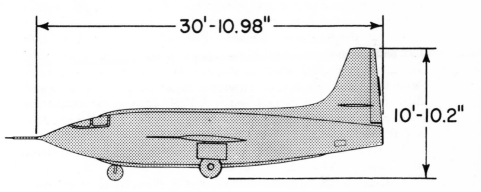

Fig. 22   USAF-NACA X-1 Rocket-Powered research airplane (Bell)

enlarged to accommodate the X-1, which would then be dropped as a glider from a height of about 30,000 feet to determine handling and aerodynamic characteristics. Beginning in early 1946, Jack Woolams, a Bell Aircraft test pilot, made twelve such gliding flights at Pinecastle Air Base, Florida.[16]

From Pinecastle, the operation moved to Muroc Army Air Base (later Edwards Air Force Base), California, on October 7, 1946; the powered-flight phase of the contractor–demonstration program was started. Beginning on December 9 and ending in June of 1947, Chalmers H. Goodlin and Alvin M. Johnston made twenty rocket

[15] NASA Langley Staff, "Conception and Background of X-15 Project," p. 7.
[16] Bonney, "Research Airplane," p. 7.

flights, successfully completing the contractor-test phase. The maximum speed attained was Mach 0.8.[17]

In the summer of 1947, the first two X-1 aircraft were delivered to the Government and flight tests were initiated under the direction of the Air Materiel Command Flight Test Division, Wright-Patterson Air Force Base, Ohio, with the NACA furnishing engineering support. Colonel Albert Boyd directed the Air Force program, selecting Captains Jack L. Ridley and Charles E. Yeager as project engineer and test pilot, respectively.[18] Lieutenant Robert A. Hoover was selected as Yeager's backup pilot. On October 14, 1947, the X-1 was attached to the B-29 carrier plane for its historic ninth flight. The B-29 crew included Major Robert L. Cardenas as the pilot; Ridley, the X-1 project engineer; and Major John P. Stapp as flight surgeon. When the carrier B-29 reached 7,000 feet altitude, test pilot Yeager was lowered into the X-1 cockpit. The X-1 was launched at 35,000 feet and climbed and accelerated rapidly to 41,000 feet where sonic speed was exceeded when it reached Mach 1.06.[19] Subsequently, NACA test pilot Herbert H. Hoover exceeded Mach 1.0 on his eighth flight in X-1 number two on March 4, 1948. He was the second man to exceed the speed of sound. Howard C. Lilly, also a NACA test pilot, was the third man to fly faster than sound on March 31, 1948, during his second flight in the number two X-1 airplane. In May, he was killed in takeoff of a D-558-I.

NACA's Walter C. Williams and his staff of twelve technical assistants, besides serving as technical observers and advisers, furnished maintenance and operation of all instrumentation during Pinecastle tests.* When the X-1 program was moved to Muroc, the NACA Muroc Flight Test Unit was formed. From 1947 through 1950, this group conducted many flight investigations with the X-1, particularly on the problems of stability and control and buffeting.

[17] Walter C. Williams, Charles M. Forsyth, and Beverly P. Brown, " General Handling-Qualities Results Obtained During Acceptance Flight Tests of the Bell XS-1 Airplane," NACA Research Memorandum, L8A09, April 1948.
[18] *Ibid.*; Bonney, "Research Airplane," p. 8.
[19] Eppley, *Rocket Research*, pp. 4-5; James M. Grimwood, *Project Mercury: A Chronology* (Washington, D. C.: 1963), p. 2; " Thirty-Five Years of Winged Rocket Flight," p. 16.
* Under the direction of Walter C. Williams, this group established permanent NACA facilities at Edwards AFB and grew to a complement of about 360 persons by 1959, at which time Williams was called by NASA to become Associate Director for Operations of the NASA Space Task Group (later the NASA Manned Spacecraft Center), with responsibility for directing operations for Project Mercury. On September 15, 1959, Paul F. Bikle was appointed Director of the NASA Flight Research Center and it has continued to grow, the present center complement being approximately 600.

During these years, the X-1 also set a number of unofficial records: in 1948, a maximum speed of 967 miles per hour and, in 1949, a record altitude of 73,000 feet. A ground takeoff was also accomplished on January 5, 1949. The X-1 had served a useful purpose and the first one, "Glamorous Glennis," piloted by Yeager in man's first flight through the sound barrier, was presented to the Smithsonian Institution in August 1950.[20] The second X-1 remained in use as a research tool under the cognizance of NACA until 1955.

There was a third X-1 airplane, designated X-1-3, delivered to Edwards Air Force Base in April of 1951. Although of the same basic geometry as the first X-1, this aircraft was provided with larger propellant tanks, a low-pressure propellant feed system, and a turbine-propellant pump. The basic engine was the same as that used in the original X-1, with the same performance characteristics. In lieu of the relatively heavy nitrogen-pressurization system, however, a turbine pump was used to deliver propellants to the rocket chambers. The pump was of the centrifugal type and was driven by the products of decomposition of 90 percent hydrogen peroxide (H_2O_2). This aircraft never accomplished powered flight. Both the X-1-3 and the B-50 carrier were destroyed by fire following a captive flight on November 9, 1951. Bell Aircraft's pilot, Joseph A. Cannon, although seriously injured in this incident, miraculously escaped death.[21]

The fact that the X-1 aircraft was able to exceed sonic speed safely was to have a tremendous effect upon the development of operational military aircraft. It eliminated the fear on the sonic phenomena and stimulated development of experimental aircraft leading to space flight.[22]

While the first two X-1 aircraft were in flight test, the Air Force ordered three additional aircraft, the X-1A, the X-1B, and the X-1D to extend the usefulness of the program. These three aircraft were different from the original X-1's in that the rocket propellants were stored in larger integral fuselage tanks, a turbine-driven pump was added in place of the heavier nitrogen-pressurization system, and an ejection seat was added. The result of these changes was about a twofold increase in performance. They were all powered by basically the same rocket engine and turbine pump as were used in the X-1-3.

The X-1D

The X-1D was the first of this series to be delivered, arriving at Edwards Air Force Base about July of 1951. It was designed to be

[20] Eppley, *Rocket Research*, p. 5-6.
[21] *Ibid.*, p. 6.
[22] Williams, Forsyth, and Brown, "General Handling Results"; Walter C.

capable of Mach 2.5 although stability problems were expected at the highest speeds. Major Frank K. Everest was the pilot for the Air Force demonstration program. On his first powered-flight attempt, August 22, 1951, the X-1D exploded while still attached to the B-50 during preparations for launch. The X-1D was jettisoned after Major Everest had egressed and returned to the bomb bay of the B-50. The subsequent accident investigation delayed the X-1A and the X-1B programs for two years.[23]

The X-1A

The actual flight-research test program on this improved version, the X-1A, began on February 21, 1953, with only the contractor's demonstration instrumentation installed. As expected, the X-1A encountered serious aerodynamic problems at Mach 2.0 and beyond when uncontrollable motions were experienced. On one of Major Yeager's speed flights, December 12, 1953, the airplane went out of control for about 70 seconds, decelerating about 1,200 miles per hour and losing 10 miles in altitude. When subsonic speeds were reached, the airplane went into a spin and normal recovery procedures were successfully accomplished. Major Arthur K. Murray encountered a similar, less violent situation on a high-altitude flight. NACA instrumentation and technical assistance were sought immediately and, according to a subsequent analysis, this anomaly was caused by an almost complete loss of directional stability, aggravated by engine-shutdown moments which resulted in sufficiently large disturbances to induce pitch-roll inertial coupling.[24]

Both speed and altitude records were nonetheless set with the X-1A: Yeager, 1,650 miles per hour on December 12, 1953 and Murray, 90,000 feet altitude on August 26, 1954. But, from the outset, the program was beset by adversities. In the fall of 1946, Bell Aircraft's only qualified test pilot, Jack Wooloms, had been killed in a P-39 (Cobra I) he was readying for the National Air Races. This had left the Air Force and Major Yeager to perform the contractor-demonstration

Williams and Hubert M. Drake, "The Research Airplane, Past, Present, and Future," presented at the National Summer Meeting of the Institute of Aeronautical Sciences, June 17-20, 1957.

[23] A. Scott Crossfield and Clay Blair, Jr., *Always Another Dawn: The Story of a Rocket Test Pilot* (Cleveland and New York: 1960), pp. 145-148.

[24] Hubert M. Drake and Wendell H. Stillwell, "Behavior of the Bell X-1A Research Airplane During Exploratory Flights at Mach Numbers Near 2.0 and at Extreme Altitudes," NACA Research Memorandum H55G25, September, 1955; Crossfield and Blair, *Always Another Dawn*, pp. 182-185; James A. Martin, "The Record-Setting Research Airplanes," *Aerospace Engineering*, Volume XXI (December, 1962). Yeager's flight was his last to date in a rocket research airplane.

flights. Later, NACA took over the flight-research effort in 1955. An explosion racked the airplane on the second attempt at flight on August 8, 1955, just prior to launch. Pilot Joseph A. Walker rapidly climbed back into the B-29 carrier. This event ended the X-1A program.[25]

The X-1B

The Bell Aircraft's X-1B was delivered in September of 1954 and flight operations began the next month. This airplane had the same general characteristics as the X-1A and its basic purpose was to serve as a pilot-training vehicle for the ultra-high performance X-2 rocket-research airplane. In December, the airplane was turned over to NACA for the conduct of a flight-research program on aerodynamic heating. As a result of the X–1A and X-1D accidents, the propulsion system was slightly modified.

Although the X-1B was not capable of achieving speeds and long-duration flights that would cause a structural weakening due to aerodynamic heating, much useful information was gathered, later applied to the X-15 program. Three-hundred thermocouples on the airframe were used to determine the flow of heat into and through the structure, the effects of heat sources and sinks, and the effects of boundary-layer transition and aerodynamic interference.

The X-1B pioneered in yet another field, that of attitude control at very high altitudes. Because the X-1B had the capability of attaining heights where the atmospheric density was so low that conventional aerodynamic-control surfaces were no longer effective, it served as an ideal test bed for the investigation of reaction-control modes that were later applicable to the X-15 and the Mercury spacecraft. These reaction controls consisted of small hydrogen-peroxide rocket motors mounted in the wing tips and nose of the airplane to produce roll, pitch, and yaw control.[26]

The X-1C

Plans had existed for an X-1C in the Air Force X-1 improvement program, but this airplane was never built, its parts and funds having been invested in the X-1A, X-1B, and X-1D programs.

[25] Crossfield and Blair, *Always Another Dawn*, pp. 200-205; NASA Langley Staff, " Conception and Background of the X-15 Project," pp. 10-11; John G. Hubbell, " If One Man Had Panicked," *Reader's Digest*, Volume LXX (April, 1957), pp. 37-41.
[26] Williams and Drake, " The Research Airplane, Past, Present, and Future," p. 5.

The X-1E

Unlike the other lettered-model versions of the X-1 series, the X-1E was not of new construction, but was a modified X-1. This airplane was extensively used by NACA for its high-speed research program from 1947 until 1952. Around the middle of 1952, NACA determined that it had fulfilled its original purpose as a transonic-research airplane. In addition, in view of the explosions resulting in the loss of the higher performing X-1D and X-3 in August and November of 1951, respectively, it was decided that it would be advisable to modify the X-1 to provide a backup to the higher-performing X-1A, X-1B, and X-1D series. A modification program was initiated by NACA which included the installation of a projected canopy, a pilot-ejection seat, a low-pressure propellant system of increased capacity equipped with a turbine-driven propellant pump as was the X-1-3, and a 50-percent reduction in the wing thickness. This airplane, which began its flight program with Walker as the pilot on December 15, 1955, was used in much the same role as the X-1B. Although the X-1E was capable of speeds approaching Mach 3.0, it was never flown above Mach 2.2 because of stability problems similar to those experienced with the X-1A. It was last flown on November 7, 1958.

The D-558-II

Concurrent with the X-1 research and development, a second D-558 series of aircraft was procured by the Navy, the first of these entering flight test in early 1948. During the early demonstration portion of the D-558-II program, turbojet engines were used, as had been the case with the first of the Navy-sponsored, Douglas-built D-558-I airplanes. In order to exceed sonic speed, these aircraft incorporated an LR-8 rocket engine, similar to the X-1 engine with turbopump. Although similar to the X-1 engine, this engine was called LR-8 because it was built for the Navy. Still not satisfied with performance, engineers removed the jet-propulsion unit and added extra rocket fuel. Only one of the D-558-II's was modified to the all-rocket configuration and launched from the modified B-29 carrier. The other two airplanes, the jet and the jet-rocket combination, used ground takeoff.[27] Before the airplane was turned over to NACA for further research, Douglas test pilot William Bridgeman attained an altitude record of 79,494 feet on August 15, 1951.[28]

After NACA accepted the D-558-II late in August of 1951, engineers

[27] "Thirty-Five Years of Winged Rocket Flight," pp. 16-17.
[28] See Bridgeman and Hazard, *The Lonely Sky*, pp. 211-309.

immediately attacked the problem of aircraft stability and control, particularly in the area of pitch-up. During the investigation a number of aerodynamic devices were evaluated on the wings, such as fences, slats, and chord extensions. Subsequent to these investigations, a NACA pilot, A. Scott Crossfield, attained a speed of Mach 2.04, the first Mach 2.0 flight, on November 20, 1953. A Marine pilot, Lieutenant Colonel Marion E. Carl, reached an altitude record of 83,235 feet on August 31, 1953. The D-558-II had performed according to its intended design.[29]

The X-2

The X-2, a third-generation rocket-research airplane, was proposed and designed to investigate the problem of aerodynamic heating. This particular project was sponsored by both NACA and the Air Force, and Bell Aircraft was selected as the contractor. The design speed was to approach 2,000 miles per hour and perhaps up to Mach 3.5 and altitudes from 100,000 to 130,000 feet. This placed the airplane well within the range of what often was termed the "thermal thicket" in speed and provided the condition of low-density atmosphere for study of stability and control.[30]

Bell Aircraft built two X-2's of stainless steel and a nickel alloy known by the trade name of Monel K. In addition to the special heat-resistant materials, the X-2 had a rocket powerplant, developed by the Curtiss-Wright Corporation and designated XLR-25. This engine consisted of two regeneratively cooled rocket chambers and a turbine pump. The chambers produced 10,000 and 5,000 pounds of thrust, respectively, at sea level. The propellants were liquid oxygen and alcohol. The turbine pump was driven by a gas generator which received its energy from burning of the engine propellants. Each of the chambers was throttleable from 50 to 100 percent rated thrust and, thus, the engine was throttleable from 2,500 to 15,000 pounds of thrust. It also had the capability to be shut down and restarted in flight. The X-2 also used landing skids in the place of wheels.[31]

During its active flight period from 1954 through most of 1956, the X-2 met with numerous adversities. After the glide tests, in which a modification to the skids was found to be necessary, Bell Aircraft's

[29] Williams and Drake, "The Research Airplane, Past, Present, and Future," pp. 4-5.
[30] NACA Study, "NACA Views Concerning a New Research Airplane," Washington, D.C., August, 1954.
[31] NASA Langley Staff, "Conception and Research Background of the X-15 Project," p. 8. See Frank K. Everest, *Fastest Man Alive* (New York: 1958).

test pilot, Jean Zeigler, and a B-50 crew member, Frank Wolko, were killed when the X-2 exploded during a captive test near Buffalo, New York. For a number of months thereafter, the Curtiss-Wright rocket motor was further developed and the landing skids, which were still causing problems and damage on landings following glide flights, were modified. Finally, the X-2 was ready for powered flight with Major Everest as the sole X-2 project pilot. NACA began instrumenting the airplane to gather data. The first flight attempt was made on October 25, 1955. It ended in an abort because of a nitrogen leak. In November, Everest completed the first powered flight.

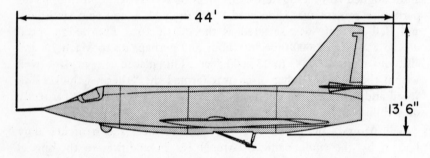

Fig. 23   USAF-NACA X-2 Rocket-Powered research airplane built by Bell Aircraft (Bell)

The X-2 subsequently made twelve successful powered flights, setting both speed and altitude records that were to stand until the advent of the X-15. Captain Iven C. Kincheloe attained 126,200 feet altitude on September 7, 1956. Some 20 days later, on the thirteenth flight which ended the program, Captain Milburn G. Apt, of the Air Force, reached a speed of 2,094 miles per hour. After attaining this record speed, Apt was turning back to the base when the airplane veered wildly out of control and began cartwheeling. The plane was destroyed and test pilot Apt was killed on his first rocket-powered flight.[32] NACA thus never received an X-2 with which to conduct its usual exhaustive research program.

[32] Richard E. Day and Donald Reisert, "Flight Behavior of the X-2 Research Airplane to a Mach Number of 3.2 and a Geometric Altitude of 126,200 Feet," NASA Technical Memorandum X-137, September 1959; Ley, *Rockets, Missiles, and Space Travel,* pp. 427-428.

The X-15

The X-15 dates back to June of 1952. The NACA Committee on Aerodynamics recommended that NACA extend its research into the problems of manned and unmanned flight to altitudes between 12 and 50 miles and at speeds of Mach 4.0 through Mach 10.0. Experienced engineers in the organization quickly pointed out that there were crucial design problems to be solved concerning aerodynamic heating and stability and control. Acting on the recommendation of the Committee on Aerodynamics, the Executive Committee of NACA indicated that manned-flight research might go beyond that proposed, mentioning in a resolution altitudes of 50 miles to infinity and speeds of Mach 10.0 to the velocity of escape from the earth's gravity.[33]

For a period of two years, NACA engineers studied fully the problems and the possibilities of the next step. By May of 1954, the basic characteristics of the X-15 had been conceived. In July, a NACA, Air Force, and Navy conference outlined the concept of the project and a memorandum of agreement was signed. Specifically, the Air Force would administer the design and construction of the airplane by the contractor, while both the Air Force and Navy would finance the venture, and NACA would have the technical responsibility. To select the best technical route, a Research Airplane Committee was formed of members from the three interested groups, with Dr. Hugh L. Dryden, Director of NACA, as chairman.[34]

At the beginning of the X-15 program, one of the most serious problems was that of obtaining a suitable rocket engine. A survey of potential contractors confirmed this fact and a decision was made to negotiate separate contracts for the airframe and the engine.

The airframe was the first order of business. Thus, throughout the spring and summer of 1955, the Research Airplane Committee studied various proposals submitted by airframe contractors. In November of 1955, North American Aviation, Incorporated, was selected to build three hypersonic X-15's.* These airplanes were to be capable of attaining a speed of 6,600 feet per second and an altitude of 250,000 feet.

Selection of a contractor to design and build the rocket engine

---

[33] NACA Committee on Aerodynamics, "Minutes of Meeting, June 24, 1952 "; Letter, NACA Headquarters to NACA High-Speed Flight Research Station, "Discussion of Reports on Problems of High Speed, High Altitude Flight, and Consideration of Possible Changes to the X-2 Airplane to Extend its Speed and Altitude Range," July 30, 1953.

[34] NASA Langley Staff, "Conception and Research Background of the X-15 Project," p. 26.

* *Hypersonic*: Pertaining to speeds of Mach 5.0 or greater.

proved considerably more difficult. In September, 1956, a contract was signed with Reaction Motors to build a 50,000-pound rocket engine (XLR-99). Liquid oxygen and anhydrous ammonia, delivered into a single-thrust chamber by a turbopump powered by hydrogen peroxide, were to be used as the rocket-engine propellants. This engine, too, is throttleable through the range of 30- to 100-percent-rated thrust and has restart capability in flight. Although the XLR-25 Curtiss-Wright engine in the X-2 incorporated a feature that allowed the turbine pump to be running prior to launch from the carrier, the X-15 carried this concept one step further in that the main rocket chamber igniter could also be operating prior to launch or separation from the carrier aircraft. This feature provided a three-phase engine-starting sequence of pump operation, pump and igniter operation and pump, igniter and main chamber operation. Such a technique of rocket-engine starting provides that approximately 90 percent of the engine-starting functions is accomplished prior to committing the aircraft to free flight and thus contributes to reliability and flight safety, particularly in view of the fact that the X-15 is launched in geographical areas that are not necessarily optimum for landing and postlanding support.

Although the thrust was relatively low in comparison with contemporary missile engines of the Atlas, Jupiter, and other weapon systems, this was a significant advance for manned-airplane engines. Conversion into horsepower presents a dramatic comparison with other conventional vehicles. The X-15 rocket engine produced slightly more than 500,000 horsepower at 4,000 miles per hour (engines of the largest aircraft carrier, the *USS Forrestal*, produce only 250,000 horsepower).[35]

While engine development demanded greater time and attention, the airframe also presented problems of consequence. The Inconel X airframe had to withstand 1,200° F. temperature, and as much as seven g's * would be experienced during acceleration and reentry.[36]

Other features incorporated in the X-15 included small rocket engines of 100 and 40 pounds of thrust, placed in the nose and wings, respectively, to provide up-and-down, right-to-left attitude, and roll control while the airplane was out of the sensible atmosphere where

[35] *X-15 Air Vehicle Press Information* (Los Angeles: North American Aviation, Incorporated, no date).

* g: An acceleration equal to the acceleration of gravity, approximately 32.2 feet per second at sea level—used as a unit of measurement for bodies undergoing acceleration.

[36] U. S. Congress, Senate Committee on Aeronautical and Space Sciences, *Project Mercury: Man-in-Space Program of the National Aeronautics and Space Administration*, 86th Congress, First Session, pp. 7-8.

conventional aerodynamic controls are ineffective. To accumulate flight data and monitor flight progress, NACA and its successor, the National Aeronautics and Space Administration, provided instrumentation that totaled some 1,300 pounds in weight. There were 1,100 sensors to record temperatures, strains, accelerations, and pressures generated at various points on the airplane. Equipment to provide proper life-support environmental conditions in the cockpit was manufactured by the Garrett Corporation's AiResearch Manufacturing Division, while the pilot's pressure suit was fabricated by the David Clark Company. As a whole, the X-15 program was designed to study performance at ultra-high speeds and altitudes, including such parameters as aerodynamic loads, heat transfer, behavior of structures in a severe thermal environment, systems, and physiological effects on the pilot.[37]

While the airframe and engine were being designed, the Air Force provided two B-52's for modification as carrier planes under a North American Aviation contract. Also, an X-15 pilot-training program had to be initiated by using high performance F-104 and F-105 aircraft as the training vehicles. The pilot team was composed of the following: Captains Kincheloe and Robert M. White of the Air Force; Walker, Neil A. Armstrong, and John B. McKay of NACA; Commander Forrest S. Petersen of the Navy; and Crossfield and Alvin S. White of North American Aviation. They received g-load training on the human centrifuge at the Navy Aviation Medical Acceleration Laboratory, Johnsville, Pennsylvania. This training was especially important in familiarizing the pilots with the problems of controlling the aircraft under conditions of rocket boost and reentry. During this program, the centrifuge was operated closed-loop for the first time; that is, the pilot controlled centrifuge accelerations and motions by operating simulated spacecraft controls in the test gondola. The movement of these controls was fed into a computer in which was stored the airplane characteristics. The computer output then controlled the centrifuge accelerations and motions as well as the pilot's displays, the same as if the airplane were in flight.

It soon became apparent that engine delivery would not coincide with that of the airframe, the first of which North American Aviation delivered in October, 1958. NASA began to explore the idea of using an interim rocket motor. Two X-1 engines, with pumps, were coupled to produce a total thrust of about 16,000 pounds. Crossfield first piloted

[37] Adrian R. Sorrells, "High Range," *Skyline*, Vol. XVII (Winter 1958-1959), pp. 5-7; "Thirty-Five Years of Winged Rocket Flight," p. 19; Thomas A. Toll and Jack Fischel, "The X-15 Research Aircraft: Part II, Research Accomplished and Planned," October, 1963.

the X-15, powered with the interim XLR-11 engines, on September 17, 1959. For the next 27 months, the program was forced to utilize the interim engines, setting both a speed record of 2,275 miles per hour and an altitude record of 136,500 feet. The Government phase of the interim-engine program began after the seventh contractor-powered flight with Walker of NASA as pilot. NASA, Air Force, and Navy pilots continued this interim phase until November of 1960, when the XLR engine was finally received.[38]

In mid-1960, when North American Aviation was static–testing the first X-15 with the XLR-99 installed, the airplane exploded because a fuel-pressure regulator failed and its attendant relief valve also failed. Crossfield had crash-landed earlier on the third contractor-demonstration flight. Thus, two of the three X-15's underwent extensive repairs in the beginning phase. On November 15, 1960, the X-15 with the XLR-99 engine was ready for flight. Crossfield, the contractor pilot, made the first of three demonstration flights. By the end of 1960, the XLR-99-engine-demonstration program was completed and the X-15 was turned over to the Government.

On March 7, 1961, the first Government-powered flight was accomplished by Captain White. From then until November 1963, the date of this text, the X-15 continuously surpassed all previous records of speeds and altitudes in 93 flights: Walker attained 354,200 feet altitude on August 22, 1963, and 4,105 miles per hour on June 27, 1962. Proving the reliability value of manned flight, data disclosed that, had the X-15 flown without a pilot on the first 81 missions, success would have been reduced from 56 to 32 percent. Also, a number of airplanes would have been totally lost without the presence of trained pilots.[39]

X-15 data proved important to the concurrent Mercury program for orbital manned flight. When solicitations were made for the most practical means of attaining early orbital flight, North American Aviation had proposed the X-15 as a third stage of a launch vehicle, but this plan was rejected.

[38] Perry V. Row and Jack Fischel, " Operational Flight Test Experience with the X-15 Airplane," presented to the American Institute of Aeronautics and Astronautics, Cocoa Beach, Florida, March, 1963; Charles V. Eppley, U. S. Air Force Flight Test Center, " Flight Log: X-15 Program," December 15, 1960; cf. Richard Tregaskis, *X-15 Diary* (New York, 1961).

[39] Joseph Weil, " Review of the X-15 Program," NASA Technical Note D-1278, Washington, D. C., June, 1962; Joseph A. Walker and Joseph Weil, " The X-15 Program," presented at the Second AIAA-NASA Manned Space Flight Meeting, Dallas, Texas, April, 1963; Robert G. Nagel and Richard E. Smith, " The X-15 Pilot-In-The-Loop and Redundant/Emergency Systems Evaluation," U. S. Air Force Flight Test Center Technical Documentary Report No. 62-20, October, 1962.

As of November, 1963, the X-15 program was by no means completed. An X-15 is currently being modified to attain higher speeds; burning time of the rocket engine is being increased from 85 to 145 seconds to produce a theoretical increase of 1,300 miles per hour in speed. Advancing rocket technology is still being applied to the research airplane that now consistently operates in a space environment.[40]

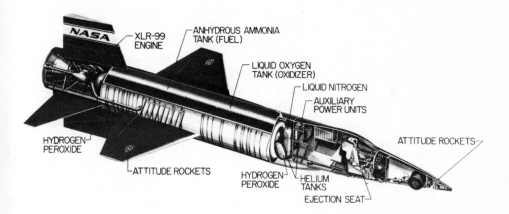

Fig. 24 Line drawing of the X-15 rocket-research airplane (NASA)

The X-20 and New Applications of Rocket Power

Very early in the X-15 research and development program, engineers realized that this airplane represented the ultimate design short of an earth-orbiting capability. Thus NACA, working closely with the Air Force's Air Research and Development Command (ARDC), suggested design criteria incorporating X-15 features into what became the Air Force Dyna Soar program (later designated the X-20). The X-20 program was initiated in November of 1956 when the Air Force approached NACA for the conduct of a feasibility study to review the ARDC sponsored studies. NACA agreed to evaluate the ARDC

[40] Grimwood: *Project Mercury: A Chronology*, p. 15; "X-15 Speed to be Boosted," *Missiles and Rockets*, Volume XIII (November 4, 1963), p. 10.

contractor studies to determine the speed and range of such a vehicle and when the project could begin.[41]

Engineers recognized that there were serious problems in the designing of a vehicle that would represent a spectacular advance over the X-15, aerodynamic heating being the most critical. To attain the objectives, the boost-glide airplane appeared to be the most attractive mode. In the 1940's, Dr. Eugen Sänger and his wife, Dr. Irene Sänger-Bredt, had originated this concept by proposing that a bomber with an 100,000-pound-thrust rocket engine be launched by a 400,000-pound-thrust rocket sled to give the vehicle the initial boost into space. The vehicle would then orbit the earth by skipping in and out of the atmosphere. Toward the end of World War II the Germans had devised plans for a manned version of the V-2, which they called A-10, that aimed at the same capabilities. Neither of these projects gained hardware status and the concept lay dormant until some of its features were applied in the X-15 and X-20 programs.

The X-20 was designed to have a rocket motor to provide an escape-maneuver capability at launch, to accelerate while in the atmosphere, or to provide retrorocket capability for reentry. It was, once de-orbited, a glider. To attain earth-orbital flight, the Dyna Soar was to have been boosted by a Titan III, which utilizes both solid- and liquid-rocket engines.* In the meantime, the United States attained orbital manned flight with Project Mercury.

This brief article has been limited to the rocket-propelled research airplanes, since it has been with this group of aircraft that the largest and most significant advances in aviation as well as in speed and altitude have been made, and, further, these aircraft provided the technological background of development and operational experience that led to this Nation's capability to accomplish successfully the Free World's first manned space-flight program, Project Mercury. The United States research-airplane program has been a fruitful one which resulted in a systematic and orderly approach to extending man's flight capabilities in both the atmosphere and space. It also provided a firm foundation on which this Nation could establish and maintain pre-eminence in space exploration.

[41] NACA Staff, "Study of the Feasibility of a Hypersonic Research Airplane," September 3, 1957, p. 3.

* Editor's note: Subsequent to the preparation of this text, the Department of Defense canceled the X-20 program in favor of proceeding with a manned orbital laboratory program.

** Author's note: Any discussion of the research-airplane program would not be complete without recognizing the early proponents of the program and their leadership, which not only established the basis for a sound effort but also made possible a successful and fruitful projection of flight technology.

Among those who provided this foresight and leadership were men like: Dr. George W. Lewis, Dr. Hugh L. Dryden, Mr. John W. Crowley, Mr. John Stack, Mr. Hartley A. Soulé, and Dr. Walter C. Williams of the National Advisory Committee for Aeronautics or of the National Aeronautics and Space Administration; General Henry H. Arnold and Colonel Albert Boyd of the U. S. Air Force; Mr. Lawrence D. Bell, Mr. Robert J. Woods, and Mr. William M. Smith of the Bell Aircraft Corporation; Mr. Lovell Lawrence, Jr., and Mr. John Shesta of the Reaction Motors Division of the Thiokol Chemical Corp.; and, Mr. Donald W. Douglas, Sr., and Mr. Edward H. Heinemann of the Douglas Aircraft Company, Inc.

Some of these men have passed away and others have either retired or are working in other fields. But they will always be remembered as pioneers in the application of rocketry to manned flight in the United States, and, thus, who established the groundwork that led to this Nation's manned space-flight achievements.

Project Mercury

WILLIAM M. BLAND, JR.*

PERHAPS NO research-and-development program aroused greater public interest than did Project Mercury, the first American manned-spaceflight program. Certainly no previous technological endeavor of such a novel and complex nature ever unfolded almost daily before the eyes of national and international observers from inception to completion. Project Mercury mobilized a truly national effort involving more than 2,000,000 persons from the National Aeronautics and Space Administration (NASA), the Department of Defense including the military services, other government agencies, the aerospace industry, and educational institutions.

In a step-by-step program of 25 space flights involving six astronauts and four animals, no living passenger or pilot was lost. Mercury was successfully concluded officially on June 12, 1963, one month after the more than 34-hour orbital flight of Astronaut L. Gordon Cooper. Within the short span of four years, eight months, and one week, all the objectives of Project Mercury initiated in October 1958 had been attained: place a man in earth orbit, observe his reactions in a space environment, and return him safely to earth at a known point where he

* Mr. Bland, Chief of the Apollo Spacecraft Program Office Test Division, at the NASA Manned Spacecraft Center, was formerly Deputy Manager, Mercury Project, at the Manned Spacecraft Center, Houston, Texas. He joined the NACA Langley Laboratory in July 1947. He is author and co-author of numerous NASA technical reports on research conducted in the areas of aerodynamics and thermodynamics of supersonic and hypersonic configurations. This research was pioneered by the use of rocket-propelled test vehicles launched from the NACA Wallops Station from 1945 under the direction of Dr. Robert R. Gilruth. While working at the Langley Research Center he was one of the early contributors to the concept that was to become the Mercury spacecraft. His contributions were in the areas of spacecraft mockup development, development of the Mercury couch design, and design of the Little Joe solid-propellant test vehicle. Bland was Deputy Manager of the Mercury Project from January 1962 to the conclusion of the project. In this capacity he directed the engineering activities of the project, including detailed operation of spacecraft systems, analysis of flight-test results, and preparation of engineering-evaluation reports. The author is greatly endebted to Mr. James M. Grimwood, capable historian of the NASA Manned Spacecraft Center, in the preparation of this article. Numerous colleagues, past and present, played indispensable roles in the achievements of Project Mercury, and it is hoped that this terse account will appear reasonably accurate to them.

could be recovered. Beyond this, Mercury demonstrated beyond all question that man himself was an invaluable part of the space-flight system as a pilot, engineer, and experimenter.[1]

Genesis

To pinpoint the exact beginning of a complex technical program is usually impossible, for more often than not it is a consequence of the scientific-research and engineering-development process underway on a broad scale, often in diverse areas. Project Mercury was no exception. Its origins are found in the rocket-research airplane program, missile-rocket technology, aerospace medicine, and missile-nosecone reentry studies. As this overall technology of flight advanced to afford greater altitudes and speeds, manned-orbital flight became a logical projection.

Perhaps the most specific date to mark the birth of Project Mercury is July 14, 1952, when the executive committee of the National Advisory Committee for Aeronautics passed a resolution that ". . . NACA devote modest effort to problems of unmanned and manned flights at altitudes from 50 miles to infinity and at speeds from Mach 10 to escape from the earth's gravity."[2] Although the immediate application of this research objective was targeted at what became the X-15 rocket-research airplane program (1954), the International Geophysical Year scientific earth-satellite program also began in 1955. It was the shock of SPUTNIK I, however, which fastened immediate attention in October 1957 upon the task of placing an American into earth-orbital flight.

In March 1956 the U. S. Air Force had initiated a study, Project 7696, entitled "Manned Ballistic Rocket Research System" with the stated task of conceiving a flight program designed to recover a manned capsule from orbital flight. Over the next two years, with NACA representatives actively participating, much fundamental work was accomplished in the study of spacecraft design, possible rocket-booster combinations, and life-support requirements. During this time, some eleven companies of the aerospace-industrial complex presented pro-

[1] MSC Staff, *Mercury Project Summary Including Results of the Fourth Manned Orbital Flight May 15 and 16, 1963* (Washington, D. C., NASA SP-45, October 1963), pp. 1-2; James M. Grimwood, *Project Mercury: A Chronology* (Washington, D. C., NASA SP-4001, 1963), p. 196. Accounting placed the total cost of the Mercury Program at $384,131,000.

[2] Letter, NACA to High Speed Flight Research Station, "Discussion of Report on Problems of High Speed, High Altitude Flight, and Consideration of Possible Changes to the X-2 Airplane to extend its Speed and Altitude Range," July 30, 1953, which contains the NACA directive. Since 1915, NACA's basic mission had been to engage in fundamental aeronautical research.

posals for accomplishing manned-orbital flight, with particular attention to the type of rocket booster that might make such a program
truly feasible. In the main, however, the industrial proposals were
based on multistage-launch vehicles some of which were still in advanced study stages. By early 1958, NACA personnel favored the
possibility of utilizing ballistic-missile boosters, with the Atlas, then
in an advanced stage of development, the logical choice.[3] Under the
management of the Air Force Ballistic Missile Division the Atlas ICBM
had been accorded highest national priorities in early 1957.

Steps to Approval

The advent of Sputnik I and its shocking impact upon American
public opinion led to the National Aeronautics and Space Act of 1958,
and the creation of NASA on October 1, 1958. It can be safely stated
that the Sputniks were the prime movers in fostering the national decision for what became known as Project Mercury. From October
1957 on, the move toward an aggressive national space program for its
own sake was accelerated.[4] Until NASA was in business a year later
numerous proposals for a manned-orbital flight were submitted. There
was, however, a considerable technical task involved before a man
could safely be committed to orbital flight by exploiting rocket technology developed exclusively for military missiles. Some of the not-so-
well known milestones deserve review here.

Technical requirements and proposed solutions had been in the
process of coalescing for more than five years prior to the initiation
of Project Mercury. In June 1952, for example, H. Julian Allen of
NACA's Ames Aeronautical Laboratory determined that a blunt shape
would be most suitable for a body reentering the earth's atmosphere,
through dissipation of 90% of the friction heat via the shock wave.

[3] House Report 1228, " Project Mercury, First Interim Report," 86th Congress
2d Session, p. 2; Memo., Maxime A. Faget, NACA Langley, to Hugh L. Dryden,
Director, NACA, no subject, June 5, 1958; in MSC Historical files; Anon., " Outline of History of USAF Man-in-Space R and D Program," *Missiles and Rockets*,
Vol. X, No. 13 (Mar. 26, 1962), pp. 148-149; Letter, Paul E. Purser, MSC, to Mary
Stone Ambrose, NASA Hq., no subject, undated, in MSC Historical files. One
of the major resultants of this era, and one in which NACA personnel also
participated, was the Air Force's X-20 Dyna Soar Program. Cf. NACA Study,
" Study of the Feasibility of a Hypersonic Research Airplane," Washington, D. C.,
September 3, 1957.
[4] Eugene M. Emme, *Aeronautics and Astronautics: 1915-1960* (Washington,
1961), pp. 91-97. The Advanced Research Projects Agency (ARPA) of the
Department of Defense had been charged with the coordination of all space
projects in November 1957.

Five years later, an Army Jupiter-C scale-model nose cone demonstrated the practicability of dissipating most of the remaining heat by the ablative process. During 1956 and 1957 NACA personnel were engaged in studying various spacecraft designs. In November 1957, a NACA presentation made in post-Sputnik Washington proposed: existing ballistic missiles were adaptable for orbital manned flights, solid-fuel retrorockets should be used to initiate spacecraft reentry, and a ballistic shape without wings should be utilized for optimum spacecraft design. To provide attitude control for a spacecraft while in orbital flight, small rocket-reaction motors were planned. Experience on such pilot control had accumulated in the X-1B and X-1E rocket-research airplane programs.[5]

In early 1958, before NASA was created, additional technical breakthroughs played a large role in assuring mission success. Safety for a test pilot was of obvious central concern, forcing attention upon all possible areas wherein failure was possible and should be circumvented. The launch vehicle itself was of highest significance for, in the event of a necessary abort (particularly on the launching pad) some means had to be perfected to provide for pilot escape. Missile-development tests, particularly in early configurations, were well known for their "unreliability" until numerous "bugs" could be identified and eliminated. To offset this lack of booster reliability a significant safety system was added to the piloted-spacecraft concept in July 1958, when Maxime A. Faget proposed a tractor-rocket system, which was later affixed atop the Mercury spacecraft on a structure commonly known as the escape tower. To employ a full-scale launch vehicle to demonstrate the escape-tower system would have been prohibitively expensive, so that a simple and reliable means of accomplishing this became the object of search. For this purpose, Paul E. Purser and Faget of the Langley Research Center conceived the idea of clustering eight solid-propellant rockets to form a simple and relatively inexpensive launch vehicle, the Little Joe. Consisting of four large rockets and four small rockets, the Little Joe could generate enough thrust to "toss" the spacecraft to the nominal orbital altitudes expected for the first manned space flight. However, the main purpose was to provide selected critical launch-environment conditions for spacecraft-systems demonstration and qualification tests.

Perhaps one of the more important engineering contributions of

[5] *Ibid.*, p. 69; Army Ordnance Missile Command, *US Army Capabilities in the Space Age*, Redstone Arsenal, Alabama, June 1959, p. 26; Presentation by Maxime A. Faget, NACA Langley to NACA Hq. Staff, November 1957.
Also see article by Kenneth S. Kleinknecht, pp. 189-211.

Faget and his associates was the design and development of the contour couch that enabled the pilot to withstand the acceleration and deceleration loads attendant upon space flight. During the two-year study period (1956-1958), opinions were widely divergent between NACA and the Air Force. The primary hypothesis of the Air Force study program, for example, was based upon a requirement that forces no higher than 12 g be imposed upon the occupant of the spacecraft. Moreover, the spacecraft was to be designed so that the pilot could be positioned optimumly during phases of the flight when the loads were great. This requirement could be met by the provision of a gimballed seat. This meant that the spacecraft would have been a relatively spacious and more complex vehicle. A second rocket-powered stage, designated the Hustler and now known as the Agena, was contemplated to support the greater spacecraft weight.

From the NACA standpoint, however, it appeared to the Faget group that if the forces from acceleration were distributed more evenly over the pilot's body, the safe operating boundary could be raised. The contour couch, which was conceived in April 1958, provided this distribution of forces. This concept was proved on the human centrifuge at the Navy Acceleration Laboratory at Johnsville, Pennsylvania. In July 1958, Carter C. Collins and others withstood loads of more than 20 g's without suffering adverse effects. Consequently, the couch became a key conceptual breakthrough in spacecraft design as it was a major factor in the final selection of the Atlas as the orbital-launch vehicle.[6]

Meanwhile, the Congress had passed the National Aeronautics and Space Act of 1958 on July 16 and the President signed the bill on July 29, 1958. In August, President Eisenhower decided that the manned-satellite program would be conducted by the civilian space agency, NASA, which absorbed NACA and opened for business on October 1, 1958. At this time, NACA personnel, under the direction of Maxime A. Faget and Charles W. Mathews at Langley Laboratory, had already drawn up preliminary specifications for a manned-satellite capsule (compiled in draft form as early as June 1958). Toward the end of September 1958, a committee headed by Robert R. Gilruth met in Washington to discuss the program and draft a plan for meeting the objectives. Between October 3 and 7, 1958, these proposals were submitted to Dr. T. Keith Glennan, Administrator of NASA, and Roy

[6] Letter, Space Task Group to AVCO-Everett Research Laboratory, no subject, May 5, 1960, contains Little Joe launch-vehicle background. Information on contour couch was extracted from notes maintained in files of Maxime A. Faget, Assistant Director for Engineering and Development, Manned Spacecraft Center.

Johnson of the Advanced Research Projects Agency of the Department of Defense. Once approved, Project Mercury was underway.[7]

Mobilizing Government and Industry Capabilities

Immediately after program approval, Administrator Glennan directed that a Space Task Group be formed at Langley to undertake the technical development of the U. S. manned-satellite program. The task which faced this small organization, consisting of only 45 people at the beginning, was monumental. Specifications for the Mercury spacecraft had to be submitted to industry and the resulting proposals evaluated for technical competence; suitable test and launch vehicles had to be procured and modified; a world-wide tracking network had to be planned and built; and engineer test pilots had to be selected and trained.

With respect to the design and development of the spacecraft, many companies had been involved in such study dating from the Air Force Man-in-Space (MIS) study program and the NACA conference on high-speed aerodynamics presented to industry in March of 1958.[8] Proposals from 12 companies were received by NASA. On February 6, 1959 the prime contract was signed with the McDonnell Aircraft Corporation. To accomplish ballistic or orbital missions, nine Atlas missiles were ordered from the Air Force; for suborbital missions to test systems and to provide early manned-space-flight experience, two Jupiter missiles and eight Redstone missiles were ordered from the Army; and a contract was signed with North American Aviation to fabricate the airframe for the Little Joe for use in a test program to perfect the escape maneuver.[9]

[7] Public Law 85-568, 85th Congress, HR 12575, "National Aeronautics and Space Act of 1958," July 29, 1958; House Rept. No. 671, *Project Mercury Second Interim Report* 87th Congress, First Session, June 29, 1961, p. 8; "(Preliminary) Specifications for a Manned Satellite Capsule," Oct. 23, 1958; NASA Minutes of Meeting, "Panel for Manned Space Flight," Sept. 24, 30, and Oct. 1, 1958; Memo., Warren J. North to NASA Administrator, "Background for Project Mercury Schedules," Aug. 14, 1960. All in MSC Historical files. As a note of interest relative to the initial objectives for Project Mercury, Arthur C. Clarke in his book *Interplanetary Flight: An Introduction to Astronautics* (New York, Harper and Brothers, Second Edition, 1960), pp. 35-37, mentions that the spacecraft would be recovered after one orbit.

[8] Unfortunately no historical accounts of the USAF MIS or MISS (Man-in-Space Soonest) programs are available.

[9] Memo., Floyd L. Thompson, Acting Director, NASA-Langley, to all Concerned, "Space Task Group," Nov. 5, 1958; Staff, NASA-Langley, "Specifications for Manned Capsule (Spec. No. S-6), Nov. 14, 1958; Compilation of Papers, NACA-Ames, "NACA Conference on High-Speed Aerodynamics, "March 18-

Besides the program hardware (the above represents only the basic requirements) Space Task Group had to plan and arrange for a time-phased test schedule involving numerous laboratories, wind tunnels, and launch sites. For the launches, facilities at NASA's Wallops Island, Virginia, were to be used for Little Joe, and the DOD's Atlantic Missile Range (now called Cape Kennedy) was to be used for the Redstone and Atlas launchings. Wind tunnels of NASA's Langley, Lewis, and Ames Centers, as well as those of USAF's Arnold Engineering Development Center and the prime contractor, were to be used in configuration tests and various rocket-component tests associated with the spacecraft. Laboratories of the entire NASA complex and many other government agencies were used to test every component; and the Department of Defense cooperated in providing the extensive flight recovery and medical support required.

The Mercury Spacecraft

The Mercury spacecraft was to become an engineering achievement dictated by the binding constraints of payload weight which could be orbited by the Atlas booster. Most remarkable in this achievement was the provision of the indispensable systems for life support and flight operations. For a given period of time, the Mercury spacecraft had to provide the pilot with all of his life-supporting requirements, means to control his orientation, and a way to deorbit and land on the surface of the earth.

In appearance, this wingless manned-flight vehicle resembled a large bell in many ways, a complete departure from the traditional winged aircraft and gliders of aviation since its beginnings. From the recovery cylinder at the top to the heat shield at the bottom, it measured 115

20, 1958; Memo., George M. Low to NASA Administrator, "Status Report No. 7, Project Mercury, Feb. 17, 1959; Memo., Warren J. North to NASA Administrator, "Background of Project Mercury Schedules," Aug. 14, 1960; Message, NASA Hq. to Commanding General, Army Ordnance Missile Command, Jan. 16, 1959; NASA-STG, "Project Mercury Status Report No. 1 for Period Ending Jan. 31, 1959," March 1959. The Jupiter order was canceled in July 1959 when NASA determined that the same or better information could be obtained by aborting one of the Atlas flights. As for the Redstone order, two of the launch vehicles were removed from the program after the second successful manned-suborbital flight, as NASA stated that nothing further could be gained. Fourteen Atlas launch vehicles were ordered for use in Project Mercury. Ten of these were used during the project. The early days of the Space Task Group are also briefly discussed in Robert R. Gilruth's "Manned Space Flight," *Space Flight Report to the Nation*, ed. by Jerry and Vivian Gray (New York, Basic Books, Inc., 1962), pp. 31-33.

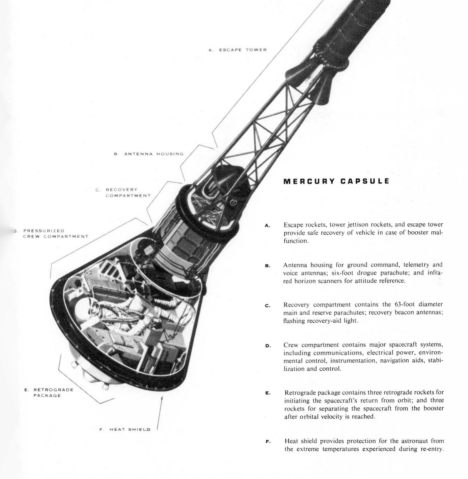

A. ESCAPE TOWER

B. ANTENNA HOUSING

C. RECOVERY
COMPARTMENT

D. PRESSURIZED
CREW COMPARTMENT

E. RETROGRADE
PACKAGE

F. HEAT SHIELD

MERCURY CAPSULE

A. Escape rockets, tower jettison rockets, and escape tower provide safe recovery of vehicle in case of booster malfunction.

B. Antenna housing for ground command, telemetry and voice antennas; six-foot drogue parachute; and infrared horizon scanners for attitude reference.

C. Recovery compartment contains the 63-foot diameter main and reserve parachutes; recovery beacon antennas; flashing recovery-aid light.

D. Crew compartment contains major spacecraft systems, including communications, electrical power, environmental control, instrumentation, navigation aids, stabilization and control.

E. Retrograde package contains three retrograde rockets for initiating the spacecraft's return from orbit; and three rockets for separating the spacecraft from the booster after orbital velocity is reached.

F. Heat shield provides protection for the astronaut from the extreme temperatures experienced during re-entry.

Fig. 25 Mercury Capsule, shown at 41° angle at which it separated from the Redstone booster on the MR-3 flight of Astronaut Alan B. Shepard on May 5, 1961 (McDonnell Aircraft drawing)

inches, and was 74 inches in diameter at its widest point—the re-entry
heat shield. Beginning at the heat shield and moving upward, the
Mercury spacecraft proper was divided into three major sections. The
first was a large truncated cone which housed the astronaut and his
supporting systems. Above this was a cylindrical section which con-

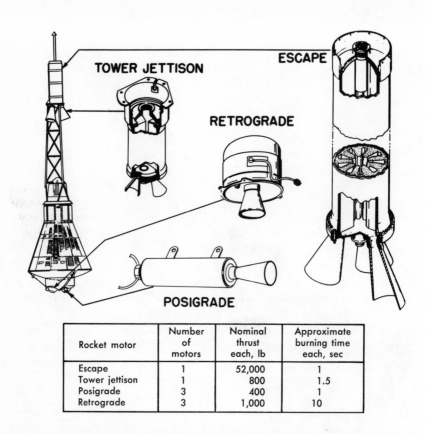

Rocket motor	Number of motors	Nominal thrust each, lb	Approximate burning time each, sec
Escape	1	52,000	1
Tower jettison	1	800	1.5
Posigrade	3	400	1
Retrograde	3	1,000	10

Fig. 26   Solid-propellant rocket motors used on the Mercury spacecraft (NASA)

tained the landing parachute, recovery aids, and certain other systems
or parts of systems. The last section was a small truncated cone
containing the communication-antenna system, horizon-sensing elements of the automatic-control system, and the drogue parachute.
Above the spacecraft, at launch, there was a triangular-shaped truss
of steel tubing forming the escape tower. This was attached to the
spacecraft-cylindrical section and it extended around and above the

antenna section. At the base of the spacecraft, the heat shield was constructed of a resin-impregnated glass fiber.[10]

Rocket power was the all-important factor determining the flight operation of the Mercury spacecraft. Affixed on the bottom of the heat shield there were six solid-propellant rockets. Three of these, known as the posigrade rockets, with each developing a nominal thrust of 400 pounds and burning for one second, were used to separate the spacecraft from the launch vehicle once orbit was achieved. The other three, designated as the retrograde rockets, each developing a nominal thrust of 1,000 pounds and burning for about 10 seconds, were employed to slow the spacecraft to initiate re-entry into the atmosphere. Prior to re-entry the retropack was jettisoned, with the exception of John Glenn's flight (MA-6) when there were erroneous indications that the heatshield had been unlocked. Then the retropack was retained to assist in holding the shield in place.

On the escape tower there were two solid-propellant rockets. One was the escape-rocket motor that was to be activated in the event a catastrophic failure was imminent. In such an event, the rocket motor, developing a nominal thrust of 52,000 pounds and burning for one second, boosted the spacecraft a safe distance from the launch vehicle. The other was the tower-jettison-rocket motor used to cast off the spent escape-rocket motor in the event it had been used. This rocket burned for 1.5 seconds and developed a nominal thrust of 800 pounds. One of the more significant engineering developments with these two rockets was the tri-nozzle which produced greater thrust effectiveness for the tower-jettison-rocket motors.

Besides the solid-propellant rockets, the Mercury spacecraft contained eighteen 90-percent hydrogen-peroxide-rocket engines (thrusters) rated at from 1 to 24 pounds of thrust. These rocket engines were used to control spacecraft attitude in either automatic or manual modes. The automatic mode used the outputs of two-attitude gyros, three-rate gyros, horizon-sensing elements, logic and programming circuits to provide attitude control.

Attitude changes could be either programmed at intervals by the automatic system or the pilot could eliminate the automatic system through switches and provide manual control. In the manual mode there was another complete set of throttleable thrust chambers that would produce up to 24 pounds of thrust for pitch and yaw control and up to

[10] Maxime A. Faget and Robert O. Piland, "Mercury Capsule and its Flight Systems," presentation at the 28th Annual Meeting of the Institute of Aeronautical Sciences, New York, New York, January 25, 1960.

6 pounds for roll control. These were operated through either a solenoid or mechanical valve by the pilot's use of the hand controller to effect pitch, roll, or yaw corrections.[11]

Each component of the spacecraft including its rocket systems underwent an exhaustive test program to obtain high reliability. While all NASA centers and many other interested organizations inside and outside of the government participated in the test program, the work accomplished at the Lewis Research Center in Cleveland is descriptive.

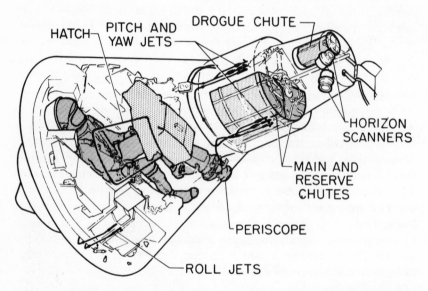

Fig. 27   Spacecraft interior arrangement showing attitude control jets (NASA)

With respect to the posigrade rockets, separation tests were conducted to determine whether the operation was adequate (sufficient impulse) and whether there would be any damage to the launch vehicle when the posigrade-rockets motors were fired. Calibration tests were conducted on the retrorockets to ascertain the amount of spacecraft-upset moment that was developed and to devise measures to minimize this moment. For the rocket-engine thrusters, Lewis engineers checked the systems to gather starting and performance characteristics of these reaction-control jets. In addition, study was made to determine the

[11] *Ibid.*; NASA-STG, "Project Mercury Status Report No. 5 for Period Ending January 31, 1960"; "Descriptive Synopsis of Project Mercury," August 1962, p. 21.

effects of the escape-rocket-motor plume on the spacecraft. These were but brief samples of the over-all test program.[12]

Significant contributions were also made in the development and operation of the spacecraft by the Mercury astronauts themselves. Their recognition of some potential shortcomings in the spacecraft resulted in incorporation of a number of improvements involving a large enough viewing window to include a view of the horizon while in retrofiring attitude so that an accurate attitude reference was available, the quick-release spacecraft hatch, and means for precisely and accurately selecting the desired control mode. Their flight experiences in space resulted in elimination of the heavy periscope and other refinements from later Mercury spacecraft.

The Launch Vehicles

To build a manned-space-flight orbital capability, a comprehensive step-by-step flight-test program was planned. In step form these included: (1) research and development; (2) primary flight qualification of production spacecraft; (3) man-rating the launch-vehicle hardware; and finally (4) the manned-ballistic and orbital flights themselves. As originally planned, four " Little Joe " and two Atlas (designated " Big Joe ") flights were scheduled for the research-and-development phase to qualify operation of the spacecraft and its systems in critical abort conditions, determine dynamic-stability characteristics, and aerodynamic-heating parameters during reentry flight. Redstones were scheduled for eight flights: two unmanned to qualify spacecraft and launch-vehicle combination, and the six remaining to train astronauts on short-space flights. Jupiter missiles were to qualify the spacecraft under extreme load conditions. And finally, three Atlas launch vehicles were designated to complete the spacecraft-qualification flights. The remainder of the Atlas vehicles were scheduled for manned-orbital operations.[13]

Special-Research-Test Vehicles

Other than the primary Mercury spacecraft-launch vehicles, two special types were employed to accomplish particular tasks in the research and development phase of the program. One of these was a five-stage, solid-propellant launch vehicle used to propel scale models

[12] Memo, Maxime A. Faget, Chief, Flight Systems Division, STG, to Project Director, " Status of Test Work Being Conducted at the Lewis Research Center in Conjunction with Project Mercury," October 22, 1959.
[13] NASA-STG, " Project Mercury Status Report No. 1 " for Period Ending Jan. 31, 1959.

in order to investigate the aerodynamic-heating characteristics of the Mercury spacecraft at high velocities in the atmosphere. This hypersonic-research-launch vehicle was 65 feet long and weighed about 7,000 pounds at lift-off.[14] Unlike other boosters in the rocket "family," it was never assigned a popular name.

The second special test-launch vehicle was the Scout, a four-stage solid-propellant rocket. In behalf of Project Mercury, it was planned that a Scout would place a pay-load of instruments into a planned Mercury operational orbit to provide a real-time test and demonstration of the world-wide tracking network. Launched on November 1, 1961, the mission failed shortly after lift-off. The failure was believed to be caused by a cross connection of two electrical connectors. No further Scout flights were planned since the Mercury-Atlas 4 and 5 missions soon thereafter provided the necessary data.[15]

Little Joe

Unlike the other major launch vehicles of Project Mercury, Little Joe was developed solely for use in Project Mercury. The Little Joe rocket was essentially a fin-stabilized cylinder with the spacecraft placed atop. It was 80 inches in diameter or about equal with the spacecraft, and including the attached spacecraft, was about 50 feet long. The eight rocket motors—four large and four small—developed a thrust at takeoff of about a quarter of a million pounds and could lift a pay-load of about 4,000 pounds on a ballistic path to an altitude of about 100 nautical miles. The purpose of the Little Joe phase was to propel full-scale, full-weight developmental and production versions of the Mercury spacecraft to some of the critical flight conditions that would be encountered during exit from the atmosphere on orbital missions for tests of the escape system.[16]

Normally, four of the small motors and two of the large motors

[14] Memo, Howard S. Carter and Carl A. Sandahl to Associate Director, NASA-Langley, "Weekly Progress Report for Week of March 8, 1959, on Langley Support of Project Mercury," March 16, 1959.
[15] Memo, Abe Silverstein to NASA Associate Administrator, "Use of Scout for Checkout of Mercury Network, May 24, 1961; Memo, George M. Low to NASA Director, Office of Manned Space Flight, "Dynamic Checkout of Mercury Ground Network with Mercury-Scout," November 8, 1961.
[16] Letter, Space Task Group to AVCO-Everett Research Laboratory, no subject, May 5, 1960; MSC Fact Sheet No. 47, "Project Mercury Little Joe Flight Test Program," no date. Note: The chronological numbered designations in the Fact Sheet are in error; the briefly stated objectives are correct. For a correct sequenced list, see the complete Project Mercury launch chronology at the end of this article.

would be ignited simultaneously at lift-off, leaving the remaining large motors to be ignited at a designated time during the mission. The nozzles of all motors were positioned so that the effective thrust passed through a combined center of gravity, especially important as the Little Joe vehicle contained no automatic guidance-control system. Rocket-motor staging times were variously used to give the desired performance on each mission. During the actual flight phase, the full-altitude boosting capabilities of the Little Joe were not utilized to attain

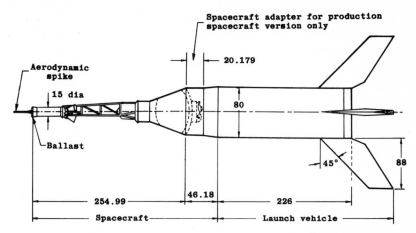

Fig. 28 Sketch of the Little Joe Launch Vehicle with production spacecraft (linear dimensions in inches). (NASA)

the critical test conditions at altitudes of 30,000 to 100,000 feet with resulting apogees of 50,000 and 280,000 feet, respectively.[17]

Progress in the Little Joe test program was rapid and systematic. It was only one year from the time that preliminary design was initiated until the first vehicle was launched in October 1959. The Little

[17] NASA Release No. 59-235, "NASA Conducts Little Joe Test Launch," October 4, 1959; NASA-STG, "Project Mercury Status Report No. 5 for period ending January 31, 1960.": Memo, George M. Low to NASA Administrator, "Little Joe 1-B (Test No. 4)," Jan. 22, 1960; Memo, George M. Low to NASA Administrator, "Report on Little Joe No. 5 and Mercury-Redstone 1," Nov. 10, 1960; Memo, Warren J. North to NASA Administrator, "Preliminary Flight Results of Little Joe 5A," March 20, 1961; Memo, Warren J. North to NASA Administrator, "Little Joe 5B Launch," Apr. 28, 1961. The total cost of the Little Joe program was about $2.5 million. The concept of a R&D rocket has been carried forward in the Apollo program with the Little Joe II.

Joe phase of the program was completed in April 1961, and during the interim there was a total of seven launches. In some of the flight tests, not all objectives were attained. During the first launch attempt on August 21, 1959, the escape-rocket motor was ignited because of a faulty circuit 31 minutes before the intended launch. On the first actual flight of a Little Joe in October of that year, early ignition of the rocket motors of the second stage increased the severity of the flight environment, thereby increasing the significance of this success-ful test. On other occasions, automatically sequenced operations did not occur as planned. An example of this type of trouble occurred during the Little Joe 5 mission of November 8, 1960 when the space-craft failed to separate from the launch vehicle. Lessons were thus learned and modifications made to correct the technical deficiencies well in advance of later manned flights. The test objectives of the Little Joe program were to demonstrate the proper operation of the escape system under the selected dynamic-flight conditions that were representative of the most severe that could be anticipated from launch to orbital conditions. As a bonus, two of the flights carried rhesus monkeys as passengers, presenting the opportunity to study the effects of acceleration and deceleration on a living being. These animals (popularly known as "Sam" and "Miss Sam") withstood the flight stresses and remained in excellent condition. Finally, judged by the useful data it provided, the Little Joe phase was inexpensive. With an energy potential about equal to the Redstone, although the lack of a guidance system prevented comparable flight accuracy, a Little Joe space vehicle cost only about one-fifth of that of a Mercury-Redstone vehicle.

Mercury-Redstone

Chosen for the task to boost the first American astronaut into space flight was a modified Redstone (Mercury-Redstone) launch vehicle (an off-spring of the V-2) developed by the Army Ballistic Missile Agency. The possibilities of using this booster for a manned-sub-orbital-space flight came to the attention of NACA personnel when the Army had proposed Project Adam in August 1958. This pre-NASA proposal described a manned-ballistic flight using existing Red-stone hardware "as a national political psychological demonstration." This proposal and an assessment of the reliable flight history that the Redstone had amassed since August 1953 were factors which influenced the NASA decision to use the Redstone. It could provide the per-formance required to place a manned Mercury spacecraft in a sub-orbital trajectory that would have an apogee altitude about equal to that planned for Mercury-Atlas orbital flights and a five-minute period of weightlessness. At this point in time—1958—the biological effects of weightlessness upon man were unknown except for the limited data acquired during zero-g aircraft experiments [18] limited in duration to seconds; therefore this capability was extremely important.

The task immediately at hand, after STG ordered eight Redstone boosters from ABMA in January 1959, was to man-rate a tactical-military missile, to provide the increased reliability desired for manned flight, satisfactory operations from a human-factor standpoint, and an adequate performance margin. A major modification program was initiated at Redstone Arsenal to provide these features.[19] To provide the required safety measure an automatic-abort system was installed to sense impending failure in the launch-vehicle systems. In such an event an automatically initiated electrical signal would terminate booster thrust, and initiate separation of the spacecraft, so that the escape rocket motor could then propel the spacecraft to a distance of several hundred feet away within one second. All innovations underwent an exhaustive component-by-component test program at the Marshall Space Flight Center under the technical direction of the Space Task Group.[20]

At the outset of the Mercury-Redstone (MR) phase, it was intended that the first two missions would be flown to qualify the spacecraft-launch vehicle combination, develop checkout procedures for both vehicles, and gain experience in the operation of the launch complex. The flight path chosen for the MR flights was to yield a maximum velocity of about 6,400 fps, a flight-path angle of about 42 degrees, and an altitude of some 200,000 feet at the end of the powered phase. This trajectory was expected to result during the accelerated portion in a 6.3 g-load. A 5-minute period of weightless flight, and an 11

---

[18] Joachim P. Kuettner, " Manrating Space Carrier Vehicles," *From Peenemünde to Outer Space*, edited by Ernst Stuhlinger, *et al.* (Redstone Arsenal, Alabama, March 1962), pp. 629-637. Kuettner mentions that for the Mercury-Redstone program, the data from about 60 Redstone and Jupiter-C launchings were available.

[19] See Wernher von Braun, pp. 107-21; David S. Akens et al., *History of the George C. Marshall Space Flight Center: July 1 to December 31, 1960*, May 1961, pp. 7-9.

[20] *Ibid.*; Jerome B. Hammack and Jack C. Heberlig, " The Mercury-Redstone Program," presentation at American Rocket Society, Space Flight Report to the Nation, New York Coliseum, Oct. 9-15, 1961; ABMA Rept. No. DG-TR-7-59, F. W. Brandner, " Proposal for Mercury-Redstone Automatic Inflight Abort Sensing System," June 5, 1959. About 800 changes were made to man-rate the Redstone launch vehicle for Project Mercury. Also see Kuettner, " Man-rating Space Carrier Vehicles," *op. cit.*, pp. 633-637.

g-load-maximum-reentry deceleration were also to be obtained. These acceleration factors closely resembled those expected in later Atlas flights. The flights also gave the added bonus of providing pilot and systems-operation experience during actual flight environmental conditions.[21]

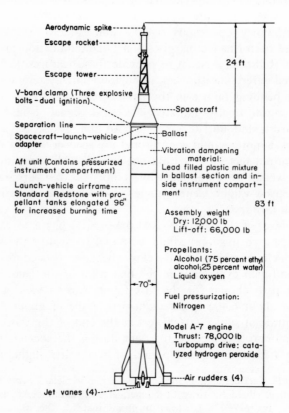

Fig. 29 Mercury-Redstone configuration (NASA)

Mercury-Redstone phase spanned a 31-month segment of Project Mercury, and during this time-frame six missions were accomplished. As usually common to research-and-development programs, there were successes and there were failures. There was, in fact, quite an unseemly start on the first flight (MR-1) attempt when early separation

[21] Hammack and Heberlig, "The Mercury-Redstone Program."

of an electrical ground line to the launch vehicle aborted the mission. The launch vehicle rose about one inch and settled back undamaged on the launch stand. On the second flight all systems worked perfectly. But problems appeared again when overacceleration in the primate "Ham" mission (MR-2) resulted in a higher trajectory and a consequent longer range than had been planned. For this reason, an extra flight, a Mercury-Redstone Booster-Development mission (MR-BD) was flown before an astronaut was committed to space flight. The MR-BD mission was completely successful. On May 5, 1961, Alan B. Shepard, Jr., became the first American in space aboard the Mercury spacecraft, FREEDOM 7 (MR-3). Astronaut Shepard demonstrated that man could operate in the space environment in performance of the necessary pilot tasks, and he found the weightless state pleasant rather than one causing any physical disorientation or discomfort. The operational phase of Project Mercury was now underway.* Virgil I. Grissom in LIBERTY BELL 7 (MR-4) made the second suborbital flight on July 21, 1961. Data from these two successful missions were sufficiently complete and informative to warrant cancelling the remaining Mercury-Redstone flights.[22]

Mercury-Atlas

To achieve the first of the stated goals of Project Mercury—to launch a man into earth orbit—the Atlas missile had been selected as the launch vehicle from the beginning. In reality when the program was approved in October 1958, there was no other rocket vehicle available for selection; that is, if the program objectives were to be reached at the earliest practicable date. It was the only off-the-shelf missile in the

* Ed. Note: On April 12, 1961, the U.S.S.R. had orbited Yuri Gagarin in VOSTOK I, and on August 6-7, 1961, Cosmonaut Gherman Titov made 17-orbits in VOSTOK II.

[22] Memo, George M. Low to NASA Administrator, "Attempted Launching of MR-1," Nov. 21, 1960; Memo, George M. Low to NASA Administrator, "Mercury-Redstone-1(A) Launching," Dec. 20, 1960; Memo, Warren J. North to Franklyn W. Phillips, NASA Code A, "MR-2 Flight Results," Feb. 1, 1961; Memo, George M. Low to NASA Administrator, "Mercury-Redstone Booster Development Test," Mar. 27, 1961; Staffs of NASA, Nat. Inst. Health, and Nat. Acad. Sci., *Proceedings of a Conference of the First U. S. Manned Suborbital Space Flight* (Washington, Government Printing Office, June 6, 1961); Staff of NASA Manned Spacecraft Center, *Results of the Second U. S. Manned Suborbital Space Flight, June 21, 1961* (Washington, 1961); Government Printing Office. For a concise statement of Mercury-Redstone missions and results see chart at end of article. Also see for general discussion on several Mercury-Redstone operations, Judith Viorst, *Projects; Space* (New York, Washington Square Press, Inc., Jan. 1962), pp. 37, 38, 40-42, 68, and 69.

American arsenal at that point in time that had the thrust capability of boosting a spacecraft into orbital flight. The USAF Atlas D was chosen as the basic configuration because its performance character- istics met most of the requirements for a launch vehicle for Project Mercury.

In dimensions, the Mercury-Atlas with the spacecraft-escape tower was 95 feet and 4 inches long, of which 71 feet and 7 inches was the launch vehicle and the spacecraft adapter. Diameter of the Atlas tank section was 10 feet, and the booster was 16 feet at the widest point. Total weight of the Mercury-Atlas at lift-off was about 260,000 pounds, and the launch-vehicle thrust delivery at that time was more than 360,000 pounds. The astronaut experienced a g-load of 1.4 at lift-off and nearly 8 at the highest acceleration achieved. The maximum g-load on the spacecraft during reentry after orbital flight corres- ponded closely with the latter figure.[23]

Similar to the Redstone phase, a modification program was necessary to prepare the Atlas ballistic missile for the Mercury mission. One of the first items of concern was pilot safety during countdown and launch. Personnel from STG, the Air Force Ballistic Missile Division (AFBMD), the Space Technology Laboratories (STL), and Convair Astronautics (later General Dynamics/Astronautics) met in February 1959 to attack this problem. The result was an abort-sensing-and-imple- mentation system (ASIS). This automatic system monitored measure- ments of engine-chamber pressures, rates of change in vehicle attitude, electrical-power status, differential-tank pressure, liquid-oxygen-tank pressure, and hydraulic-source pressure. Deviations of these parameters beyond established limits, if confirmed by the system, caused the initiation of a signal that resulted in engine shutdown, spacecraft release, and ignition of the spacecraft escape-rocket motor. These events then would result in boosting the spacecraft a safe distance from the launch vehicle in about one second. By April 1959, STG believed that a reliable ASIS had been conceived. Relative to the guidance, STG believed that the existing system was quite adequate based on the suc- cessful PROJECT SCORE satellite launching by an Atlas system of December 18, 1958.* For mating the Mercury spacecraft with the Atlas launch vehicle, a special adapter section was required. STG assigned the task of building the adapter to the Mercury prime con-

[23] General Dynamics/Astronautics, " Mercury-Atlas MA-9 Launch Information and Notebook," Circular, April 1963. See Robert L. Perry, pp. 142-161.

* Ed. Note. PROJECT SCORE or the " talking Atlas " was the communication- relay satellite which involved the placement of an entire Atlas into orbit (8,750 lbs.).

tractor (McDonnell Aircraft Corporation). The first one was ready in April 1959.[24]

The Space Task Group had begun its initial negotiations for the procurement of Atlas launch vehicles with the Air Force Ballistic Missile Division in October 1958. In November, one Atlas C was ordered for the purpose of flight checking the aerodynamics of the

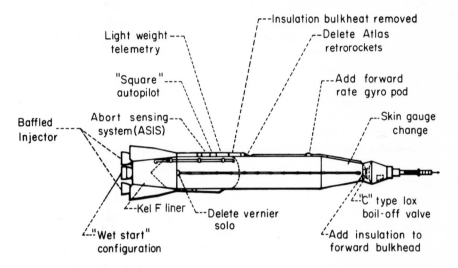

Fig. 30   Atlas launch vehicle with modifications for Mercury (NASA)

spacecraft in a ballistic-reentry heating test. However, Atlas D's became available the next month, with STG ordering nine, and plans were adjusted to the Atlas D launch vehicle, only. Later, five other Atlas vehicles were ordered by NASA for a total of 14.[25]

[24] NASA-STG, "Project Mercury Status Report No. 1 for Period Ending Jan. 31, 1959"; NASA-STG, "Project Mercury Status Report No. 2 for Period Ending April 30, 1959"; Brochure, General Dynamics/Astronautics," Project Mercury"; also see, John L. Chapman, *Atlas: The Story of a Missile* (New York, Harper and Brothers, 1960), pp. 174-175.

[25] Message, NASA NDA, Ralph Cushman, Contracting Officer, NASA, to Commanding General, Air Force Ballistic Missile Division, Nov. 24, 1958; Memo, Warren J. North to NASA Administrator, "Background of Project Mercury Schedules," Aug. 14, 1960. It must be remembered that the so-called "missile race" placed a high strategic value on each Atlas manufactured at this time.

The flight phase of the 57-month Atlas phase of the Mercury Project began with the launch of the successful Big Joe Atlas boiler-plate spacecraft on September 9, 1959. Although major objectives were attained and a planned second similar flight was cancelled, problem areas appeared. Achieved velocity was below the expected value as the Big Joe vehicle had failed to stage. The launch of Mercury-Atlas 1 on July 29, 1960, with the first production spacecraft to be mounted on an Atlas launch vehicle, ended after about 60 seconds of flight. The spacecraft was destroyed upon impact, since no spacecraft-escape system was used in this mission. An intensive investigation, conducted between August 1960 and February of 1961 resulted in modifications to stiffen the adapter and to increase the thickness of the material in the launch-vehicle skin near the adapter. An interim version of a "fix" was successfully used on the flight of MA-2, but the final version was not proved until the flight of MA-4 since the MA-3 mission failed soon after lift-off from another cause.[26]

The first orbital flight of the Mercury spacecraft (MA-4) occurred on September 13, 1961, presenting the opportunity to check out the world-wide communication network and the all-important recovery operations with an actual mission. Slightly more than two months later (November 29), Enos, a trained chimpanzee, was launched on a planned three-orbit mission (MA-5) as the last qualification flight prior to the manned program. During the flight, an abnormal performance of the attitude-control system was noted and the spacecraft was returned to earth after two orbits. The MA-5 flight was successful, but if an astronaut had been aboard the flight could have been continued for the third orbit by use of a manual redundant system (demonstrated under similar conditions during the later flights).

After delays caused by unfavorable weather conditions and launch-vehicle fuel-tank leaks, Astronaut John H. Glenn, Jr. was launched into orbital flight (MA-6) on February 20, 1962. The initial objectives of Project Mercury had been attained. Glenn suffered no debilitating effects and successfully demonstrated pilot capabilities during a three-orbit space flight. This was followed by the successful three-orbit

[26] Memo, George M. Low to NASA Administrator, "Big Joe Shot," Sept. 9, 1959; Memo, George M. Low to NASA Administrator, "Mercury-Atlas 1, Post Launch Information," July 29, 1960; files maintained in office of Paul E. Purser concerning the Rhode-Worthman Committee investigation of Big Joe and MA-1 failures. Also see George Alexander, "Atlas Accuracy Improves as Test Program is Completed," *Aviation Week and Space Technology*, Feb. 25, 1963, pp. 75-76; Martin Cardin, *Man Into Space* (New York, Pyramid Books, May 1961), pp. 66-73. The latter contains a relatively complete discussion on the MA-3 failure.

flight (MA-7) of M. Scott Carpenter, in which an attitude misalign-
ment at retrofire time caused a 250-mile landing overshoot, delaying his
recovery for several hours after landing. In preparation for a day-
long mission, Walter M. Schirra piloted a six-orbit mission (MA-8) on
October 3, 1962. By employing drifting-flight modes to conserve some
of the more critical consumables, Schirra demonstrated without question that the Mercury spacecraft was capable of longer-duration missions. And as mentioned earlier the 34 plus-hour flight of L. Gordon
Cooper culminated the successful Mercury program.[27]

Lessons and Accomplishments

Without doubt Project Mercury provided the basic foundation for
the further exploration by man of the unfriendly environment—space.
The confidence engendered by the experience of Project Mercury
generated the follow-on programs of manned-space flight—Gemini
and Apollo—long before Mercury had been concluded.

Along the often rough route, we added considerably to our technical
know-how. Launch vehicles developed as missiles were adapted for
manned space flight to improve greatly the chances for pilot safety
and mission success; a craft capable of transversing space was conceived, tested, and proved; rocket power was harnessed to provide
launch capability, emergency-operation capability, spacecraft control,
and return of spacecraft from orbit. In addition, we achieved our
primary objective, that of learning that man could perform in space
if provided with reliable systems producing his normal life-sustaining
environment. Communications and tracking systems were improved
to monitor minutely the entire flight, its pilots, and major spacecraft
systems from lift-off to recovery.

The compressed time-frame of this tremendously complex project
appears equally unique, one made possible by the concurrent develop-
ment-and-testing approach. By moving forward concurrently on the
major elements of the program—flight-hardware research and development; flight-crew program, tracking, and network; and flight tests—
the steps of qualifying each phase before moving sequentially to

[27] NASA Manned Spacecraft Center, *Results of the First United States Manned
Orbital Space Flight, February 20, 1962* (Washington, Government Printing Office
1962); NASA Manned Spacecraft Center, *Results of the Second United States
Manned Orbital Space Flight, May 24, 1962* (NASA SP-6) (Washington, NASA
SP-6, 1962); NASA Manned Spacecraft Center, *Results of the Third United
States Manned Orbital Space Flight, October 3, 1962* (NASA SP-12); NASA
Manned Spacecraft Center, *Mercury Project Summary Including Results of the
Fourth Manned Orbital Flight, May 15 and 16, 1963* (Washington, NASA SP-45,

Fig. 31   Mercury flight program summary (NASA table)

Mission [a]	Spacecraft [b]	Launch date	Flight duration [c], hr:min:sec	Occupant
LJ–1	BP	Aug. 21, 1959	00:00:20	
Big Joe	BP	Sept. 9, 1959	00:13:00	
LJ–6	BP	Oct. 4, 1959	00:05:10	
LJ–1A	BP	Nov. 4, 1959	00:08:11	
LJ–2	BP	Dec. 4, 1959	00:11:06	Rhesus monkey "Sam"
LJ–1B	BP	Jan. 21, 1960	00:08:35	Rhesus monkey "Miss Sam"
Beach abort	S/C 1	May 9, 1960	00:01:16	
MA–1	S/C 4	July 29, 1960	00:03:18	
LJ–5	S/C 3	Nov. 8, 1960	00:02:22	
MR–1	S/C 2	Nov. 21, 1960	00:00:00	Simulated man
MR–1A	S/C 2	Dec. 19, 1960	00:15:45	
MR–2	S/C 5	Jan. 31, 1961	00:16:39	Chimpanzee "Ham"
MA–2	S/C 6	Feb. 21, 1961	00:17:56	
LJ–5A	S/C 14	Mar. 18, 1961	00:23:48	

Mission [a]	Basic test objectives [d]	Summary of results [e]
LJ–1	Max. dynamic pressure abort; evaluate launch escape and recovery systems.	Object. not met; inadvertent abort initiated during countdown.
Big Joe	Ballistic flight; evaluate heat-protection concept, aerodynamic shape, and recovery system.	Successful.
LJ–6	Ballistic flight; qualify launch-vehicle structure; evaluate command system.	Successful.
LJ–1A	Max. dynamic pressure abort; same as LJ–1.	Primary object. not met; escape motor ignition was late.
LJ–2	High-altitude abort; evaluate launch, abort, and reentry dynamics of S/C; recovery.	Successful.
LJ–1B	Max. dynamic pressure abort; same as LJ–1A; evaluate launch and abort.	Successful.
Beach abort	Off-the-pad abort; qualify structure and launch escape system for simulated pad abort.	Successful.
MA–1	Ballistic flight; S/C-launch-vehicle compatibility; thermal loads in critical abort.	Object. not met; mission failed at about 60 sec. after lift-off.
LJ–5	Max. dynamic pressure abort; qualify launch escape system and structure.	Object. not met; S/C did not separate from launch vehicle.
MR–1	Suborbital flight; qualify S/S-launch-vehicle compatibility, posigrades, ASCS.	Test object. not met; launch vehicle shutdown at lift-off.
MR–1A	Suborbital flight; same as MR–1	Successful; cutoff overspeed caused overshoot.
MR–2	Suborbital flight; qualify ECS, landing bag.	Successful; launch vehicle failed to shutdown until fuel depletion, S/C overshot by 130 miles.
MA–2	Ballistic flight; same as MA–1	Successful.
LJ–5A	Max. dynamic pressure abort; same as LJ–5.	Object. not met; escape rocket ignited early.

Mission [a]	Spacecraft [b]	Launch date	Flight duration [c], hr:min:sec	Occupant
MR–BD	BP	Mar. 24, 1961	00:08:23	
MA–3	S/C 8	Apr. 25, 1961	00:07:19	
LJ–5B	S/C 14A	Apr. 28, 1961	00:05:25	
MR–3	S/C 7 FREEDOM 7	May 5, 1961	00:15:22	Alan B. Shepard
MR–4	S/C 11 LIBERTY BELL 7	July 21, 1961	00:15:37	Virgil I. Grissom
MA–4	S/C 8A	Sept. 13, 1961	01:49:20	
MA–5	S/C 9	Nov. 29, 1961	03:20:59	Chimpanzee " Enos "
MA–6	S/C 13 FRIEND- SHIP 7	Feb. 20, 1962	04:55:23	John H. Glenn, Jr.
MA–7	S/C 18 AURORA 7	May 24, 1962	04:56:05	M. Scott Carpenter
MA–8	S/C 16 SIGMA 7	Oct. 3, 1962	09:13:11	Walter M. Schirra, Jr.
MA–9	S/C 20 FAITH 7	May 15, 1963	34:19:49	L. Gordon Cooper, Jr.

[a] LJ–Little Joe launch vehicle mission; MA–Mercury-Atlas (launch vehicle) mission; MR–Mercury-Redstone (launch vehicle) mission; BD–Booster development.

[b] BP–Boilerplate spacecraft; S/C–spacecraft; S/C 10, 12, 15, 17, 19 not used in flight program.

Mission [a]	Basic test objectives [d]	Summary of results [e]
MR–BD	Suborbital flight; evaluate modifications to correct MR–1 and MR–2 malfunctions.	Successful.
MA–3	One-pass orbital flight; evaluate all S/C systems, network, recovery forces.	Object. not met; launch vehicle failed to follow roll program; S/C escape system operated.
LJ–5B	Max. dynamic pressure abort; same as LJ–5 and LJ–5A.	Successful.
MR–3	Suborbital flight; familiarize man with space flight; evaluate response and S/C control.	Successful; first American astronaut in space.
MR–4	Suborbital flight; same as MR–3.	Successful; after landing premature hatch release caused S/C to sink; astronaut recovered.
MA–4	One-pass orbital flight; same as MA–3.	Successful; circuit anomaly control system caused S/C to land 75 miles uprange.
MA–5	Three-pass orbital flight; qualify all systems, network, for orbital flight recovery.	Successful; control system malfunction terminated flight after two passes.
MA–6	Three-pass orbital flight; evaluate effects on and performance of astronaut in space; astronaut's evaluation of S/C and support.	Successful; first American to orbit earth; control system malfunction required manual retrofire and reentry; erroneous T/M signal, retropack retained through reentry: S/C landed 40 miles uprange.
MA–7	Three-pass orbital flight; same as MA–6; evaluate S/C modifications and network.	Successful; horizon scanner circuit malfunction required manual retrofire; yaw error caused S/C to land 250 miles downrange, recovery in 3 hr.
MA–8	Six-pass orbital flight; same as MA–6 and MA–7 except for extended duration.	Successful; partially blocked ECS coolant valve delayed stabilizing suit temperature until 2nd pass; S/C landed 4½ miles from primary recovery ship.
MA–9	Twenty-two pass orbital flight; evaluate effects on man of up to 1 day in space; verify man as primary S/C system.	Successful; short circuit late in flight disabled ASCS, inverters, prompted manual retrofire and reentry; S/C landed 4½ miles from ship.

[e] Duration measured from lift-off to landing.

[d] ASCS—automatic stabilization and control systems; ECS—environmental control system.

[e] Object.—objectives of flight; prop.—propellant; T/M—telemetry.

another were omitted. Risks were always involved, problems were quickly solved to prevent extended delays. Thus, even program management in this mode of complexity and urgency came to represent a newly developed asset. Project Mercury appears to have been one of the most successful major research-and-development programs ever accomplished in the United States.

The 25 major flight tests of the project were accomplished in a 45-month period at an average of one flight test in each eight-week period. During late 1960 and early 1961, the pace was much more rapid with ten flight tests accomplished in less than six months. In spite of the rapid pace, careful selection of space equipment and precise preparation and testing of the spacecraft and launch vehicles resulted in an unique flight record. The six astronauts and the four animals were recovered safely at the end of their assigned missions. Some failures did occur during the earlier development-and-qualification flights as deficiencies under actual flight stress appeared. The most significant of these failures were caused by deficiencies in interface areas; that is, the launch vehicle-spacecraft interface area on the Little Joe 5 and 5A flights and the MA-1 mission, and the launch vehicle-ground-equipment interface during the MR-1 launch. These emphasized the need for close examination of the areas between systems that could not be completely qualified during ground simulation tests.

The seven Little Joe test vehicles proved to be effective and reliable tools for the project. They were relatively inexpensive, they were easy to prepare for launching, and they provided performance that generally matched the different mission requirements very closely, particularly for such an unsophisticated system. Where differences did occur because of launch-vehicle anomalies, they fortunately resulted in more severe qualification conditions that were successfully passed by the test articles.

The performance of the Mercury-Redstone launch vehicle proved the applicability and effectiveness of the changes made for manned flight. Systems anomalies did occur during the unmanned qualification flights without causing serious consequences. During the MR-2 mission, an anomaly in the launch-vehicle engine, when the thrust-regulation subsystem caused unplanned fuel depletion, proved the effectiveness of the automatic abort-sensing system by commanding an abort. Subsequent changes resulted in near perfect performance for each of the manned ballistic space flights.

Similarly, the performance of the Mercury-Atlas launch vehicle confirmed the effectiveness of the changes made to man-rate that tactical missile; even the catastrophic failures in the MA-1 and MA-3 missions proved the proper operation of the automatic failure-sensing system. Excellent performance by the last six of the Mercury-Atlas launch vehicles in succession appears almost unbelievable when the exacting performance requirements of each of these orbital missions is considered. Also, the sheer complexity of each launch vehicle should be noted because each of the hundreds of thousands of components had to work as required to accomplish each mission. A notable exception was the MA-3 mission where analysis indicated that a failure of a single electrical signal could have been the reason for the failure of the launch vehicle to follow the prescribed path.

The performance of the Mercury spacecraft itself through all of the missions was very satisfactory, particularly when cognizance is taken of the strenuous qualification flights that were made and of the fact that the new flight environment of weightlessness was maintained for appreciable periods for the first time. Some spacecraft components and system failures did occur during these missions; however, the significance of these failures was minimized by pilot use of redundant systems. All manned missions were accomplished as planned. The performance of the spacecraft systems must be considered excellent, even with some component failures, when it is noted that each spacecraft consisted of more than 80,000 nonstructural parts, identifiable by part number. Also, there were almost a quarter of a million solder joints and 600 plumbing connections that had to maintain their integrity for the mission to be accomplished.

In general, the performance of those spacecraft systems included in the area of rocket technology performed very well. All of the solid-propellant rocket motors performed within tolerance and without failure. The rocket engines, or thrusters, used in the attitude-control system had a number of performance anomalies; however, any mission degradation was successfully attenuated by use of redundant components. As a result of these experiences, specialists have improved design-and-qualification requirements and component selectivity. They have learned also the significance of contamination in the weightless environment and know the importance of avoiding contamination and of protecting against it.

The pace of technological advances in manned space flight continues to demand our greatest skill and ingenuity for the difficult tasks ahead. In the words of Dr. Hugh L. Dryden, Deputy Administrator of NASA, "Mercury was only a first step in the development of American space transportation. . . . Yet it offers us a catalog of processes by which man progresses from ideas originating in the human mind to the physical devices for man's travel to the moon and beyond." [28] When the full history of Project Mercury is available the use as well as the further development of rocket technology thereby accomplished will be more completely detailed.

[28] In the Foreword to *Project Mercury—A Chronology* (Washington, D. C., NASA SP-4001, 1963), p. v. Attention of the reader is also invited to the appendices of this volume which summarize the following: time-graph of Project Mercury History; Test Objectives; Flight-Data Summary; Launch-Site Summary; Budget Summary; Key-Management Progression; Contractors and Sub-contractors; and Government Agencies.

The First Rocket-Belt

ROBERT D. ROACH, JR.*

ONE OF MAN's ageless dreams—unencumbered free-flight by a man utilizing an integrated propulsion system—was realized on April 20, 1961. Early that chilly morning, a small dedicated group of men gathered on the fringes of Niagara Falls Airport, New York. Here in a community better known for its scenic display, engineers of many disciplines had long worked for the demonstration of man's first controlled, individual free-flight with a rocket-belt. A conquest of nature's physical constraints, man's first rocket-belt flight, traversing more than 100 feet at an altitude best measured in inches, was the culmination of an eight-month development program conducted by Bell Aerosystems Company for the United States Army Transportation Research Command.

The desire to fly has appealed to man since he first noticed the birds and the flight of objects thrown through the air, and harbored the thought of reaching the heavenly bodies. A well-known legend of personal flight tells of Daedalus and Icarus who tried to fly with wings constructed of feathers and wax. Early inventors experimented with kites, gliders, flapping wings.[1] Leonardo da Vinci conceived a fundamental helicopter design; Cyrano de Bergerac, Jonathan Swift, and, later, Jules Verne described concepts of aircraft and spacecraft, as is well known. Free flight with lighter-than-air craft was achieved by the Montgolfier Brothers in 1783. Powered flight of a heavier-than-air craft did not occur for another 120 years, until the Wright brothers made the first controlled airplane flights in 1903. Now, at the dawn of the space age, it was almost ironic that man would pause to fill in one

* Mr. Roach of the Rockets Department of Textron's Bell Aerosystems Co. (Buffalo, N. Y.) has been associated with the rocket industry for over 12 years. From 1950 to 1952 he was Supervisor of the Solid Propellant Analytical Laboratory at Picatinny Arsenal; he joined Bell Aerosystems in 1952 as a rocket project engineer, working with both solid and liquid-fuel rockets and missiles. He is the author of numerous technical papers.

This article received Honorable Mention in the Robert H. Goddard Historical Essay Competition for 1962, sponsored by the National Space Club, Washington, D. C.

[1] Cf. Lynn White, Jr., "Eilmer of Malmesbury, an Eleventh Century Aviator," *Technology and Culture*, Vol. II (Spring 1961), pp. 97-111.

of the blanks in flight achievement that had been passed over in the rapid aeronautical and astronautical progress of the twentieth century.

Recent previous attempts to provide personal propulsion had centered in flying platforms and one-man helicopters. The thought of affixing a rocket to a man's back was neither new nor untried by the time Wendell F. Moore, a rocket engineer at Bell Aerosystems Company, first gave it serious thought in 1953.[2] During the heyday of amateur rocketry in Germany in the 1930's an enterprising, fearless young man, outfitted with a rocket on his back, attempted to zoom through the streets on roller skates. The bruises and burns he sustained from being cartwheeled and dragged across the ground discouraged further rocket excursions by roller-skaters.

But Wendell Moore wasn't considering using wheels or skates. His idea was to join man with rocket and accomplish flight on this integrated man-machine suported by the rocket thrust alone. Assigned to Bell's X-airplane programs (for the U.S. Air Force and the National Advisory Committee on Aeronautics) at Edwards Air Force Base in California, Moore had scratched the first "engineering drawings" of the rocket belt in the desert sands with a pointed stick, while he discussed his concepts with Jim Powell, Bell's flight research engineer for the X-2 rocket-powered research aircraft.

Man is not a very stable flying object! Therefore, stability and control actually presented a much more severe technical challenge than the development of the rocket propulsion system. In order to obtain basic information on stability characteristics, to determine where the thrust nozzles should be positioned, and to what portion of the human body the lift force should be attached, a nitrogen gas test rig was first constructed. Made entirely of steel tubing, the test rig had two underarm stirrups to lift the operator. A flexible hose, draped over a 15-foot high support, delivered the nitrogen to the tubing at a point above and behind the operator's head. From there, the flow was divided equally to both sides of the man at approximately shoulder height, where two downward-pointing tubes were fitted with flow-control orifices.

Operation of the device was controlled by a test engineer on the

---

[2] Source material for this article was the technical and informational reports and papers of the SRLD (Small Rocket Lift Device) program, as well as select interviews. The author conducted personal interviews with the following: Wendell F. Moore, SRLD Technical Director; Edward Ganczak, SRLD Project Engineer; Harold M. Graham, Jr., SRLD Operator; Dr. F. Tyler Kelly, Bell Aerosystems Plant Physician; Ralph E. Flexman, Bell Aerosystems Human Factors Engineer; and Ernest Kreutinger, SRLD Crew Chief.

ground with a valve which increased or decreased nitrogen flow through the lift device nozzles. The experimental system was crude, and its limitations were readily discernible: the flex hose would restrain the freedom of movement of the rig; the nozzles might be mismatched thrust-wise; and the operator could only attempt to control in one plane—pitch—by means of arm pieces attached to the tubing to permit rotation of the rig about his shoulderline.

On a cold day in the winter of 1958, with ropes tied about his waist and lines from them running fore and aft to several stalwart gentlemen, in order to control any violent maneuver, Wendell Moore signaled thumbs-up—"take it on up." The blast was ear-shattering. The dust really flew. The control valve was a bit too coarse in furnishing thrust corrections, thus resulting in some rapid up-and-down maneuvers. But, it was a beginning. Jim Powell then took a turn at it and tried to move fore and aft by tilting his arm-control levers. The success of such maneuvers was not readily measured because of all of the rope and flex hose restraints. At this point, one very important factor in the philosophy of flight by a man-rocket was dramatically portrayed for the group at the test site.

Jim Powell had been through a check-out ride on the jet platform with which the National Advisory Committee for Aeronautics had been experimenting at Langley, Va. He reported that for movement fore and aft or to the sides, it almost sufficed to "think" about the direction of travel in order to move that way.

When another Bell engineer, one with firm convictions of the instability of such a man-machine configuration, attempted to "fly" the nitrogen test rig, he made repeated attempts to get up to an altitude of several feet. Each time he went through violent side-to-side swings accompanied by over-corrective foot motions which only aggravated the condition of instability. His flying-belt career drew to a close quickly when on one violent side swing, he dashed himself against the wall! Fortunately, he was not injured, but he was more convinced than ever that the arrangement was unstable. Then the Bell motion picture photographer who had been recording the tests, Tom Lennon, volunteered to take a brief ride in the "rig."

Lennon gave the "thumbs-up" signal, and away he went—five, ten, almost 15 feet into the air—up, then down; up again, down and up for the next three minutes without the slightest hint of instability. This experience, with different operators with the same equipment and identical test conditions, indicated that even though a stable configuration might be forthcoming in the actual rocket belt designs, the psychological attitude of the operator himself would play a significant role in success or failure of the test.

The early work with the nitrogen rig established the feasibility of underarm lifting for a rocket belt and hinted that stable operation could be achieved. Some insight on proper nozzle location was gained when one rocket engineer managed to have the sleeves of his sport coat unraveled by the jet blast while he was in flight. The hazard would be much greater, of course, when the hot gases from an actual rocket were employed in the prototype designs. So, the nozzles were deployed further from the operator's body and canted outward in subsequent designs.

U. S. Army interest in the rocket belt began to mount about this time. While Wendell Moore and Jim Powell took up other assignments for Bell in Baltimore, Maryland, the Army requested proposals for a study program of a Small Rocket Lift Device (SRLD).[3] A contract for the study program went to Aerojet-General Corporation.[4] By the time that the study program was complete, the configuration for a SRLD for manned flight had been defined. Wendell Moore, now back at Bell's main plant, rekindled Bell's interest in the next phase of the U. S. Army's program. Phase II was to be the fabrication of the SRLD and a manned flight program, first on a tether (safety harness) for safety and experience, then finally to negotiate free and controlled flight.

A contract award was received by Bell Aerosystems from U. S. Army TRECOM (Transportation, Research and Engineering Command) in August 1960.[5] Project Officer for the Army was Robert Graham. This was to be a minimum cost feasibility program. Wendell Moore, now technical director for Bell's SRLD program, set out to use proven "shelf" items such as oxygen breathing bottles, for propellant and pressurant tanks. Moore was an inspired man—the job was one that he wanted, earned, and cherished; this was not just an ordinary, run-of-the-mill engineering assignment. Moore selected Eddie Ganczak, as the Project Engineer, and Ernie Kreutinger, as the rocket technician and general "man-Friday." Others, too numerous to mention, participated throughout the development program.

Initial SRLD design configurations were compatible with the

[3] Bell Aerosystems Company, "Proposal for a Study of Small Rocket Lift Devices" (Report No. R8085-945-001, June 1959).

[4] Aerojet-General Corporation, "Feasibility Study of a Small Rocket Lift Device" (Final Report No. 1751, Feb. 1960).

[5] Bell Aerosystems Company, "Proposal for Small Rocket Lift Device" (Final Report No. D8123-953001, April 1960).

recommendation of the Aerojet study, and so, with approval of the Army, fabrication was initiated. A 280-lb. thrust rocket motor was constructed and tested; this unit would supply hot gas to the nozzles on each side of the SRLD. A throttle valve, resembling the one designed for use by the astronaut in the Mercury Capsule manual reaction-control system, was selected as controller device. The valve was operated through cable linkage with a squeeze throttle located on the operator's right armrest. The left armrest was fitted with levers to operate jetavator-type gas deflectors around the nozzles, to effect yaw control.

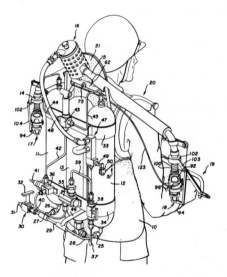

Fig. 32 Detail of first rocket-belt propulsion unit (Bell Aerosystems, U. S. Patent 3,021,095 for a controllable rocket propulsion device, February 13, 1962)

Mating of all of this machinery with the man was a minor challenge. A major concern was the support of the 125-lb. loaded weight of the propulsion system. A form-fitting fiberglass corset was made to the body contour of the first intended operator—and this, of course, was an honor (at that time a dubious one) reserved for Wendell Moore.

The test program was laid out in a "walk-before-you-run" manner. First, the peroxide rocket was test fired, the control valve was flow tested, and the full system was installed in a rocket test cell with a remote control linkage to operate the throttle. The assembly was allowed to move up and down on guide wires and it was ballasted to equal full launch weight of the man-machine combine. As testing progressed and confidence increased, Wendell Moore positioned the SRLD in a holding fixture and backed up to it so that he could operate the controls from the same position as in flight. Satisfied with the rocket propulsion system, the time had come for the final assembly of this mostly human flying machine.

Donning a special set of protective coveralls and a crash helmet, Moore was carefully tethered at the waist as a safety precaution during tests. Because a lower tether attached to his legs proved too restricting, it was removed and tethered flights continued in the less congested out-of-doors. It was winter, and the rapid condensation of the steam produced billowy white clouds which obscured observation of the operator.

The remaining tethered flights were made in the hangar in which they had originated. After 15 or 20 tethered flights, Wendell Moore had located many bugs in the system. A tendency to yaw (rotation of the operator about his vertical centerline) was one of the most difficult stability problems to overcome. The jetavators gave the best control in the yaw direction. While experimenting with the effects of forceful body movements, Moore would occasionally induce a pendulum movement with his body which could not easily be stopped. During such maneuvers, he adopted a practice of cutting the rocket thrust and allowing himself to be supported and lowered on the tether line.

On one morning test, while he was approximately ten feet above the concrete hangar floor, Moore cut the rocket power, expecting to be safely lowered by the tether. Unbeknown to the flight test crew, the tether line had been sawing back and forth on a sharp metal bracket on the propulsion system. At rocket cut-off, with Moore's full weight on the line, it failed. He fell to the floor sustaining a fractured knee cap. Subsequent permanent grounding deprived Moore of personal fulfillment with his project. He never achieved a free-flight.

Harold Graham, a 27-year old rocket test engineer, volunteered and was selected to fill the breach. Graham had worked with some of the SRLD components and was not entirely unfamiliar with the program. This meant that Graham would start cautiously with tethered flights and gradually build up the experience required for the first free-flight. During 36 tethered flights, Graham conducted final de-bugging flights, practiced landing letdown procedures, and evaluated the installation of additional pads and supports under arm and at the waist as well as an abdominal support plate suggested by Dr. F. Tyler Kelly, the plant physician. Dr. Kelly's contribution soon became known as the "Kelly Belly Plate."

Harold Graham's proficiency and confidence grew with each succeeding flight. On the morning of April 20, 1961, all conditions were "go" for an attempt at free flight. Everyone on the field had an assigned task. Observers were positioned along the flight path, as were motion picture and still photographers. Dr. Kelly was on hand to monitor the operator's vital capacity—and blood pressure and pulse measurements—both before and after the flight. Ed Ganczak ran through the check list, a practice well-defined by experience during 56 previous tests. Ernie Kreutinger stood close by with a hand fire extinguisher to act in the case of fuel leakage and consequent fire hazard.

The check list run-through was now complete. Ganczak accepted the safety locking pin from the throttle control and signalled Harold Graham that he was on his own. The tanks were pressurized, and Graham flexed his arms and back muscles to ascertain familiarity with his 125-lb. propulsion system. He was ready. Whoosh! A short burst to check out the operation of his propulsion system, but only for an instant, and insufficient in thrust to move him. Now, satisfied that both he and the equipment were ready, Graham applied the throttle, rose to a height of about 18 inches and immediately began moving forward at about seven to ten miles per hour.

Rapidly condensing steam in the cold air obscured Graham from view until he began to move along the flight path. Photographers rushed alongside to get an unobscured shot. On a nearby highway, cars came to a rapid halt while amazed early morning travelers became eyewitnesses to a bit of history. When he touched down proudly at the end of his 112-foot flight (eight feet less than the Wright Brothers' first powered flight), Graham had been airborne in free and controlled flight for 13 seconds. Man had begun a new chapter in the conquest of flight!

This, of course, was merely a beginning. A number of flight accomplishments were to follow in the remaining month the initial Army contract was to run. Graham flew up and over a 30-foot hill with an approximate 60-degree slope while maintaining a flight path approximately parallel to the ground at an altitude of three to four feet. He flew across a 12-foot wide stream of water, made circular flight paths, flew over obstacles such as trucks, and slalomed through a course of flags.

The first public demonstration requested by the Army on June 8, 1961, at Fort Eustis, Virginia, brought wide acclaim to this modest SRLD program. While Harold Graham flew over an Army 2-½ ton truck, the G. I. driver relaxing comfortably in the cab, the crowd of several hundred officers, VIP's, and guests watched awestruck. The moment he landed, as with every single SRLD flight that ever had an audience, the crowd broke into spontaneous applause—and Graham's reply was a jaunty salute thrown from his white helmet. Within a week after this first public unveiling, " The Belt," as even the average citizen was calling it, was readied for a performance on the Pentagon lawn. Approximately 30 general officers and an estimated 3,000 other Pentagon workers took a ten-minute break to witness the Army's newest method of mobility on parade. For this particular demonstration, Graham flew high over an Army staff car which had been purposely placed as an obstacle in his flight path. The flight was perfect, the applause thunderous, and—Graham's salute was improving.

Flights conducted in subsequent months were many and varied. To learn more about the stability and control characteristics, test flights were instrumented and data was telemetered to a ground station. Meanwhile, requests were filled, with Army approval, for numerous public appearances throughout the country. Thousands of other requests to demonstrate the rocket belt at state fairs and even on a world-wide tour had to be denied for economic reasons. Company mail contained unsolicited ideas which ranged from totally ridiculous to criminally suspicious. One gentleman demanded his own rocket-belt so that he could put his hands on a $1,000,00 treasure which, he said, could not otherwise be reached. Such a request could not be granted, of course, due to the experimental nature of the SRLD. But one cannot help but wonder whether the walls of Ft. Knox might not have been the obstacle in mind!

Graham went on to complete 83 free flights with the rocket-belt and retired from the program. Although never seriously injured during his tenure, he did have a few bad spills and collected many bruises. Perhaps his most memorable flight was a command performance for President John F. Kennedy at Fort Bragg, North Carolina. As Graham flew from the deck of an off-shore amphibious vehicle to land in front of the President, he tossed off one of his now perfected salutes. The President returned it in fine Navy style.

Interest still runs high in the potential applications of the rocket-belt for tactical and rescue missions by the U. S. Army and others.[6] Now a second generation of rocket belt operators are trained and are continuing the research necessary to make this device a successful military tool. The two current rocket-belt pilots at Bell Aerosystems Company present a study in contrast. Youngest is Peter Kedzierski, 19, who

⁶ U. S. Army Transportation Research Command, " Small Rocket Lift Device," (TCREC Technical Report No. 61-123, Nov. 1961).

finished an aviation mechanics course in a vocational high school and was doing some additional study there when Bell Aerosystems Company selected him for training as a rocket-belt pilot. The second operator, Robert F. Courter, Jr., is a 36-year-old veteran pilot with combat flight experience in World War II and Korea.

For the future, the prospect of more rocket-belts and more trained operators is already beyond the planning stage. Only time will tell the extent of the role to be played by this man-machine mode of flying in the future of man's transportation. Some see it as the answer for the traffic-jammed commuter. Others see humane rescues from points of difficult access.

The 1965-1980 era brings with it a need for man to maneuver himself about in space or on lunar or planetary surfaces. The rocket-belt fulfills these needs. It can be compacted to a light weight installation, for the thrust required for movement through a vacuum at zero gravity is extremely minute.

Preliminary studies have also been completed for a lunar rocket-belt designed specifically for locomotion over the surface of the moon. Such a propulsion system may be integrated with a life-support system, thus giving excellent mobility to a space-suit clad lunar explorer. Already proved on earth, the SRLD requires no further demonstration of feasibility for lunar use. On the other hand, since the support of only one-sixth of earth flight weight is involved, the duration of rocket-belt operation on the moon could be extended to many minutes rather than being limited to seconds. Other concepts for locomotion of a man on the moon are dependent upon the surface characteristics of the moon itself, which are presently undefined. The lunar SRLD may well become man's preferred choice for radial exploration from a spacecraft after landing on the surface of the moon.

Whatever the future, the immediate past was a dream from the dawn of man. The year which saw the first suborbital space flight of a Mercury astronaut—1961—may also be remembered for the first rocket-belt flight.

RELATED TECHNOLOGY

"What is the purpose of a newborn baby? We find out in time."

—*Michael Faraday*

The Origins of Space Telemetry

WILFRID J. MAYO-WELLS*

IN THE HISTORY of rocketry and astronautical research, the common bond of space telemetry and ground-based instrumentation gleams as a thread of continually advancing progress and may well be considered today one of its most vital characteristics. It has been only comparatively recently that the importance of the telemetry and other forms of instrumentation has been recognized along with the longer established and more spectacular fields of rocketry and space flight such as propulsion, guidance, and re-entry. This recognition has recently been assisted by the increasing use of the term "telemetry." Orbital and scientific space missions have effectively demonstrated their dependence upon reliable and accurate instrumentation for ground checkout and on reliable radio telemetry before and after launch.

Telemetering, or as it is today generally written, "telemetry," is the art of measurement at a distance in which the physical quantity being measured is converted to another quantity for transmission to receiving and recording equipments. Space telemetry cannot, however, be fully documented without consideration of the origin of using a wire link in place of the more recent radio link between the transmitter and its accompanying receiver.

Origins of Ground-Based Checkout Instrumentation

Two divisions of space telemetry have been combined into the complex systems of the present programs for manned and un-manned space flights: the ground-based checkout instrumentation and the radio telemetry vehicular and earthbound installations. The former, using largely a line link between the rocket or capsule and the recorders or indicating panels, appears to have had its origins in the early part of

* Mr. Mayo-Wells of the Vitro Corporation of America, Vitro Laboratories Division (Wheaton, Maryland), has been associated with radio, radar, and tele-metering for many years, with the R. A. F. during World War II and the Applied Physics Laboratory of Johns Hopkins University (1945-56). He was a founder of the National Telemetering Conference in 1950.

This article received Honorable Mention in the Robert H. Goddard Historical Essay Competition for 1962, sponsored by the National Space Club, Washington, D. C.

the nineteenth century when, as reported by P. L. Shilling, the Russians telemetered the successful firing of remotely activated mines to stem the French invaders during the War of 1812.[1] The problem of establishing the exact dates of this and subsequent Russian inventions is made more difficult by the order of Tsar Nicholas of April 28, 1844, putting under secret classification all applications of electromagnetic circuits and associated scientific developments. This action resulted in the disappearance of many records, but fortunately, since some of these reports were written in French and German, they escaped detection by the secret police of that time and have found their way to libraries in Europe and America.

European Progress and American Developments

Of direct application to future ground telemetry systems was the establishment[2] by B. S. Yakobi in 1845 of a data transmission circuit between the Tsar's Winter Palace and the Russian Army Headquarters for an exchange of logistic information. Simultaneously, General K. I. Konstantinov with Dr. Poulié developed a telemeter[3] to transmit and record automatically the speed of flight of a cannonball using besides an original relay and a novel rotation speed regulator, the forerunner of the modern commutation-switch with 16 contacts. By 1857 warships were being equipped with electromagnetic signalling[4] between the bridge and engine room and other strategic locations such as the gun emplacements. In 1874, the electrical engineer, Olland, developed a telemetry circuit[5] to transmit three measurements from the slopes of Mont Blanc over the 350 kilometers to Paris utilizing electric impulses applied to the long land line. These early telemetered quantities, or measurands, of snow-depth, temperature, and barometric pressure were displayed on suitable large-diameter dials at a subsequent Paris exhibition and attracted much comment. All these demonstrations of the potential value of telemetry, although they were of great local interest, did not achieve universal appeal in Europe until the next century.

Meantime, in the United States, the first glimmering of future glory

---

[1] *Bulletin de l'Academie de Saint Petersburg*, Vol. 7 Supp. 1 (1864), p. 1; P. F. Mottelay, *Bibliographical History of Electricity and Magnetism* (London, 1922), pp. 420-23.

[2] *Archives de l'Électricité* (Paris and Geneva), vol. 5, (1845), p. 574.

[3] *Journal Ministère Russie Defense*, Vol. 47, Section 7, (1845), p. 25.

[4] B. S. Yakobi, *Bulletin Physico-Mathematique de l'Academie de Saint Petersburg*, Vol. 15, (1857), p. 145.

[5] Olland, *Arch. nederl. Sci.*, Vol. 10 (1874), p. 241; and E. Kleinschmidt, *Handbuch der Meteoroligischen Instrumente* (Berlin, 1935), p. 556.

for American telemetry engineers was indicated by the issue of a patent[6] to P. Moennich in 1889 for the "inductive adjustment of an interrupted current for telemetering."[7] In 1901, C. J. A. Michalke obtained a patent for a position motor which would be considered the father of the present widely-known selsyn and of many servomechanisms employed in today's space vehicles.[8]

Russian developments also continued. In 1906 B. B. Golizen set up an elaborate teleseismic telemetry measuring and recording station at Pulkovo, near Saint Petersburg.[9] This system included such important developments as inductive and induction transmitters for remote transmission of data recorded by sensitive seismographs. At the receiving end Golizen employed moving coil galvanometers. Thus, by 1906, at least in Europe, an ancestor of modern telemetry was beginning to take shape.

For comparable developments in America, we must wait another six years, until in 1912 a paper by O. J. Bliss[10] appeared in the transactions of the young pioneer engineering society, the American Institute of Electrical Engineers, describing an installation of a load dispatching telemeter by the Commonwealth Edison power company at Chicago. With the publication of this paper telemetry may be said to have emerged from the status of a laboratory curiosity to that of a potentially valuable industrial tool. Its future value in research in nearly every field of technical and scientific endeavor, including those connected with space exploration, was as yet unrecognized save by the few exceptionally gifted seers in engineering. In 1913-1914, the opening of the Panama Canal, with its extensive telemetry systems to report water level and other physical phenomena, further emphasized the brilliant future of this new art as evoked in many technical and popular articles.[11]

[6] U. S. Patent 416,006 (1889).

[7] The original term was 'telemetering." The term "telemetry" is synonymous but of later observed origin.

[8] U. S. Patent 684,579 (1901).

[9] B. B. Golizen, *Investia Imperatore Academie Nauk*, Vol. 1, No. 1. (Dec. 13, 1906), p. 45, and "Die elektromagn. Registrier-Methoden" in *St. Petersburg Bulletin de Seism. Komm.*, Vol. 2 (1906). See Pozgendorff, *Biographisch-Literarisches Handworterbuch*, Vol. V (1904-1922), p. 408.

[10] O. J. Bliss, "Electrical Transmission of Electrical Measurements," AIEE *Trans.*, Vol. 31 (1912), pp. 1537-40. See AIEE Reports S-111, Vol. I, Part 3, Bibliography, "Telemetering, Supervisory Systems and Associated Channels," June 1959, p. 37.

[11] C. H. Hill and C. T. Hentschel, *G. E. Review*, Vol. 17 (Jan. 1914), p. 19; also, E. H. Jacobs and H. M. Stevens, *ibid.*, p. 31.

Progress between the Wars

In sharp contrast to the rapid developments in telemetry occasioned by the incessant military demands for better weapon systems in World War II, World War I moved very slowly in telemetry utilization. The weapons were still relatively unsophisticated and scarcely required telemetry systems such as characterize modern rocket and guided missile programs. Only one major development before the restoration of an uneasy peace appears worth noting, namely, the announcement by German engineers in 1918 of the "unbalanced bridge system of telemetering" employing current division, dual rheostatic transmitters, and a symmetrical ratiometer with crossed coils (similar to the World War II goniometer) to telemeter "angular rotating meters." [12]

From 1920 to 1926 rapid advances in telemetry took place on both sides of the Atlantic. Although still largely concerned with the utilities, other applications of the growing art were appearing. Pride of place in the 26 references listed in the *AIEE Telemetering Bibliography* (1959) must go to P. A. Borden's epoch-making paper "Electrical Measurement of Physical Values." [13] Here was the signpost so long delayed since the pioneer efforts of the European engineers in the latter half of the nineteenth century to the first decade of the twentieth, pointing to the future multitudinous measurements of modern telemetry.

The thermal converter first patented in the United States in 1890 [14] by M. E. Thompson serves to illustrate graphically a delayed application. After the patent was granted no further interest was shown in this device until in 1925 it reappeared in a moderately-sized installation in an English power distribution network. Only in 1926 was this now widely used device adopted by the Hydro-Electric Power Commission of Ontario, Canada, for extensive exploitation in their Toronto power systems. [15]

A potential new factor in the fast-growing art of telemetry had been born since the first shots of World War I. Wireless or radiotelegraphy was destined to play a decisive role in the expansion of telemetry to new fields, particularly to the exacting sciences of aeronautics and astronautics. The accounts of the first documented use of

[12] *Brief History of the Development of Telemetering Techniques*, p. 2 (translated from the Russian: *Teleizmerenive Chast 1 Sistemy Intensivnosti*, by G. M. Zhadanov, Moscow-Leningrad, 1952).

[13] P. A. Borden, "Electrical Measurement of Physical Values," *AIEE Trans.* Vol. 44 (1925), pp. 238-63.

[14] U. S. Patents 425,269 and 425,270 (April 8, 1890).

[15] P. A. Borden, *Electr. News* (Toronto, 1926), p. 35. See P. A. Borden & W. J. Mayo-Wells, *Telemetering Systems* (New York, 1959), pp. 4, 31-38.

radio telemetry, which forms the second division of space telemetry, are to be found in two papers [16] by French physicists of the revolutionary experiments with a balloon beginning on the third of March 1927 and continuing through 1932. The initial equipment was called by the two pioneers, R. Bureau and P. Idrac, "une radiosonde," and the first successful measurements were made in 1930 following a period devoted to the improvement of the original transmitter "de faible puissance." [17] It is of considerable interest to learn that this "sonde," and the telemetry chronometric impulse system employed by Olland in his Mont Blanc-to-Paris meteorological relay, formed the precise basis for the radiosonde flown by Dr. A. V. Astin and Dr. L. F. Curtiss in their famous 1936 experiments on the stratosphere.[18] Thus all-unknowingly the two divisions of space telemetry were united in an early experiment only to be widely separated by the security curtain of World War II. This can now be seen to have set back all effective cooperation and to have generated two schools of thought, to the detriment of both fields of telemetry research and development.

Industrial vs. Aircraft/Missile/Ordnance Telemetry

While the industrial and utility telemetry engineers were making rapid strides, in the full glare of publicity, by expanding their systems to serve many new industries as well as by improving their services to the utilities, with the advent of World War II the aircraft/missile/ordnance group were shut in behind closed doors. Here, these classified teams, composed in the main of young graduates or professors direct from college and having only a limited acquaintance with industrial or utility telemetry, developed their own unique technology and used a self-coined terminology among themselves. The "old" notion of 50 cycles per second as an upper limit for frequency response was replaced when need arose for thousands and, ultimately, for millions of cycles per second. Equipment had to be very small, rugged to withstand unaccustomed forces and conditions, and reliable for a brief exciting

[16] R. Bureau, "Sondages par ballons munis d'un émetteur radioélectrique," *La Météorologie* (Sept. 1931); A. Corriez, & A. Perlat, "La methode radiogoniometrique de l'onm pour la mesure de la direction et la vitesse due vent par temps couvert," *La Météorologie* (Aug. 1935).

[17] Private letter, A. Perlat to the author, (Paris, 1 June 1959).

[18] L. F. Curtiss & A. V. Astin, "High Altitude Stratosphere Observations," *Science*, Vol. 83 (1 May 1936), pp. 411-12 and A. V. Astin & L. L. Stockmann, "Receiver for Radio-Meteorograph," *Rev. Sci. Inf.*, Vol. 7 (Dec. 1936), p. 462; L. F. Curtis & A. V. Astin, *Journal of the Aeronautical Sciences*, Vol. 3 (Nov. 1935), p. 35; L. F. Curtis & A. V. Astin, L. L. Stockmann & B. W. Brown, *Jo. Res. Bu. Stds.*, Vol. 22 (Jan. 1939), p. 97.

life of at most a few minutes. Heavy, long-life, slow-operating units, as used by the industrial and utility group, could not be tolerated in a world where space was limited almost to the point of absurdity and where telemetry was a "necessary nuisance" to be tolerated only so long as the vehicle was experimental or the equipment remained unproven. Telemetry engineers were a "service" group with no operational future; they were at the base of the totem pole in the weapon system's research and development hierarchy with little say as to the course of their own programs or as to the direction of their advanced planning for research.

In this compartmented atmosphere, it was inevitable that much duplication of effort should result from a lack of intercommunication between teams working on related projects but separated by the prevalent wartime security regulations. It was not until 1948, when the National Telemetering Forum was formed, that a regular attempt was made to effect the desired information exchanges, although isolated attempts such as the Princeton University's Palmer Laboratory Conference of 1946 had been made from time to time.[19]

Altogether some 50 independent airborne telemetry systems were evolved, plaguing the test field facilities which were expected to provide receiving and recording stations to accept any one of these systems. Rivalry centered in the selection of a standard system, and fierce arguments arose defending the use of a variable frequency or a variable pulse as the physical characteristic to be transmitted as representing the value of the measured quantity at all times. These two systems, known as "frequency division" and "time division modulation" respectively, are applied to the radio frequency carrier signal just as speech, music, or pictures are transferred in radio and television broadcasting. With the frequency system the modulation can be considered as a bunch of tones, known as subcarrier bands, transmitted simultaneously and each varying according to a specific measured quantity. In the pulse system, a train of pulses is transmitted sequentially, each pulse being modified in accordance with the changes in a specific measurement and each quantity being sampled in turn.

The First FM/FM Telemetry System

Early in the war effort, the Princeton Palmer Laboratory had produced and employed the first frequency modulated sub-carrier telemeter in conjunction with a radio transmitter to measure the aero-

---

[19] *Bumblebee Report on 1946 Telemetering Conference* (No. 42) at Princeton, Feb. 19 & 20, and at APL, Dec. 10, 1946 (Declassified 8 July 1954).

dynamic characteristics of a test vehicle in flight. This pioneering installation first transmitted two, and subsequently four, acceleration and pressure channels, using one sub-carrier band for each; it was the forerunner of the standard 18-band system for modern FM/FM telemetry used in the space program. One of the first organizations to adopt the Palmer system was the Applied Physics Laboratory of the Johns Hopkins University. Working on the series of Bumblebee guided missiles for the defense of the U. S. Navy, under the authority of the Bureau of Ordnance, this laboratory rapidly expanded the original plan of four sub-carrier bands first to a six, and later to a ten, sub-carrier band system. At the same time it developed new pickup devices, or transducers, to accommodate new measurements such as temperature, vibration, roll, linear motion, rotary motion, and even to transmit the high frequency signals present in the guidance beams. These new units were tested in various types of flight vehicles, each engaged in a special series of experiments, such as ones on guidance, propulsion, aerodynamics, or control. It is highly significant that scarcely ever was it necessary to flight test a vehicle for the sole purpose of proving out a new telemeter unit or device, although new components did occasionally take a ride for their testing as an additional load item for a vehicle under test.[20] Concurrently in other laboratories throughout the land, many other telemetry systems were evolved as described in Dr. S. F. Brinster's declassified report of 1947.[21]

Keeping pace with these airborne telemetry advances, the ground station equipment had been continuously improved and its versatility increased.[22] Recording techniques especially had progressed from the early disc recorder similar to the phonograph record cutting machine to the magnetic oscillograph and magnetic tape recorder. With these developments had come a capability to record ever increasing frequen-

[20] H. W. Haas, " Telemetering Notch Antenna 225.0 mc/sec Aerobee Hi Rocket," New Mexico College of Agriculture & Mechanical Arts Paper (February 1956).

[21] J. F. Brinster, " A Survey Report of Telemetry," The Johns Hopkins University (Prepared for the U. S. Navy, Bureau of Ordnance, and Applied Physics Laboratory), May 1947.

[22] G. S. Sloughter and R. T. Ellis. " Linear Discrimination for FM Telemetering," *Electronics*, Vol. 24 (June 1951), pp. 112-15; L. L. Rauch and C. E. Howe, " Filters for Telemetry," *National Telemetering Conference Record* (1953), pp. 159-76; M. S. Redden, Jr. and H. W. Zancanata, " A New Crystal-Controlled Ground Station Telemetering Receiver," *National Telemetering Conference Record* (1955), p. 127; C. E. Gilchrist, " Application of the Phase-Locked Loop to Telemetry as a Discriminator or Tracking Filter," *IRE Trans.* (TRC-4) (June 1958), pp. 20-35.

cies until the 100,000 cycles per second limit of the 70 kc. sub-carrier band had been successfully stored and reproduced as a visible recording. New antenna designs,[23] including the notch, turnstile, and helical beams, had raised the gain of both airborne and receiving aerial systems to increase greatly signal reception reliability and the range of satisfactory transmissions. Most of these developments were never reported in the technical press but rather were disclosed at meetings in the form of conference papers. However, they are to be found in greater numbers after 1948 in the 11 classified volumes of the National Telemetering Forum's *Minutes*[24] and, commencing in 1950, in the published minutes of the National Telemetering Conference.[25]

Cooperative Efforts

Early in its second year of operation, the National Telemetering Forum was rudely awakened by an anguished cry from the AIEE Telemetering Committee, which angrily demanded an explanation of the Forum's existence and its use of the word "telemetering" in its title, since the Committee had heard it was a "space radio organization"! At once a meeting was arranged for Good Friday at the AIEE Headquarters in New York and resulted, in the words of the chief AIEE delegate, Mr. Perry Borden, "in the formation of a beautiful friendship" between that delegate and the Forum's chairman. From this humble beginning arose the ultimate reunion between the industrial and missile/ordnance telemetry groups, the invaluable exchange of ideas, and the restarting of the undivided space telemetry national effort, begun long ago with Dr. Astin's stratospheric sondes.

The missile group learned with considerable surprise of the advanced state of the telemetry art as represented in the industrial applications. A glance at the AIEE Bibliography[26] shows the startling increase from eight references in 1927, through 34 in 1936, to 56 in 1948. Both groups had utilized the commutating-switch for sampling measurements in sequence, to supplement the continuous channel systems, and had developed the same five major modulation systems—although their terminologies were often different.

[23] J. D. Kraus, "Helical Beam Antennas for Wide-Band Application," *Proc. IRE*, Vol. 36 (1948), p. 1236.

[24] *Minutes of National Telemetering Forum, 1948-1950.*

[25] "Problems of Telemetry Data Analysis," B. S. Benson. Joint AIEE/NTF Conference on Telemetering 1950, *AIEE Special Publication S-41* (August 1950), pp. 201-04; L. M. Biberman, "The Sun as a Primary Reference for Internal Instrumentation of Rockets." *Ibid.*, pp. 173-76.

[26] *AIEE Report S-111*, Vol. I, Part 3, pp. 37-43.

New environments and new data needs in many fields, such as nuclear power plants, oceanographic studies, biomedical and space research, were demanding ever increasing capabilities and strength in the new telemeters and their associated equipment. These new requirements led to the development of radical test facilities, both to simulate and to test for performance in different environments of single physical conditions, or combined groups of physical conditions such as are found in an orbiting capsule or a re-entering space vehicle. The National Bureau of Standards extended its range of testing facilities to include these new environments and stepped up efforts to develop improved standards for the manufacturers of space vehicles and systems equipment.[27] Surveys were made by the Aerospace Industries Association [28] of the needs and availabilities of these standards and of techniques for precision measurements necessary to achieve a greatly increased reliability factor for space flight. In all these activities the space telemetry industries played an increasingly important role as the conditions at the measurement point grew more formidable for common materials, not to mention for the human observer.

An indication of the growing recognition of telemetry in national weapon systems development was the issuance of standards by the Committee on Guided Missiles of the Research and Development Board (RDB) of the Department of Defense.[29] In the establishment of these initial standards for radio telemetry, the Applied Physics Laboratory played an important part. Their contribution was enhanced by the initial publication of a telemetry handbook and of a carefully organized and monitored program of industrial production by the contractors to the U. S. Navy.[30] The original standards were in two parts: one for an 18-band sub-carrier system, and one for a pulse width modulated system. Commutation schedules for each system were in-

---

[27] R. D. Smith and P. S. Lederer, " The Shock Tube as a Facility for the Dynamic Testing of Pressure Pickups," NBS Paper for AIEE Pacific General Meeting (June 1959); T. A. Perls and C. W. Kissinger, " High-g Accelerometer Calibrations by Impact Methods with Ballistic Pendulum, Air Gun, and Inclined Trough," NBS Paper for *ISA Weekly*, Pittsburgh (March 1955); W. A. Wildhack and R. O. Smith, " A Basic Method of Determining the Dynamic Characteristics of Accelerometers by Rotation," NBS Paper for *ISA Weekly*, Pittsburgh (March 1955).

[28] " Industry Calibration Survey," Feb. 1961.

[29] Telemetering Standards, RDB Working Group for Telemetry of the Panel on Test Ranges and Instrumentation of the Committee on Guided Missiles (May 1948).

[30] *The FM/FM Telemetering Handbook*, published by the U. S. Navy Bureau of Ordnance and compiled jointly by the Johns Hopkins University APL and the Bendix Aviation Corporation, Pacific Division (1954).

cluded. These standards were revised several times until the Board's dissolution in 1951, just after the latest revision.[31]

Following the RDB work, a new authority known as the Inter-Range Instrumentation Group of the Range Commander's Conference took over; its first revised recommended standards were published soon after its establishment.[32] These six standards have now been combined and issued [33] with a glossary of terms used in the standards together with the revised version of Telemetry Frequency Utilization Parameters and Criteria (IRIG Document #101-59 revised) of the Frequency Coordination Working Group.

Early Pulsed Radio Telemetry Systems

As early as 1946, the Palmer Laboratory at Princeton had developed and tested two pulse systems for Pulse Amplitude Modulated (PAM) telemetry under a National Defense Research Council contract. Dr. M. H. Nichols, leader of this project, has described the high-speed electronic commutating circuit employed in one of these systems to switch 21 channels at a rate of 20,000 samples per second or at a frame rate of 952 per second.[34] The Applied Physics Laboratory also introduced PAM/FM modulation to telemeter a considerable number of low frequency channels on a single sub-carrier band for their propulsion test vehicles.[35] Subsequently, in 1947, the Naval Research Laboratory published details of V-2 Rocket experimental flights utilizing two types of Pulse Position modulation (PPM) telemetry.[36] PPM/AM telemetry was also used successfully with coincidence radiation counters in Aerobee and Viking launchings.

The Applied Science Corporation of Princeton had by 1948 tried to secure equal recognition with FM/FM telemetry of their Pulse Dura-

[31] MTRI 204/6 Telemetering Standards RBD g. v.

[32] IRIG Recommendation No. 101-55, Testing for Speed Errors in Instrumentation-Type Magnetic Tape Recorders; 101-57, Magnetic Recorder/Reproducer Standards; 101-60; Magnetic Recorder/Reproducer Standards; 102-55, Telemetry Standards for Guided Missiles; 102-56, Standards for Pulse Code Modulation (PCM) Telemetry; 102-59, Revised Telemetry Standards for Guided Missiles.

[33] IRIG Document 160-60, approved Nov. 1960. Secretariat IRIG, White Sands Proving Ground N. M. of the Panel on Test Ranges and Instrumentation.

[34] M. H. Nichols and L. L. Ranch, *Radio Telemetry* (2nd edn., New York, 1956), p. 274.

[35] W. J. Mayo-Wells, *Telle-Tech and Electronic Industries*, Vol. 13 (Jan. 1954), p. 85.

[36] V. L. Heeren, C. H. Koeppner, J. R. Kauke, S. W. Lichtman and P. R. Shifflet, "Telemetering from V-2 Rockets Electronics," Vol. 20 (Mar. 1947), pp. 100-05 and (Apr. 1947), pp. 124-27.

tion (Width) modulation (PDM or PWM) telemetry system, designed to transmit economically a large number of relatively low frequency channels.[37] For this reason, and to avoid further controversy, the RDB standard included a section of PDM telemetry. All these systems closely paralleled the industrial telemetry impulse modulated installations which had been in use for many years.[38] Of these the Bristol Metameter is probably the most universally used impulse-duration telemeter in space telemetry installations, along with the Leeds and Northrup Micromax. The latter employs the self-balancing potentiometer invented by the German engineer, G. Keinath, and reported by him in a series of papers in the German technical press.[39]

A radically new development, resulting from the use of digital signals for high speed automatic computation, was the Pulse code modulation (PCM) technique for telemetry. An early system, of PCH, was developed at Melpar Inc. by B. D. Smith and reported by him at the 1953 National Telemetering Conference.[40] A very complete series of papers were presented three years later at the Dayton Airborne Electronics meeting by which time a number of telemetry system's manufacturers were actively engaged in PCM production.[41] Of special note is the AN/AKT-14 equipment built by Radiation Inc. for the Air Force. The importance of this new modulation was recognized after another three years development by the IRIG, which issued a tentative standard for range launchings in 1959.[42] This was revised in November 1960 after consideration by the National Telemetering Conference's Standards Committee and reissued in December of the same year.

[37] P. A. Borden and W. J. Mayo-Wells, *Telemetering Systems* (New York, 1959), pp. 101-03.

[38] B. H. Smith and A. R. Rutter, *Trans. AIEE*, Vol. 43 (1924), p. 297; B. H. Smith, *Electrical Journal*, Vol. 21, (1924), p. 355; F. B. Bristol and G. S. Lunfe, *G. E. Review*, Vol. 42 (1939), p. 584.

[39] G. Keinath, " Electrical Remote Recording Methods " (in German), *Electrotech.*, Vol. 50 (1924), p. 1509; " Telemetering of Electrical Quantities " (in German), *Messtechnik*, Vol. 4 (Apr. 22, 1928), p. 85; "Electrical Remote Recording " (in German), *Electrotech. v. Nasch*, Vol. 46 (Nov. 11, 1928), p. 1058.

[40] B. D. Smith, " A PCM Telemetering System," *National Telemetering Conference Record* (1953), pp. 194-98.

[41] G. S. Shaw, R. P. Bishop, D. C. Howard, J. A. Petersen, C. A. Campbell, and G. F. Anderson, *IRE Transactions on Telemetry and Remote Control*, TRC-2, Vol. 1 (1956), p. 5.

[42] Telemetry Standards (Document Number 106-60), IRIG (December 1960).

Telemetry for the First Earth Satellite

When the Vanguard program was inaugurated at the Naval Research Laboratory, it was realized that the exceptional requirements for the first U. S. satellites—extremely small size, low power drain, and long-life reliability, but coupled with considerable data capacity—could not be met with existing systems. It was accordingly decided to design a new modulation technique [43] utilizing magnetic cores [44] and other novel components of great reliability and simplicity. This system was ultimately called Pulse Frequency Modulation (PFM) and should not be confused with earlier techniques of the industrial engineers whose PFM system was quite different. It has since been used in a large number of NASA programs, both for early satellites and space probes. A particularly notable achievement was its use in the International ARIEL (UK-1) Satellite jointly prepared by four British Universities and the NASA Goddard Space Flight Center.[45] This unit is still transmitting enormous volumes of data from 63 channels, some of which are transmitted continuously while others are recorded on a miniature tape recorder installed in the vehicle. On command from the ground, the tape recording system is switched to the " playback " mode, and the stored data, with its frequency of playing multiplied 48 times, is transmitted in the intervals between the continuous data.

Concurrently with the designs for spaceborne earth satellite telemetry, radical new systems were developed for the accompanying ground-station network. A series of telemetry ground stations located alongside minitrack tracking [46] stations, and embodying data relay facilities for retransmission of received information to NASA network center, were constructed around the world. These stations employ the latest techniques and devices to insure reliable reception of the precious telemetry signals, which carry the " pay-off data " of each space mission.

[43] W. Mathews, "Earth Satellite Instrumentation Program," *National Telemetering Conference Report* 1-A-1 (1957); also, "Earth Satellite Instrumentation," *Elec. Engineering*, Vol. 76 (July 1957), p. 562, and "Telemetering in Earth Satellites," *Ibid.* (Nov. 1957), p. 976.

[44] R. W. Rochelle, "Earth Satellite Telemetry Coding System using Transistors and Magnetic Cores," *National Telemetering Conference Report 1-A-3* (1957); also "Earth Satellite Telemetry Coding System," *Elec. Engineering, Vol.* 76 (Dec. 1957), p. 1062.

[45] Charles LaFond, "UK-1 Satellite Turns up Surprises—Joint US-UK Ionospheric Explorer indicates Atmosphere Hotter at High Latitudes; a Detailed Report," *Missiles and Rockets*, Vol. 11 (July 16, 1962), pp. 3, 26.

[46] R. L. Easton, "The Mark II Minitrack System," *Project Vanguard Report* No. 21. Minitrack Report No. 2, *Journal Brit. Interplan. Soc.*, Vol. 16 (May-June 1959), p. 390.

The Problems of Longer Flights and Greater Ranges

As the time of flight and ranges for transmissions were greatly increased, new problems arose both at the transmitter and receiver locations. At the National Telemetry Conference in Denver in 1959, Eberhardt Rechtin of the Jet Propulsion Laboratory, Pasadena, presented a status report and forecast of the telemetry transmission problem.[47] Rechtin prepared the following table on "Long Term System Capabilities":

Characteristic	1958	1960	1962
Transmitter Power	0.1 watt	10 watts	100 watts
Vehicle antenna gain	6 db	16 db	36 db
Receiver sensitivity (Noise temperature)	2000° K	400° K	40° K

Information Bandwidth for S/N = 10 and above characteristic values:

	1958	1960	1962
1. Satellite Installation	0.6 mc/s	10 mc/s	10 mc/s
2. Lunar application	60 mc/s	0.3 mc/s	10 mc/s
3. Mars application	————	30 cps	0.3 mc/s
4. Edge of Solar System	————	————	30 cps

The projected pace of development toward these capabilities has been exceeded in the intervening years, especially for the receiver noise improvement where the use of masers has already resulted in receiver noise temperatures of less than 10° K. The Mariner R telemetry successfully negotiated 36 million miles of space to transmit at the rate of eight bits per second. It proved its capability to be 33 bits per second, which more than meets the 1959 prediction by extrapolation.

With the long life times, reliability becomes a very serious consideration. The practice of redundancy is one possible answer. Operation at only long intervals and for very short duration during the outward flight is another. However, non-operative shelf-life failures would appear to rule out cold storage until the "target" planet is approached. In addition, there may be transistor or tube "sleeping sickness," which occurs in a bi-stable element which is allowed to remain in one state too long; on excitation the device does not respond, and so switching action to the alternate state is not achieved.

[47] E. Rechtin, "Communication Techniques for Space Exploration," California Institute of Technology, *The Realities of Space Exploration Colloquium* (March 20, 1959).

Most serious of all problems, however, is that of distinguishing and reading the signal through the galactic, solar, and atmospheric noise. Frequently it is a severe task to decide whether the signal received is a noisy but true signal or just noise with a signal-like characteristic! Modern pseudo-noise and orthogonal coding techniques used in conjunction with biphase modulation and auto-correlation circuits have gone far to overcome this difficult problem.[48] However, as the missions are further extended the same problems will return to plague the engineers; for example, in telemetering from the planets orbiting beyond the sun, the transmission loss will exceed 300 dbs for radio waves.

Although the single radio transmitter-multichannel telemetry used in modern spacecraft boosters represents a great advance on the two-channel systems used by Bureau, and later the Palmer Laboratory, the number of measurements for future spacecraft boosters is an order of magnitude higher. Thus for the early Saturn booster tests, ten radio frequency transmitters are planned employing four of the previously described modulation techniques and, in addition, the use of Single Side Band FM (SS/FM).[49] This development of Marshall Space Flight Center creates a single side band with suppressed carrier, as in the well-known commercial UHF transmitting systems, and uses this signal to modulate an FM transmitter. In all, 603 measurements are planned for Saturn I and 613 for Saturn II. Ground testing will be even more complex with 743 measurements to be recorded. Recorders will be of four types, namely Digital (368), Stripchart (195), Oscillograph (475), and magnetic tape (82).[50]

Biomedical Telemetry and Manned Space Flight

No history of space telemetry would be complete without the inclusion of a short section on biomedical telemetry. Just as telemetry is an essential part of the space program, so biomedical telemetry is vital for the manned space flights. Without the continuous monitoring of the physiological conditions of the astronaut, the margin of safety for his life would not be adequate to justify the risk involved. Moreover, during his extensive training and preparation, the astronaut must be

[48] C. C. Kirsten, " Interplanetary Telemetry," Paper delivered before Washington IRE-PGSET (October 30, 1962).

[49] Walter O. Frost, " A New Telemetry Technique," Marshall Space Flight Center Papers No. MTP-G and C-1-61-39 (October 16, 1961).

[50] The numbers in parenthesis give the number of channels on this type of recorder.

constantly supervised by telemetric measuring devices for his heart beat, pulse, temperature, and other physiologic characteristics.

At a conference on Physics and Medicine of the Upper Atmosphere, several members of the USAF School of Aviation Medicine at San Antonio presented papers on space medicine.[51] The first reference in the AIEE Telemetering Bibliography is of a radio cardiograph in a French journal in 1956.[52] Dr. B. Jacobson of Sweden was already at work on his endoradiosondes, minute telemetry transmitters designed to be swallowed.[53] Once in the stomach the battery would be activated and certain physiologic measurements would be transmitted. By the time of the National Telemetering Conference of 1958, when the first Biomedical Session was held, many other telemetry devices for medical research[54] and monitoring had been developed. The Systems Research Laboratory of Dayton developed for the Air Force an automatic blood pressure measuring device for pilots which performs all the steps of the usual manual operation in 10-15 seconds and records the calculated blood pressure. The principles are identical to those of a large rack-mounted equipment developed at the NBS under Dr. Broida a little earlier, but the whole instrument has been rigorously miniaturized.

In 1961 another Biomedical Session at the National Telemetering Conference revealed the great progress made since 1958. Research instruments for astronauts had been constructed[55] using Pulse Position Modulation (PPM) transmitting six channels with 40 cycles per second frequency response each. The personal telemetry must be lightweight (less than 30 ozs.) and use very little power (113 m watt). Measurements included EKG, respiration, and body temperature. EEG data, especially the α-wave, are of great value in selecting astronauts, and Vector has developed a three-channel package[56] for EEG, EKG, and respiration designed to fit in the space occupied by a crash helmet.

[51] Clayton S. White and Brig. General Otis O. Benson, Jr., eds. *Physics and Medicine of the Upper Atmosphere* (Albuquerque, N. M., 1952).

[52] E. Evard and J. Rens, "Radio Transmission of an Electrocardiogram," (in French) *Rev. H. F.*, Vol. 3 (1956), p. 193.

[53] B. Jacobson, "A PH Endoradiosonde," *Lancet*, Vol. 272 (1957), p. 1224.

[54] D. A. Morken and P. E. Morrow, "A Remote Control Measuring System for Physiological Study," *National Telemetering Conference* (1958), p. 103-06; J. W. Still, "Telemetering in Biology—With Special Reference on the Problems of Research into Space Biology," *National Telemetering Conference* (1958), pp. 107-09.

[55] A. R. Marko, "Multichannel Personnel Telemetry System Using Pulse Position Modulation," *Proc. National Telemetering Conference* 13-1 (1961).

[56] H. Boreen, F. Shandelman, and R. Berman, "Bio-Medical Telemetry." *Ibid.* (1961), pp. 13-19.

From these humble beginnings, the modern astronaut's suit-system and additional external pickups have been developed to telemeter all the necessary physiological and psychophysiological characteristics during a manned flight. With the increase in flight time, and particularly for extended periods of weightlessness, more precise and complex measurements may prove necessary to achieve maximum efficiency of the crew members.

Space Telemetry—Horizons Unlimited

It is clear that both divisions of space telemetry, the ground test facilities and the spaceborne system, will require constant refinement and increased performance as space missions are extended in time and range. The history of telemetry development, however, provides a rational basis for confidence in the ability of telemetry to meet all challenges ahead of the other dynamic fields of endeavor in space technology. It must be remembered that telemetry is practically always installed to measure or monitor some other unit or to transmit a characteristic of an environment; hence telemetry must be so reliable that its presence has no measurable effect on the measured qualtity. Hopefully, techniques will be found to reduce long countdowns before launch to a minimum while assuring rapid detection and identification of any source of fault in a system in flight, however complex. These techniques must be based on a sound organization of knowledge, both theoretical and practical, which telemetry always enhances.

EVOLUTION
OF ROCKETRY
IN THE
SOVIET UNION

"Do you realize the tremendous strategic importance of machines of this sort? They could be an effective straight-jacket for that noisy shopkeeper Harry Truman. We must go ahead with it, comrades. The problem of the creation of transatlantic rockets is of extreme importance to us."

—Premier I. V. Stalin, at a meeting of the Politburo, on March 15, 1947.

"The successes of the Soviet conquerors of space reflect the great achievements of the Soviet people in the development of the mighty productive forces of our homeland, the indisputable advantages of socialism, and its superiority over the capitalist system. The most reasonable representatives of the western world cannot fail to admit that socialism, as Comrade Khrushchev puts it, is indeed the reliable launching pad from which the Soviet Union launches its spaceships."

—Editorial in Pravda upon the anniversary of the orbital flight of Yuri Gagarin in VOSTOK I on April 12, 1962.

Soviet Rocket Technology

G. A. TOKATY*

THE AIM OF THIS PAPER is to depict the background of well known
and not so well known Soviet achievements and failures in the field of
space technology, irrespective of whether it agrees or disagrees with
numerous existing books, pamphlets, articles, and rumors on the subject.

In June 1959, I received, from an influential Western (not British)
organization, an invitation to testify before a powerful constitutional
body and in the press that the Soviet Sputniks, Laikas, Luniks, etc.,
were no more than " rude Communist propaganda "–a " Big Red Lie."
A few months later, while looking at the capsule of the Mercury
Project at the McDonnell Aircraft Corporation, St. Louis, Missouri,
a well known scientist and educator said to me: " Well, here we have
something new, real, and outstanding, while the Russians make only
propaganda announcements." Then, in April, 1961, a few hours after
Major Gagarin's successful re-entry and landing in the USSR when I
refused to give "Yes" and "No" answers, my interviewer in a Los
Angeles hotel stated boldly that "the so-called Gargarin's Space
Flight," too, may well prove to be "another Russian hoax." Finally,
in a document (in front of me as I write) prepared for official use, a
Western intellectual advises his superiors that, according to results
of his "first-hand study," the Russian and "other Eastern Slavonic
nations" appear to be "much less inventive and imaginative" in
science and technology than the Anglo-Saxon nations.

I could enlist dozens of publications, radio broadcasts, and even TV
plays, in which the cold war sergeants, some of them known as "Russian experts," depict the Soviet Union as the old Tsarist Russia with its
notorious longbearded Muzhiks and Oblomov-like intellectuals, with
no real scientific and technological progress.

* Dr. Tokaty was former chief of the aerodynamics laboratory of the Zhukovsky
Academy of Aerodynamics of the Soviet Air Forces in Moscow and Chief Rocket
Scientist of the Soviet Government in Germany (1946-47). He is now head of
the Department of Aeronautics and Space Technology, Northampton College of
Advanced Technology, London.
This paper was originally presented at a meeting of the British Interplanetary
Society in London on September 22, 1961, and was printed in Spaceflight, Vol. V,
No. 2 (March 1963). It is published here through the kind permission of the
British Interplanetary Society and the editors of Spaceflight.

But the realities are quite different. The October Communist Revolution destroyed, abolished, and replaced *that* Russia by a fundamentally different state organization called the Union of Soviet Socialist Republics, or simply the Soviet Union, in which there are no private or even semi-private industrial companies or corporations, research establishments or laboratories, educational establishments, or technological publications. Everything and everybody in the USSR belongs to the State and is employed, financed, directed, and controlled by the State. The latter itself " belongs " to the Central Committee of the Communist Party of the Soviet Union.

The second basic difference is that the Soviet Union is a country of a single and permanent official *Ideology* (Marxism-Leninism) serving a single and permanent national purpose, or aim, or sense of life, or destiny (Communism). Whoever you may be and whatever you may be doing, your efforts are predetermined, once and forever, by this single and permanent aim. And so are the efforts of the entire Soviet people. Tsarist Russia, on the other hand, was a jungle of philosophies and ideologies with no uniting national purpose.

There are, of course, many other differences as well but, ad hoc, these two are the decisive ones. They make the USSR not only the country of a dictatorship with a very high degree of centralization but also one of the most dynamic state formations in modern history, or perhaps the most dynamic, knowing clearly where it wants to go, and why and how. And this is precisely what puts such fields as aeronautics and space technology in an advantageous position in comparison with those in, say, the United States and the United Kingdom.

The general philosophy, purpose, and history of the Soviet Space Technology began, however, long before the October Revolution. Russian engineers and scientists, N. I. Kibal'chich, K. I. Konstantinov, N. S. Sokovin, A. P. Fyodorov, K. E. Tsiolkovsky,[1] I. V. Meschersky, and others, independently, had put forward ideas, projects, and the theories of rockets as far back as 1881-97. Daniell Bernoulli, Leonhard Euler, Lomonosov, Ostrogradsky, Gromeka, Bobylev, Petrov, Mendeleev, Mayevsky, Meschersky, Zhukovsky, and many other members of the St. Petersburg Academy of Sciences or professors of Russian institutes and universities, had created and maintained excellent traditions in mathematics, theoretical mechanics, and theoretical physics. K. I. Konstantinov's publications *On Military Rockets* (1856) and on *Military Rockets in European Armies* (1855) were particularly well received. Professor I. V. Meschevsky's book on *The Dynamics of a Point of Variable Mass* (1897), laying down the foundations of what we call today " Theoretical Rocket-dynamics," attracted great atten-

[1] Ed. Note: American orthographic practice uses the form " Ziolkovsky."

tion from scientists and engineers and gave a powerful impulse to the later studies in the field.

Konstantin Eduardovich Tsiolkovsky (1857-1935), the man of " great efforts and little rewards," is, however, considered to be the " father " of present Soviet achievements in rocket technology. He gave Russia a spaceship project which was, for 1903, absolutely unique. But being what he was—a mere teacher in a remote provincial school, a technologist rather than a theoretician—his project did not attract the attention it deserved. Besides, Tsarist officialdom's technological dreams did not rise above St. Petersburg's chimneys.

The first wind tunnel in Russia, although a small and rather primitive one, was designed and built in 1890 by the same Tsiolkovsky. But he was not the only enthusiast of aeronautics and astronautics. Professor Nikolai Egorovich Zhukovsky (1847-1921), the "father of Russian Aviation," constructed in 1902 the second wind-tunnel, at Moscow University. Then, in 1904-06, the engineer Dmitri Pavlovich Ryabouchinsky designed and built up the famous Kuchino Institute of Aerodynamics. Finally in 1910-12 in the Moscow Higher Technological College (M. V. T. U.), again under Professor Zhukovsky, one more laboratory was designed and built. Thus, as far as ideas, theories, projects, and aerodynamics laboratories were concerned, towards the eve of the first World War, Russia was no longer a backward country.

Tsiolkovsky continued his research. Zhukovsky was lecturing on problems of general aerodynamics, mechanics of flight, and aeroballistics. Professor S. A. Chaplygin (1869-1942), the author of the well known work on gas streams (1902-04), continued his basic research into problems of theoretical gasdynamics, the importance of which for high-speed aeronautics and rocketry became evident only decades later. Ryabouchinsky, in collaboration with General Pomortsev designed and tested (1916) a tactical military rocket-bazooka. Several Russian scientists, Professor Rynin among them, began writing and publishing popular books and articles on rockets and space travel, etc.

Immediately after the October Revolution, Lenin empowered Professor Zhukovsky to begin the building of a completely new and up-to-date center of aeronautical research, under the name " Tsentral'nyi Aero-Gidrodinamicheskii Institute " (Ts. A. G. I.), the Soviet NACA; this was initiated in 1918 and completed partly in 1924 and fully in 1927.

Equally important was the creation (1919) of the now famous Zhukovsky Academy of Aeronautics in Moscow, with its ever improving teaching and experimental facilities. Today there are in the USSR 15 such or comparable academies, institutes, and higher colleges, exclusively of aeronautics and space technology, plus a great number of aerospace tekhnikums (i. e., technical colleges), plus a number of departments and chairs of aeronautics and astronautics in universities. Each of these has laboratories of its own. All the 15 institutions are not only teaching but also doing basic research. Thus the problem of preparation of aerospace scientists, engineers, technologists, and technicians was solved drastically and effectively. The consequence is that, in my opinion and experience, the present Soviet aerospace *intelligentsia* is not only the most numerous but also the most directed and the most effective in the world.

This is not all. The "Pyatiletkas" (i. e., five-year plans of industrialization) gave the USSR a modern aerospace industry, which, in turn, created favorable conditions for the creation of huge research establishments. One of these is the "New Ts. A. G. I." (built in 1933-38), with superb wind tunnels and other facilities. A second is the "Newer New Ts. A. G. I.," the Institute of Fluidmechanics of the Academy of Sciences in Novosibirsk (built in 1959-60), with academicians S. A. Khristionovich and M. A. Lavrentev in charge. Then there are the Central Institute of Aerospace Propulsion Systems (Ts. I. A. M.), the All-Union Institute of Aerospace Materials (V. I. A. M.), the Flight Research Institute (L. I. I.), the Scientific Testing Institute of the Soviet Air Forces (N. I. I. V. V. S.), the Scientific Testing of Air Armaments (N. I. I. A. V.), the Scientific Institute of Air Instruments (N. I. I. A. P.), the State Scientific Research Institute Number One (NII—No. 1) (Rockets), the Baikanur launching base (the Cape Canaveral of the USSR), etc., etc. Do not have illusions: both by their quantity and quality, they are all as impressive and powerful as those in any other country in the world. What is even more important, their activities are well planned, well coordinated, well aimed, and absolutely free from financial worries.

If we now have a closer look at the space developments proper, we notice that the Soviet government has manifested its keen interest in the field throughout the entire history of its existence. A special Central Bureau for the Study of the Problems of Rockets (Ts. B. I. R. P.) was created as far back as 1924. In the same year, an All-Union Society for the Study of Interplanetary Flights (O. I. M. S.) was formed in Moscow. In 1927, Ts. B. I. R. P. and O. I. M. S. organized in Moscow an international exhibition of rocket technology. In 1928-30, a number of closed and open conferences of Soviet rocket enthusiasts took place. Each conference discussed the one single major topic: what should be done in order to proceed from theories and projects of rockets to practical rocket technology? This was precisely what the government wanted.

Tsiolkovsky's last major contribution to Soviet space technology was his well formulated and clearly presented idea of a multistage rocket (1929). He was already an old man in poor health, and his activities in the projects of the 'twenties and 'thirties could not be more than symbolic. But the second generation of Soviet rocket engineers was already deep in the field. Boris Sergeevich Stechkin, then still an ordinary engineer of Ts. A.G. I., but today an eminent member of the Academy of Sciences of the USSR and Head of the Department of Aerospace Propulsion at the Zhukovsky Academy, published in 1929 an article on the theory of jet propulsion, which made an important contribution also to the theory of rocket propulsion.

Y. V. Kondratyuk put forward, in 1928, the idea of braking re-entry vehicles by aerodynamic means and proposed the use of ozone as an oxidant in rocket fuels. His book *Rockets*, published in 1929, was a valuable contribution to the subsequent achievements of Soviet space technology. G. A. Tsander (1887-1933) was another rising star. He began working in the field only in 1919, but already in 1926-38 he had become "another Tsiolkovsky." He put forward several original ideas and projects of jet and rocket engines. Two of them, OR-1 and OR-2, with gasoline-air and gasoline-liquid oxygen fuels respectively, were built and tested successfully in 1930 and 1932, developing absolute thrusts up to 50 kg. He also designed jet engines with 5-ton and 600 kg. thrusts. In 1932, he published an important book entitled *Problems of Reactive Flight*. The years 1929 to 1933 were, on the other hand, years of great happenings. Stechkin was arrested and imprisoned for many years. Some of the Ts. B. I. R. P. and O. I. M. S. members were pronounced enemies of the regime. Tsander died. Tsiolkovsky was a retired sick old man. The entire higher educational system and industrial and agricultural economy were in a state of radical reorganization and Stalinization. Ts. B. I. R. P. and O. I. M. S. were disbanded.

Naturally, these happenings confused the work of the Soviet rocket engineers, but this was for a short period only, and the government was far from abandoning its "rocket interest." Quite the opposite: it demanded a doubling of efforts in the field. Professor V. P. Vetchinkin (1888-1950) was asked to form a group of scientists in the Ts. A. G. I., with the aim of studying foreign experience in the field and carrying out basic research on the mechanics of rocket flight. This group began working in 1930. In 1931, a completely new Group for the Study of Rocket Propulsion Systems (G. I. R. D.) was formed in Leningrad. A few years later, the G. I. R. D. became the State Rocket Scientific Research Institute, which is known today as NII—No. 1.

Vetchinkin's group translated into Russian and published numerous foreign works on the subject, including those by Max Valier and Eugen Sänger. In 1933-35, Vetchinkin himself developed and published excellent theories of rocket flight.

But to return to G. I. R. D., which continued Tsander's and others' projects and initiated new ones. One rocket, built and tested in 1933, powered by a liquid propellent engine, was 245.7 cm. long, 160 mm. in diameter, and 20 kg. in weight. It rose to an altitude of 4500 m. But none of the projects, with the exception of the so called "GRID-X," proved to be successful enough. "GRID-X" was, in fact, a further development of an earlier project by Tsander. Its length, diameter, and weight were respectively, 2.2 m., 0.14 m. and 30 kg. It was fired successfully in November 1933, but did not reach the design maximum altitude of 5000-6000 m.

The active majority of G. I. R. D. consisted of the third generation of Soviet rocketists, i. e., those who were educated under the new regime. V. P. Glushko, S. P. Korolev, M. K. Tikhonravov, A. C. Kostikov, Yu. A. Pobedonostsev, L. S. Dushkin, and others, who are today leading figures in the design and production of Soviet rockets, sputniks, and spaceships, began their efforts in G. I. R. D. The years have since proved that they were vigorous, imaginative, inventive, and able, although some "experts" insist that "dictatorship paralyzes talents."

For instance, Tikhonravov designed, built, and tested successfully (1934) a liquid fuel rocket. I knew this rocket and its further versions fairly well and would like to say that, for its time, it signified a remarkable jump forward. The rocket was supposed to be secret, but in 1945 my group found its drawings in the Nazi Air Ministry. Tikhonravov not only developed interesting rocket projects—he also published many valuable articles and a book *Raketnaya Tekhnika* (1935) full of detailed information on rocket design.

A. G. Kostikov, on the other hand, dedicated his talent and energy to the development of small military rockets named "Katyusha," The work of his group began in 1936; in May of 1940 "Katyusha" was accepted for mass production and was widely used during the Soviet-Nazi War.

S. P. Korolev's work on rockets began in the early 'thirties. In 1934 the Ministry of Defence of the USSR published his book *Rocket Flight in the Stratosphere.* During the following years he worked in the Ministry of Aircraft Production, then in the Ministry of Armaments, and in the Rockets Research Institute, continuously in charge of rocket research and development. In 1945 he was made responsible for the further development of the German V-2. Some years later his group designed an intercontinental ballistic missile, the successful launching of which was announced on 27 August 1957. Today he is one of the chief designers of rockets for carrying Sputniks and "Vostok" capsules. An active member of the Soviet Communist Party, an excellent organizer, a Lieutenant-General of Aviation, a Hero of Socialist Labor, a Corresponding Member of the Academy of Sciences, a highly imaginative and inventive engineer with tremendous concentration—such is this leading rocket engineer of our times.

Then there is V. P. Glushko, one of the outstanding experts in the field of powerful liquid fuel rocket motors. He too entered this field in the early 'thirties. Together with G. Langemak, Glushko published (1935) a book on *Rockets, Their Construction and Application*, which influenced the future of this field. The authors also played an active role in the work of such rocket organizations as the Aviation Engineering-Technological Society Aviavnito (1934-40) and Osoaviakhim. In 1935 they presented papers at the All-Union Conference on the use of rockets for the study of the upper layers of the Atmosphere. The various contributions were published in a book entitled *Reactive Motion*, which could be obtained by anyone at home or abroad.

Pobedonostsev, a gasdynamicist and former member of the Ts. A. G. I. staff, joined NII—No. 1 in the late 'thirties and worked full-time on the aerodynamic problems of rockets. After the war, for several years, he was in charge of a large group of German engineers who worked on the Peenemuende V-2.

Among the younger Soviet rocket engineers, I should like to mention I. A. Merkulov, L. S. Dushkin, and A. H. Lyul'ko. In 1935, while an aeronautical engineering student, Merkulov designed, built, and tested (1936) a two-stage rocket. Its first and second stages were propelled, respectively, by gunpowder motors and a "uniflow" jet-engine. In 1937, a further version of this rocket was mounted on a conventional air force fighter, as a booster, and showed good results. In March 1941, at the Zhukovsky Academy of Aeronautics, I was visited by I. S. Merkulov and L. K. Baev. They put on my desk a completely new project for a two-stage rocket. Undoubtedly, this was much more advanced than anything I had seen before. There was a general feeling that the two bright young men must be given a chance to go ahead with their idea, but the Soviet-German War, which began two months later, made this impossible.

Then there was, of course, Lyul'ko, a promising Zhukovsky Academy graduate. His first contribution was his Diploma Project (1938), which turned out to be quite a step forward. The authorities gave him good opportunities, and he continued working on his top secret propulsion system during the war years. But then, in 1945, my group found full drawings and detailed descriptions of the project in the Luftwaffe Ministerium in Berlin. This was a shock for us and very bad luck for Lyul'ko. Today, however, he is once again working in the field.

The first Soviet experimental rocket fighter, roughly of the Me-163A [2] type and size, was designed by V. F. Bolkhovitinov in 1939-40; built in 1940-41 it was transported to one of the Moscow military aero-dromes for flight tests in October, 1941. The rocket motor of the fighter was designed in 1937-38, built in 1938-39, and tested in 1939-40 by Dushkin, who is, undoubtedly, one of the leading figures behind the present Soviet aerospace technology. I have good reason to believe that he is now about to finish a long and hard task on a new rocket propulsion system which will give the USSR new advantages capable of surprising the entire aerospace world. He began with an engine of the calibre of the well known HWK-109-509 and finished up with a monstrously powerful rocket engine.

It may well be asked why, if the USSR had so many rocket scientists, technologists, engineers, projects, and prototypes, there were no rockets and jet aircraft until much later, after the war? There are reasonable explanations:

(1) it is not true at all that there were no rockets in the Soviet Union; "Katyushas" of several types were in mass production and wide-scale use in 1941-45;

(2) the main industrial centers of the USSR had been either occupied by the Germans or evacuated to the East, and this caused serious delays;

(3) resources and efforts had to be concentrated on the immediate needs of defense;

(4) the Soviet industry was still young and inexperienced;

(5) as admitted by the XXth Congress of the Communist Party itself, Stalin and his lieutenants had committed too many mistakes in preparing the country's defenses.

Now about the post-war period. One reads and hears time and again that the present Soviet space achievements are due to "hundreds of German rocket scientists and engineers deported from Peenemuende and Berlin to Russia."

But what are the facts? Peenemuende, Berlin, and other rocket centers were destroyed by Anglo-American bombing, fully or partly. At least 130 leading rocket scientists and technologists, with their theories and projects, were evacuated and later taken to the United States. Wernher von Braun and General Dornberger were among

[2] Ed. Note: German Messerschmitt.

them. The underground factory of V-2 rockets in the Harz Mountains was captured by the U. S. Army, quickly dismantled, and sent, together with its staff, to the United States. Nothing was left behind.

And the USSR? Let me put facts right: the USSR did not get a single *leading* V-2 rocket engineer or administrator, not a single complete rocket factory, and not a single new project. "This is absolutely intolerable," said Marshal Stalin some time later to Colonel-General I. A. Serov, in my presence. "We defeated Nazi armies; we occupied Berlin and Peenemuende; but the Americans got the rocket engineers. What could be more revolting and more inexcusable? How and why was this allowed to happen?"

The only thing that could be done in the circumstances was to sort out the ruins, put pieces together, and study them. Well, we succeeded. With the help of ordinary German engineers, technicians, and workers, we restored not only the general picture but also some laboratories and workshops. Some time later, all this was transported to the USSR, where work was resumed on a wider basis.

What were our impressions of Peenemuende? This is an extremely interesting question, and I would like to answer it frankly. We were quite clear on three things:

(1) in the field of original ideas and rocket theories, the USSR was not behind Germany; in some respects it was even ahead of Peenemuende;

(2) in the field of practical technology of rockets of the V-2 calibre we were definitely behind the Germans;

(3) having seen and studied Peenemuende, we came to the conclusion that there were in the USSR rocket engineers as able and gifted as elsewhere.

I mentioned this in my detailed report to G. M. Malenkov and to the C.-in-C. of the Soviet Air Forces. One year later, in March 1947, I made the same statement at the meeting of the Politbureau and of the Council of Ministers of the USSR. In this sense, we, the Soviet aerospace scientists and technologists, were not worried by the fact that the leading rocket engineers of Peenemuende were in the U. S. A. What we badly needed was the practical technological experience, and this was obtained much sooner than was anticipated. With the help of hundreds of German workers and ordinary engineers who were transported to the U. S. S. R. in 1945-46, V-2 production was fully restored, with some improvements as compared with that at Peenemuende.

From September 1949 there existed in the USSR full scale serial production of big single-stage rockets (the greatly improved versions of the V-2, under the name "Pobeda") with maximum range about 900 km. and with a fairly reliable guidance system. This production was under Soviet administrators and engineers, by Soviet workers, from Soviet materials, on Soviet soil. Some of the Germans had been sent home. The others continued working on isolated problems in isolated places, under Soviet scientists. To generalize, I would say that the Peenemuende V-2 level of 1944 (before the Anglo-American air raid) was reached by the USSR roughly in 1946-47, while in 1949-50 it was far above that level in terms of both quantity and performance. The first Rocket Divisions (armed with V-2's and "Pobedas") of the Soviet Armed Forces were formed in 1950-51. The exploration of the upper layers of the atmosphere by V-2 type rockets began in the autumn of 1947. From 1949, it was continued by "Pobedas."

This leads me to the question addressed to me dozens of times in various countries. Are the present Soviet space achievements due to mere good luck or to something else? Well, the Soviet philosophies do not believe in "good luck." Of course, if it comes it is welcome, but the Soviet Sputniks, Luniks, and Vostoks are the children of knowledge, not luck. More than that, the Soviet philosophies demand that any education and scientific knowledge must have an aim, a purpose.

The aims of Soviet space technology are twofold, strategic and space exploration. Bearing this in mind, Marshal Zhigarev, then the C.-in-C. of the Soviet Air Forces, in the autumn of 1946, in Berlin, said to me "We must admit that our V-2 type rockets do not satisfy our long-term needs; they were good to frighten England, but should there be an American-Soviet war, they would be useless; what we really need are long-range, reliable rockets capable of hitting target areas on the American continent. This is an aim that should dominate the mind and efforts of your rocket group." On 14 March 1947, in the Kremlin, at a meeting of aircraft and rocket designers, G. M. Malenkov, in turn, made it quite clear to us that the program of V-2-type rockets did not conform to the long-term aims of the country. "No, Comrades," he said, "I am not happy with our V-2's; we cannot rely on such a primitive weapon; besides, should there be another war, it would be a war not against Poland; our strategic needs are predetermined by the fact that our potential enemy is to be found thousands of miles away."

One day later, on 15 March, at a meeting of the Politbureau and of the Council of Ministers of the USSR, I. V. Stalin made the aim even clearer. "Under Hitler, German scientists have developed many interesting ideas," he said with utmost seriousness. "This 'Sänger

Project' seems to represent one of them. Such a rocket could change the fate of the war. Do you realize " (Stalin was looking into my eyes) "the tremendous strategic importance of machines of this sort? They could be an effective straightjacket for that noisy shopkeeper Harry Truman. We must go ahead with it, comrades. The problem of the creation of transatlantic rockets is of extreme importance to us."

Such was the general line, and so were formulated the strategic needs of the country. Accordingly, the Soviet government undertook a number of steps which changed the scale and pattern of rocket production. On 15 March 1947, Stalin personally suggested, and the Council of Ministers agreed immediately, the formation of a special State Commission for the study of the problems of long range rockets (Pravitel'stvennaya Komissiya po Raketam Dalnego Deistviya, PKRDD). It consisted of Colonel-General I. A. Serov (1st Deputy Minister of NKVD, Chairman), Professor-Colonel G. A. Tokaty-Tokaev (Chief Scientist and Deputy Chairman, from the Soviet Air Forces), Professor M. V. Keldysh (member, from the Ministry of Armaments), Professor M. A. Kishkin (member, from the Ministry of Aircraft Production), and Major-General V. I. Stalin (member).

This was an extraordinary decree. It signified a turning point. It was made known to the rocket groups already in existence and influenced their further work very sharply. Towards the end of 1947, as A. G. Kostikof put it, "everybody wanted to design a transatlantic rocket."

In November and December 1947, the state of rocket technology in the USSR was roughly as follows:

(1) the problem of small military rockets had been solved fully and completely;
(2) rockets of the V-1 calibre (but of different types) and of V-2 type were already in serial production;
(3) rockets of the "Pobeda" type were in a state of design;
(4) there were, as far as I knew, already *two* draft projects for long-range rockets. One of them, known as "project TT-1," was developed by my group and presented to the Government in September, 1947. It was a three-stage liquid fuel rocket for extremely high altitude and orbital flights. Had the group been allowed to continue its work without interference from outside, the USSR might well have succeeded in putting a Sputnik round the earth sometime in 1950-52. But for reasons which had nothing to do with the project itself or with our professional qualifications, we found ourselves in a difficult position. Towards the end of 1947 our work was paralyzed. Some of us were compelled

to seek refuge in the West, and others were arrested; the rest had to wait. Here I should like to mention that Professors Keldysh and Kishkin did not take part either in the project or in our tragedy.

You may guess that, politically and ideologically, I am not an admirer of the Soviet Government. I have always disagreed also with many of its practical acts. But this does not prevent me from having a high opinion of the Soviet Government where rocket technology is concerned. I am in no doubt whatever that no other government contributed to space technology as effectively as the governing officials of the USSR. They made up their minds a long time ago. They instructed the corresponding learned bodies to work out a single long-term national program of space technology. They have never been reluctant in providing the necessary sum of money and supporting facilities.

The consequences? We know them all. Already in 1949-50 rockets of the " Pobeda " type were in actual production and use for both military and space exploration purposes. In 1954 the second of the above-mentioned multi-stage rocket projects was accepted (we shall call it " Project USSR-1 "). In April 1956, several " USSR-1 " missiles were ready for test. In August, 1957, *TASS* announced to the world that the Soviet Union had fired successfully a transcontinental ballistic missile. Finally, on 4 October 1957, Sputnik I began circling the Earth.

None of these events surprised me, because there was in the USSR a general policy and a national plan of space research and development. I certainly felt sorry for some Western nations with no such policy and plans.

Here, again, we could learn from the experience of " those Russians." They realized a long time ago that rocketry is the elite of modern science and technology and cannot be successful under non-experts. Accordingly, all Soviet ministers, deputy ministers, top administrators, planners, and co-ordinators of aerospace efforts are distinguished aerospace scientists, technologists, and engineers. It is therefore easy for them to understand each other. They do not need to be accompanied by advisers and consultants at governmental meetings. If we add to this the fact that there exists a single central Commission for the co-ordination of all the space research and development work throughout the USSR, which also consists of eminent experts in the field, then it will be clear that Soviet space technology has every reason to be as successful as it is today.

When one analyzes accomplishments and studies numerous publications, broadcasts, etc., one begins to see that Soviet space technology moves into the future with great confidence. It does not step forward until everything that has gone before is fully worked out. No experiment or design is undertaken unless the theoretical aspects of the problems have been studied. Rightly or wrongly, the Soviet philosophies assert that the field is too complicated, too expensive, and too important to be allowed to grow in any other manner. This explains, at least partly, why the Soviet Union has so few failures in rockets and sputniks.

The progress emerges logically from the general program of space research, which is based on the idea of a systematic step-by-step expansion of efforts. The same general trend can be observed in total rocket thrust, in size of vehicle, etc. I should expect, for instance, that during the next three or four years or so the total thrust of the heavy Soviet liquid-propelled carrier rockets will be nearly doubled. I personally believe that this can be achieved not in a single rocket motor but by combining powerful rocket motors with special-purpose jet and ramjet engines. This is one of the fields of intensive investigation in the USSR at present. Such a sharp increase in the total thrust, of course, would mean that the problem of delivery of H-bombs by long-range rockets would be solved fully and finally.[8] It would also mean that, for exploration purposes, the USSR would be able to put into orbit much more sophisticated sputniks.

A rocket engineer will understand immediately that the combination of rocket motors and jet and ramjet engines will require practically a new rocket vehicle. Soviet designers are working on it now. On the other hand, the multi-stage vehicles already in existence are still far from being perfect. This became particularly clear after Gagarin's and Titov's flights. Hence the conclusion that during the forthcoming years a good proportion of effort will be absorbed by further improvement of existing vehicles.

It is also known that there has existed in the USSR, for a number of years, a powerful group of scientists and engineers which works on the problem of a real spaceship. There is no specific information on the progress of this project, but if I may be allowed to advance a rough guess, I would say that it is not behind the corresponding American project.

Finally, there are good reasons and indications to believe that the USSR is now working very intensively on the project for placing a permanent space-station round the earth. The general ideas of the

---

[8] Author's note: These words were written in August 1961.

project are not new; but whether it is supposed to house people or to be an automatic station, remains unknown. However, exploiting once again the basic philosophies guiding Soviet space technology, I would suggest that it will be a purely automatic station.

REFERENCES

M. V. Lomonosov, *Selected Philosophical Works* (Moscow, 1950).

A. Sternfield, *Iskusstvennye Sputniks* (Moscow, 1958).

I. V. Meschersky, *Dinamika Tochki Peremennoy Massy* (St. Petersburg, 1897). *Soviet Man in Space*, Soviet Booklet No. 78 (London, 1961).

G. A. Tokaty, *Aeronautical Engineering Education and Research in the USSR* (University of Kansas, 1960).

G. A. Tokaty, "Progress in Astronautics," *Eastern and Indian Engineer*, 104th Anniversary Issue (1963).

V. P. Vetchinkin, *Selected Works*, Volume I (Moscow, 1956).

Oleg Pisar Zhevsky, *A Glance at Soviet Science* (Moscow, 1960).

V. I. Feodosiev and G. B. Siniarev: *Introduction to Rocket Technology* (New York–London, 1959).

F. R. Gantmakher and L. M. Levin, *The Theory of Flight of an Unguided Rocket* (Moscow, 1959).

S. P. Korolev, *Rocket Flight in the Stratosphere* (Moscow, 1934).

A. E. Primenko, *Reaktivnye Dvigateli* (Moscow, 1946).

Pravda (1957-61).

Vestnik Vozdushonogo Floto (1959, 1960, 1961).

G. A. Tokaty, "Soviet Rocket Technology," articles in *Russkaya Mysl* (1957-58-59).

Moscow Radio, Special Lectures on Space Problems (1957-61).

Bibliographical Note

ARTHUR G. RENSTROM *

This bibliographical note lists the principal general published sources relating to rocket technology and thus provides a brief guide to the available literature on rocketry, space flight, and related technologies. Time for selection and space available did not permit an exhaustive listing of pertinent materials, not to mention the growing tide of related publication. The primary aim here was to cite the significant bibliographies and source materials compiled to date.

Bibliographies have been broadly interpreted to include not only material published as such, but also material which appears as references or source notes accompanying books, journal articles, technical reports, or research papers. Some handbooks, technical symposia, and other treatises are included; while they are not bibliographies, they constitute a framework for further reading, provide basic information, and have extensive lists of references. Individual works not well documented and not of assistance to the student for further research are not ordinarily cited. Some foreign sources, including French, German, and Russian, have been included.

Many publications deal with several or many aspects of rocket technology and its impact so that it was difficult in many instances to classify them into specific categories. The attempt was made so that related items have been arranged alphabetically by author or issuing agency according to the following major subject categories: (1) history and chronology; (2) general bibliography; (3) biography; (4) rocket technology; (5) space law; (6) space sciences; and (7) abstracting and indexing services.

Sources cited are generally those available in the Library of Congress. Most should also be available in large public, university, or specialized research libraries.

* Science Reference and Bibliographical Specialist, Science and Technology Division, Library of Congress. Mr. Renstrom has been associated with the Aeronautics, Technical Information, and Science and Technology Divisions of the Library of Congress since 1931. A contributor to aviation, bibliographical, and library journals, he is the compiler and editor of numerous bibliographies, including *Aeronautic American; A Bibliography of Books and Pamphlets on Aeronautics Published in America before 1900; Aeronautical and Space Serial Publications; Aeropolitics; United States Aviation Policy;* and "Wright Brothers Bibliography" in the *Papers of Orville and Wilbur Wright.* He is bibliographical editor of the *Journal of Air Law and Commerce.*

285

(1) HISTORY AND CHRONOLOGY

Adams, Carsbie C., *et al. Space Flight: Satellites, Spaceships, Space Stations, and Space Travel.* New York: McGraw-Hill Book Company, 1958. 373 p.
  References appended to each chapter. Includes "The History of Astronautics," pp. 1-35, with "Chronology," pp. 22-26, and "Bibliography," pp. 26-35; "The Rocket," pp. 36-66, with "Bibliography," pp. 64-66; and "Sputniks, Prelude to Man in Space," pp. 150-170, with "Bibliography," pp. 169-170.

Akens, David S. *Historical Origins of the George C. Marshall Space Flight Center.* Huntsville, Ala.: NASA George C. Marshall Space Flight Center, 1960. 168 p. (MSFC Historical Monograph No. 1).
  Includes numerous footnote references. Chapter I, "Historical Highlights," pp. 1-22, is a chronology covering the period July 1, 1939 through December 19, 1960.

Bailey, James O. *Pilgrims Through Space and Time: Trends and Patterns in Scientific and Utopian Fiction.* New York: Argus Books, 1947. 341 p.
  Includes "The Cosmic Romance. 1. In Space," pp. 123-132; "Space-Fliers," pp. 274-275; and "Bibliography," pp. 325-333.

Benecke, Th., and A. W. Quick. *History of German Guided Missiles Development* (First Guided Missiles Seminar, Munich, Germany, April, 1956) Brunswick, Germany: E. Appelhans and Co., 1957. 420 p. (Advisory Group for Aeronautical Research and Development. AGARDograph No. 20)
  Comprises 26 papers, most with references appended.

Boucher, Anthony. "Prophets of the Space Age; the Writers of Science Fiction," *Air Force and Space Digest,* v. 42 (February 1959) pp. 76-79.
  Brief survey of space science fiction, 1726-1953.

"A Chronology of Fiscal 1962," *Missiles and Rockets,* v. 11 (July 30, 1962), pp. 136-145.
  Covers world missile, rocket, and space events, July 21, 1962 through July 2, 1963. Compiled annually. "A Chronology of Fiscal 1963," *Missiles and Rockets,* v. 13 (July 29, 1963), covers period July 21, 1962 through July 2, 1963.

Clarke, Arthur C. "Space-Travel in Fact and Fiction," *British Interplanetary Society Journal,* v. 9 (September 1950), pp. 213-230.
  A survey of the literature, 1638-1949.

Cleator, Philip E. *Rockets Through Space: the Dawn of Interplanetary Travel.* New York: Simon and Schuster, 1936. 227 p.
  Early chapters are historical and 24 early works on rockets are cited, pp. 211-212.

Cleaver, A. V. "Rocket Propulsion and Its Implications to Human Society," *Royal United Service Institution Journal,* v. 100 (August 1955), pp. 368-383.
  Includes references, p. 379.

Dornberger, Walter. *V-2.* Translated by James Cleugh and Geoffrey Halliday. New York: Viking Press, 1954. 281 p.
  An account of German developments in the liquid-fuel rocket field between 1930 and 1945.

Emme, Eugene M. *Aeronautics and Astronautics; an American Chronology of Science and Technology in the Exploration of Space, 1915-1960.* Washington: National Aeronautics and Space Administration, 1961. 240 p.
  Part II, pp. 89-135, is entitled "The First Three Years of the Space Age, October 1957-December 1960." Appendix A, pp. 139-151, is a chronicle of earth satellites and space probes, 1957-1960. Includes bibliography, pp. 207-212, and a subject and name index. Kept up to date by NASA Historical Staff with annual supplements. Chronology for 1961 is entitled *Aeronautical and Astronautical Events of 1961,* by Eugene Emme and F. W. Anderson

(Washington: U. S. Govt. Print. Off., 1962, 113 p.). Chronology for 1962 is entitled *Astronautical and Aeronautical Events of 1962* (Washington: U. S. Govt. Print. Off., 1963, 370 p.).

Gartman, Heinz, ed. *Raumfahrtforschung.* Munich: R. Oldenburg, 1952. 200 p. Includes "Die Geschichte des Raumfahrtgedankens," by Willy Ley, pp. 9-26, and "Bibliographie der Raumfahrt," pp. 193-195, a chronological list of references.

Gove, Philip B. *The Imaginary Voyage in Prose Fiction: a History of Its Criticism and a Guide to Its Study, with an Annotated Check List of 215 Imaginary Voyages from 1700 to 1800.* New York: Columbia University Press, 1941. (Columbia University Studies in English and Comparative Literature, No. 152)
    A bibliography of books and articles relating to the study is included, pp. 403-420.

Gray, George W. *Frontiers of Flight, the Story of NACA Research.* New York: A. A. Knopf, 1948. 362 p.
    A review of the activities of NACA, emphasizing its technological contributions in World War II.

Green, Roger L. *Into Other Worlds; Space-Flight from Lucian to Lewis.* New York: Abelard-Schuman, 1958. 190 p.
    Includes bibliography.

Grimwood, James M. *Project Mercury: a Chronology.* Washington: Office of Scientific and Technical Information, National Aeronautics and Space Administration, 1963. 238 p. (NASA Publication SP-4001)
    Part I, "Major Events Leading to Project Mercury," covers period March 16, 1944 through October 1958. Part II, "Research and Development Phase of Project Mercury," covers period October 1958 through June 19, 1963.

Hausenstein, Albert. "Zur Entwicklungsgeschichte der Rakete," *Zeitschrift für das gesammte Schiess- und Sprengstoffwesen,* v. 34 (May-December 1939), pp. 135-139, 170-174, 206-210, 237-242, 286-288, 306-308, 331-333; v. 35 (January-February 1940), pp. 8-9, 32-34.
    Includes numerous references.

Hillegas, Mark W. *The Cosmic Voyage and the Doctrine of Inhabited Worlds in Nineteenth-Century English Literature.* Ann Arbor: University Microfilms, 1957. 258 p.
    Ph. D. thesis, Columbia University. Includes bibliography, pp. 244-258.

Holme, Molly. *First Five Years of NASA: a Concise Chronology.* Washington: NASA Historical Staff, National Aeronautics and Space Administration, 1963. 68 p. (NASA Historical Report)
    Covers the period October 1, 1958–September 13, 1963. Compiled to show highlights of NASA's administrative, organizational, and policy experience; major NASA milestones in space science and technology; representative items reflecting contributions of NASA offices, centers, and individuals; major policy statements by the President and NASA administrators; and summary items reflecting evolution, growth, and accomplishments of NASA.

Hunsaker, Jerome C. *Forty Years of Aeronautical Research.* Washington, D. C.: Smithsonian Institution, 1956. From *The Smithsonian Report for 1955,* pp. 241-271. (Smithsonian Publication 4237)
    Discussion of the National Advisory Committee for Aeronautics, 1915-1955.

Huzel, Dieter K. *Peenemünde to Canaveral.* Englewood Cliffs, N. J.: Prentice-Hall, 1962. 247 p.
    Appendices include: (1) "Rocketry in Germany; Historical Note," pp. 232-234; (2) "German Rockets of the 'A' Series," pp. 235-238; and (3) "Test Facilities at Peenemünde (P-1-P-12)," pp. 239-241.

Lasser, David. *The Conquest of Space.* New York: Penguin Press, 1931. 271 p.
    Cites early references to rocket propulsion.

Ley, Willy. *Rockets, Missiles, and Space Travel.* Rev. and Enl. for the 1960's.
New York: Viking Press, 1961. 528 p.
Includes extensive bibliography, pp. 513-548. Earlier versions of this bibliography appeared in all editions of this book, first published in 1944 under
title *Rockets; the Future of Travel Beyond the Stratosphere.* Briefly anno-
tated list of books arranged according to the language in which book was
printed. Some British and U. S. Government publications are listed. Section
3, pp. 542-544, is entitled " Literary History of Imaginative Literature on
Space Travel."
Maxwell, W. R. " Some Aspects of the Origins and Early Development of
Astronautics," *British Interplanetary Society Journal,* v. 18 (September/Decem-
ber 1962), pp. 415-425.
Includes " References (27)," p. 425.
Nicholson, Marjorie. "' Spaceflights of Fancy," *Air Force and Space Digest,* v.
43 (January 1960), pp. 82, 85.
A discussion of space flight as portrayed in the early literary classics.
Nicolson, Marjorie. *Voyages to the Moon.* New York: Macmillan Co., 1948.
297 p.
Includes selected annotated bibliography, pp. 258-288, arranged chronologi-
cally, covering literature through 1783.
Parry, Albert. *Russia's Rockets and Missiles.* Garden City, N. Y.: Doubleday,
1960. 322 p.
" Bibliographical Note," pp. 357-360, lists 31 English books and articles deal-
ing with Soviet rocketry.
Quick, A. W. " Possibilities of Aeronautical and Space Research in the
Federal Republic of Germany," *Journal of the Aerospace Sciences,* v. 28 (April
1961), pp. 257-283, with " References (60)," pp. 281-283.
Rosen, Milton W. " The Influence of Space Flight on Engineering and Science,"
Washington Academy of Sciences Journal, v. 56 (March 1956), pp. 79-84.
A bibliography (12 references) is appended, p. 84.
Rosen, Milton W. " Twenty-Five Years of Progress Toward Space Flight,"
Jet Propulsion, v. 25 (November 1955), pp. 623-626.
Includes " References (12)," p. 626.
Rosen, Milton W. *The Viking Rocket Story.* New York: Harper, 1955. 242 p.
Seifert, Howard. " Twenty-Five Years of Rocket Development," *Jet Propulsion,*
v. 25 (November 1955), pp. 594-603, 632-633.
Includes " References (68)," pp. 632-633.
" Spaceflight; the First Five Years," *Spaceflight,* v. 5 (May 1963), pp. 87-101.
A comprehensive table of artificial earth satellites and space probes.
Stehling, Kurt R. *Project Vanguard.* Garden City, N. Y.: Doubleday, 1961.
312 p.
A history of the U. S. I. G. Y. Project under the Naval Research Laboratory.
Appendix B, pp. 269-281, is a " Flight Summary," covering the period
December 8, 1956-June 22, 1959.
Stemmer, Josef. *Die Entwicklung des Raketenantriebes in allgemein verständ-
licher Darstellung.* Zürich: E. A. Hofmann, 1944-45. 3 v. (Hofmann-Bibliothek,
Nr. 106-108)
'Literaturverzeichnis," v. 3, pp. 211-216.
Stemmer, Josef. *Raketenantriebe, ihre Entwicklung, Anwendung und Zukunft;
eine Einführung in das Wesen des Raketenantriebes, sowie Raketen- und
Weltraumfluges.* Zürich: Schweiser Druck- und Verlagshaus, 1952. 523 p.
(SDV Fachbücher)
Includes " Chronologischer Bericht (3000 B. C.-September 1951)," pp. 14-52,
and " Literaturverzeichnis," pp. 515-523.
Stuhlinger, Ernst. " Army Activities in Space—a History," *IRE Transactions on
Military Electronics,* v. MIL-4 (April/July 1960), pp. 64-69.

Appendix I, p. 68, is a chronology (May 1947-October 13, 1959) of Army's
record in the missile and space field and Appendix II is a list of Army
orbital and space launches, January 31, 1958 through October 13, 1959.
Sutton, George P. "History, Problems, and Status of Guided Missiles," *Jet
Propulsion*, v. 25 (November 1955), pp. 615-622.
Includes references (18), p. 622.
U. S. Air Force. Systems Command. *The Rocket Research Program, 1946-1962.*
Edwards Air Force Base, Calif.: Air Force Flight Test Center, 1962.
U. S. Congress. House. Commitee on Science and Astronautics. *A Chronology
of Missile and Astronautic Events.* Washington: U. S. Govt. Print. Off., 1961.
189 p. (87th Cong., 1st Sess. House Report No. 67)
Covers period 1686-February 22, 1961. Also includes chronological lists of
Congressional bills, documents, hearings, and reports, 1958-1960.
U. S. Library of Congress. Air Information Division. *Comprehensive Analysis
of Soviet Space Program (Based on Soviet Open Literature).* Washington, 1961.
177 p. (*Its* AID Report 61-72)
Includes references (20) with English titles, pp. 147-159.
U. S. National Aeronautics and Space Administration. *Historical Origins of the
National Aeronautics and Space Administration.* Washington: U. S. Govt.
Print. Off., 1963. 22 p.
Includes " Select Historical References (84)," pp. 20-22.
Von Braun, Wernher. "Survey of Development of Liquid Rockets in Germany
and Their Future Prospects," *British Interplanetary Society Journal*, v. 10
(March 1951), pp. 75-80.
Includes references.

(2) GENERAL BIBLIOGRAPHY

Advances in Space Science and Technology. New York: Academic Press, 1960-
1962 (v. 1-4) Annual.
Chapters of volumes accompanied by extensive lists of references and
bibliographies.
Air Force and Space Digest. *Space Weapons; a Handbook of Military Astro-
nautics.* New York: Praeger, 1959. 245 p.
Includes slightly expanded version of " Bibliography of Space Literature,"
by J. F. Sunderman, originally published in *Air Force*, v. 41 (March 1958),
pp. 168-174.
Aleksandrov, S. G. and R. Ye. Fedorov. *Soviet Satellites and Cosmic Rocket.*
Translation Prepared by Liaison Office, Technical Information Center, MCLTD,
Wright-Patterson Air Force Base, Ohio. Wright Patterson Air Force Base,
1960. 245 p.
A translation of the 1959 edition of *Sovetskie Sputniki i Kosmicheski Korabli*,
including bibliography (18 references), pp. 241-242. An expanded and ex-
tensive bibliography of Russian books and periodical articles in this field is
included in the second revised and enlarged edition of this book (Moscow,
Izdatel'stvo Akademii Nauk SSSR, 1961, 439 p.), pp. 427-436.
Ax, Paul. *Exploration of Space.* San Francisco: Pacific Air Forces, 1963. 72 p.
(PACAF Basic Bibliographies)
First issued in 1958 and revised periodically. Comprises books published
1958-1960 arranged in seven subject categories. Section one is " Rocket-
Missile History and Research."
Bates, David R. and Patrick Moore, eds. *Space Research and Exploration.* New
York: W. Sloane Associates, 1958. 287 p.
Each chapter accompanied by references. Chapter 2, "History," by P. E.
Cleator, includes six references, p. 41.

Benton, Mildred C. *The Literature of Space Science and Exploration.* Washington: U. S. Naval Research Laboratory, 264 p. (U. S. Naval Research Laboratory. Bibliography No. 13).
An annotated list of 2274 books, periodical articles, and research reports covering the period 1903 through June 1958. References are listed chronologically with an author and subject index. Emphasizes the progress, development, and scientific uses of instrumented vehicles.

Berkner, Lloyd V., ed. *Manual on Rockets and Satellites.* London, New York: Pergamon Press, 1958. 508 p. (Annals of the International Geophysical Year. Vol. 6)
Includes references (104), pp. 500-503.

Booser, R. J. "Selected Bibliography and Glossary of Missile and Rocket Literature," *Special Libraries,* v. 53 (April 1962), pp. 201-206.
Lists 77 books, indexes, periodicals, and special sources useful to a library.

California Institute of Technology. Jet Propulsion Laboratory. *Publications of the Jet Propulsion Laboratory, January 1938 through June 1960.* Pasadena, 1961. 336 p. (*Its* Bibliography No. 39-1)
Annual supplements bring list up to date. Lists "Open Literature Surveys," "Literature Searches," and other pertinent space publications issued by JPL.

Estep, Raymond. *An Aerospace Bibliography.* Maxwell Air Force Base, Ala.: Documentary Research Division, Research Studies Institute, Air University, 1962. 158 p. (Air University Documentary Research Study, AU-290-61-RSI)
A briefly annotated bibliography of 3100 books and periodical articles published 1930 through January 1962 arranged alphabetically under 48 broad subject categories with subject and author index. Includes "Aerospace Literature and Bibliography (38 titles)," pp. 3-4; "Biography, Autobiography, and Memoirs (66 titles)," pp. 55-58; and "History (127 titles)," pp. 73-78. Combines in one volume the coverage formerly furnished in *An Airpower Bibliography* (Maxwell Air Force Base 1956) and later in *A Space Bibliography* (Maxwell Air Force Base, 1959).

Fiock, Ernest F. and Carl Halpern. *Bibliography of Books and Published Reports on Gas Turbines, Jet Propulsion and Rocket Power Plants.* Washington: U. S. Govt. Print. Off., 1951. 64 p. (National Bureau of Standards. Circular 509)
"Rockets," pp. 43-51; "Guided Missiles," pp. 44-45. References are arranged chronologically and cover period 1940-1950. A supplement (Washington: U. S. Govt. Print. Off., 1954, 110 p.), covers the period January 1950 through December 1953.

Gamble, William B. *History of Aeronautics; a Selected List of References to Material in the New York Public Library.* New York: New York Public Library, 1938. 325 p.
Includes early historical references to rocket propulsion, p. 314.

Gantz, Kenneth F. *Man in Space; the United States Air Force Program for Developing the Spacecraft Crew.* New York: Duell, Sloan and Pearce, 1959. 303 p.
Includes "A Reading List of Books on Astronautics," compiled by Raymond Estep, pp. 279-285.

Herzliková, Vlasta. Meziplanetarni Lety; Soupis Literatury Knizni a casopiseckych clanku. Pro potrebu knihoven, ryzkumnych ustavu a pracovniku hvezdaren. Brunn: Statni Technická Knihovna, 1959. 35 p.
A Czech bibliography of books and periodical articles relating to interplanetary flight compiled for the use of libraries, research institutes, and astronomers.

Humphries, John. *Rockets and Guided Missiles.* New York: Macmillan, 1957. 231 p.
Includes bibliography, pp. 207-225.

Koelle, Heinz H., ed. *Handbook of Astronautical Engineering*. New York: McGraw-Hill Book Company, 1961.
  Bibliographies, some extensive, accompany each chapter. Includes a chronology, " Milestones of Astronautical History," by D. E. Koelle, pp. 1-17-1-22.
Koelle, Heinz H. and H. J. Kaeppeler. *Literaturverzeichnis der Astronautik. Literature-Index of Astronautics.* Tittmoning/Oberbayern: W. Pustet, 1954. 100 p.
  A bibliography of books and periodical articles published 1914-1953 arranged in accordance with a three-place decimal system developed by Dr. Eugen Sänger. Many peripheral topics are included. Has an author index.
Krieger, Firmin J. *Behind the Sputniks; a Survey of Soviet Space Science.* Washington: Public Affairs Press, 1958. 380 p.
  Part I lists books and monographs dealing with historical, scientific, and technical aspects of rocketry and astronautics. Part II contains references drawn from various Russian newspapers, popular magazines, and serious technical journals. Includes " Bibliography of Soviet Books, Monographs, and Periodicals on Space," pp. 339-376, arranged alphabetically by author and covering period 1928-1957.
Krieger, F. J. " Soviet Space Experiments and Astronautics," *Aerospace Engineering*, v. 20 (July 1961), pp. 8-9, 28-37.
  Includes " Bibliography (17 References)," pp. 36-37.
Lent, Constantin P. *Rocketry: Jets and Rockets; the Science of the Reaction Motor and Its Practical Application for Aircraft and Space Travel.* New York: Pen-Ink Pub. Co., 1947. 254 p.
  Includes " List of Rocket and Jet Patents and Rocket Societies," pp. 241-250.
Levantovskii, Vladimir I. *Raketoi k Lune* (To the Moon by Rocket) Moscow: Fizmatizdat., 1960. 379 p.
  Includes bibliography, pp. 367-371.
Magnolia, L. R. and J. R. Trew. *Lunar Problem; a Bibliography in Two Volumes.* Los Angeles: Space Technology Laboratories, 1961. 2 v.
Moore, Patrick. *Space Exploration.* Cambridge, Eng.: Cambridge University Press, 1958. 36 p. (Reader's Guides, 3d ser.)
  An annotated list of 120 English-language books arranged in nine subject categories.
National Aviation Education Council. *A Bibliography of Adult Aerospace Books and Materials.* Compiled for National Aeronautics and Space Administration. Washington: U. S. Govt. Print. Off., 1961. 36 p.
  Comprises books, reference materials, films and filmstrips, and related materials, most non-technical and most published 1958-1961, with an index of authors and titles. Similar lists for younger readers are entitled *Aeronautics and Space Bibliography for Secondary Grades* (Washington: U. S. Govt. Print. Off., 1961) and *Aeronautics and Space Bibliography for Elementary Grades* (Washington: U. S. Govt. Print. Off., 1961)
Ordway, Frederick I. *Annotated Bibliography of Space Science and Technology, with an Astronomical Supplement. A History of Astronautical Book Literature— 1931 through 1961.* 3d ed. Washington: Arfor Publications, 1962. 77 p.
  First published in 1955 under title *Specialized Books on Space Flight and Related Disciplines.* A list of 352 English-language astronautical and 151 astronomical books arranged chronologically. Includes multi-language proceedings of international astronautical conferences and significant translations from French, German, and Russian.
Ordway, Frederick I. and Ronald C. Wakeford. *International Missiles and Space-Craft Guide.* New York: McGraw-Hill Book Company, 1960.
  Chapter 1 is a " Chronology of Missile Progress," pp. 3-16. A bibliography (6 p.) follows the main body of the book, comprising a list of English-language journals containing information of interest to the rocket, missile,

and astronautical fields; books primarily concerned with rockets and missiles; and books primarily of astronautical interest.

Philp, Charles G. *Stratosphere and Rocket Flight (Astronautics); a Popular Handbook on Space Flight of the Future, Including a Section on the Problems of Interplanetary Space Navigation.* London: Sir I. Pitman, 1935. 118 p.

"Books on Rockets and Astronautics," pp. 116-118, lists 14 English titles.

Progress in the Astronautical Sciences. New York: Interscience Publishers, 1962 to date.

Extensive lists of references accompany each chapter.

Rand Corporation. *An Annotated Bibliography of Rand Space Flight Publications.* Santa Monica, Calif., 1958 (rev. 1959). 53 p. (*Its* Report RM2113-1; and Report AD-21608)

Cites 172 items.

Rand Corporation. *Space Handbook: Astronautics and Its Applications,* by Robert W. Buchheim and the Staff of the Rand Corporation. New York: Random House, 1959. 330 p.

A revised and up-dated edition of House Committee on Astronautics and Space Exploration Document 86 (Washington: U. S. Govt. Print. Off., 1959) which was originally issued in 1958 as Rand Corporation's Research Memorandum RM-2289-RC under title *Astronautics and Its Applications.* Notes at end of each chapter include bibliographical references.

Rynin, Nikolai A. Mezhplanetnye soobshchenia [Interplanetary Communications] Leningrad: N. A. Rynin, 1928-32. 3 v. (9 pts.)

Includes bibliography. the most extensive published to this date, v. 3, pt. 9, pp. 110-189, the first part arranged chronologically, the second part grouped into five sections, each arranged alphabetically by authors: 1, Fiction in the Russian language; 2, Fiction in foreign languages; 3, Motion pictures dealing with space flights; 4, Scientific research publications in the Russian language; and 5, Scientific research publications in foreign languages.

Sänger, Eugen. *Raketen-Flugtechnik.* München und Berlin. R. Oldenbourg, 1933. 222 p.

Includes "Literatur zum Abschnitt Triebkräfte," pp. 4-5, listing 41 books and periodical articles published 1911-1941, and "Literatur zum Abschnitt Luftkräfte," pp. 76, listing six books.

Scherschevsky, Alexander B. *Die Rakete für Fahrt und Flug; eine allgemeinverständliche Einführung in das Raketenproblem.* Berlin-Charlottenburg: C. J. E. Volckmann, 1929. 134 p.

Includes "Literaturverzeichnis," pp. 130-134.

Sokoll, Alfred H. *Literatur zur Aero- und Astronautik; ein bibliographischer Wegweiser.* München: Alkos-Verlag, 1961. 89 p.

A guide to the literature of aeronautics and astronautics listing pertinent materials under the following categories: bibliographies; documentation services; reference works; news services; bulletins, notes, papers, and reports; and periodicals. Includes author and subject index.

Space Technology Laboratories. *Flight Performance Handbook for Orbital Operations; Orbital Mechanics and Astrodynamic Formulae, Theorems, Techniques, and Applications.* New York: J. Wiley, 1963.

References accompany sections and chapters.

Sunderman, James F. "A Missile and Space Bibliography," *Air Force and Space Digest,* v. 45 (April 1962), pp. 175-183.

Books are listed alphabetically by author under the following categories: rockets and missiles; astronautics; spaceflight; the men; earth satellites; human factors; and research and reference. An expanded version of lists originally appearing in this journal April 1958, pp. 168-174 and June 1960, pp. 169-181.

U. S. Air Force. Air Materiél Command. *Bibliography of German Guided Missiles.* Dayton, Ohio, 1946. 145 p. (*Its* Bibliography No. 2)

Lists German World War II documents available on microfilm at the Air Documents Division, Air Materiél Command. Arrangement is by eleven broad subject categories.

U. S. Air Force Academy. Dept. of Astronautics. *Astronautics.* Rev. Denver, 1961. 22 p. (Air Force Academy. Library. Special Bibliography Series. No. 5)
> A list of English-language titles arranged under five subject categories: course reference materials, background data, popular and historical accounts, periodical titles, and periodical indexing media.

U. S. Armed Services Technical Information Agency. *Bibliography of Bibliographies (Unclassified Title),* Compiled by Katye M. Gibbs and Elizabethe H. Hall. Arlington, Va., 1962. 268 p. (ASTIA Report AD-281 900)
> The section "Guided Missiles," pp. 90-102, lists pertinent bibliographies relating to the space sciences.

U. S. Dept. of the Army. *Missiles and Ventures into Space; Progress Report, 1961-1962.* Washington, 1962. 110 p.
> A bibliography covering the period April 1961 to March 1962 and including approximately 700 titles of books, articles, and studies, partly abstracted and annotated.

U. S. Dept. of the Army. *Missiles, Rockets and Satellites.* Washington, 1958. 5 v.
> A bibliographic survey covering the period 1957 through March 1958. Contents comprise.—v. 1. U. S. S. R.—v. 2. United States.—v. 3. Great Britain, France and other free countries.—v. 4. Technology: Means and Methods.—v. 5. Earth Satellites and Space Exploration.

U. S. Dept. of the Army. *Missiles, Rockets, and Space in War and Peace.* Washington, 1959. 94 p. (Dept. of the Army Pamphlet 70-5-6)
> Continues Dept. of the Army pamphlet 70-5. A partially annotated list of 1300 books and periodical articles published 1957-1959.

U. S. Dept. of the Army. Army Library. *Guided Missiles.* Washington, 1956. 91 p. (*Its* Special Bibliography No. 4)
> A comprehensive list of over 800 titles of books, periodical articles, and studies, with abstracts and annotations. Includes section entitled "History of Development."

U. S. Dept. of the Army. Army Library. *Guided Missiles, Rockets and Artificial Satellites, Including Project Vanguard; a Selected List of Titles.* Washington, 1957. 153 p. (*Its* Special Bibliography No. 11)
> A partially-annotated list of about 1,000 pertinent books, documents, periodical articles, and motion pictures.

U. S. Dept. of the Army. Army Library. *Military Aspects of Space Exploration; a Selected List of Titles.* Washington, 1958. 55 p. (*Its* Special Bibliography No. 16)
> Lists approximately 300 titles in alphabetical order within major and subordinate subject groups.

U. S. Dept. of the Army. Army Library. *Space Travel, a Selected List of Titles for Lecturers and Students.* Washington, 1956. 11 p. (*Its* Special Bibliography, No. 2)
> A general bibliography, partially annotated, listing about 100 books and periodical articles published 1952-1955.

U. S. Dept. of the Army. Office of the Chief of Research and Development. *U. S. S. R.: Missiles, Rockets and Space Efforts; a Bibliographic Record, 1956-1960.* Washington, 1960. 49 p. (Dept. of the Army. Pamphlet 70-5-8)
> An annotated list arranged alphabetically by author within major and subordinate subject groups. Section IX, Source Materials, lists ten titles.

U. S. Engineer School. Library. *Guided Missiles and Rockets, a Bibliography, 1946-1956.* Fort Belvoir, Va., 1956. 50 p.
> English-language periodical articles are cited.

U. S. Library of Congress. Aerospace Information Division. *USSR Missile and Rocket Program; Bibliography.* Washington, 1961. 66 p. (*Its* AID Report 61-62)

> The bibliography, consisting of 709 entries arranged alphabetically within eight major subject categories, serves as a guide to the Soviet literature of astronautics and the problems of space flight. The materials listed comprise Russian monographic titles given in transliterated form and followed by an English translation, periodical articles; conference proceedings, newspaper references, and other public sources.

U. S. Library of Congress. Legislative Reference Service. *Guided Missiles in Foreign Countries.* Prepared for the Committee on Armed Forces, United States Senate, by Eilene Galloway. Washington: U. S. Govt. Print. Off., 1957. 73 p.

> Includes bibliography, pp. 58-62, listing selected references on guided missiles in Australia, Canada, France, Great Britain, Italy, Sweden, Switzerland, and U. S. S. R. and satellites; preceded by general section.

U. S. Library of Congress. Science and Technology Division. *Space Science and Technology Books, 1957-1961; a Bibliography with Contents Noted.* Washington: U. S. Govt. Print. Off., 1963. 133 p.

> Arranged chronologically and by country within each of the given years. Includes subject and author indexes.

U. S. Office of Scientific Research and Development. National Defense Research Committee. *Summary Technical Report of Division 3, Vol. 1. Rocket and Underwater Ordnance.* Washington, 1946. 381 p.

> Declassified August 26, 1960 (nearly all Division 3 reports were classified when issued). Includes "General Bibliography of Technical Reports Issued under Division 3, NDRC," pp. 307-365.

U. S. Works Progress Administration. *Bibliography of Aeronautics. Part 49. Rocket Propulsion.* New York: Institute of the Aeronautical Sciences, 1937. 27 p.

> Chronological list of books, pamphlets, and periodical articles with author index.

U. S. Works Progress Administration. *Bibliography of Aeronautics. Part 50. Stratospheric Flight.* New York: Institute of the Aeronautical Sciences, 1937. 35 p.

> Chronological list of books and articles published 1904-1936 with author index.

Weiss, Sylvia E. and Elizabeth E. McCue. *A Catalog of OSRD Reports. Division 3, Rocket Ordnance.* Washington: Navy Research Section, Library of Congress, 1950. 21 p.

> Reports are listed under name of contractor with author, OSRD and report numbers, and subject index.

(3) BIOGRAPHY

Bergaust, Erik. *Reaching for the Stars.* Garden City, N. Y.: Doubleday, 1960. 407 p.

> Essentially a biography of Dr. Wernher von Braun.

Brügel, Werner, ed. *Männer der Rakete, in Selbstdarstellungen.* Leipzig: Hachmeister & Thal, 1933. 144 p.

> Includes biographical sketches of the thirteen contributors—all early rocket pioneers.

Emme, Eugene. "Yesterday's Dream . . . Today's Reality"; a Biographical Sketch of the American Rocket Pioneer, Dr. Robert H. Goddard," *Airpower Historian*, v. 7 (October 1960), pp. 216-221.

> Includes "Biographical Notes," pp. 221, citing 19 references and other sources.

Epstein, Beryl and Samuel Epstein. *The Rocket Pioneers on the Road to Space.* New York: Messner, 1958. 241 p.
> Chapters are devoted to Goddard, Oberth, Tsiolkovsky, and other early rocket pioneers.

Gartmann, Heinz. *The Men Behind the Space Rockets.* Translated from the German by Eustace Wareing and Michael Glenny. New York: D. McKay Co., 1956. 185 p.
> Contains biographical sketches of Ganswindt, Goddard, Oberth, Sänger, Tsiolkovsky, von Braun, Valier, and Zborowski.

Hartl, Hans. *Hermann Oberth: Vorkämpfer der Weltraumfahrt.* Hannover: Theodor Oppermann, 1958. 238 p.
> Includes "Zeittafel," covering the period 3200 B. C.-1958, pp. 231-238, and "Quellenverzeichnis," p. 240.

Kosmodem'ianskii, Arkadii A. *Konstantin Tsiolkovsky: His Life and Work.* Translated from the Russian by X. Danko. Moscow: Foreign Languages Pub. House, 1956. 101 p.
> The most extensive biography of Tsiolkovsky available in English.

Lehman, Milton. *This High Man: the Life of Robert H. Goddard.* New York: Farrar, Straus, 1963. 430 p.
> Includes reading list in "Sources and Acknowledgements," pp. 410-416.

Thomas, Shirley. *Men of Space; Profiles of the Leaders in Space Research, Development, and Exploration.* Philadelphia: Chilton Co., Book Division, 1960-63. 6 v.
> The six volumes issued contain 46 biographical sketches of outstanding figures engaged in astronautical research, development, and exploration, each sketch accompanied by a list of references.

U. S. Library of Congress. Aerospace Information Division. *L. I. Sedov; a Survey and Evaluation of His Works and Activity.* Washington, 1961. 116 p. (*Its* AID Report 61-136)
> Consists principally of annotated bibliography of Sedov's writings.

U. S. National Aeronautics and Space Administration. *Space Scientists and Engineers: Selected Biographical and Bibliographical Listing, 1957-1961.* Washington: U. S. Govt. Print. Off., 1962. 332 p. (*Its* Publication NASA SP-5)
> Contains brief biographical data for 1,000 scientific personnel who are making significant contributions to the advancement of space science and technology and a list of their published writings during the period 1957-1961. Eighteen countries are represented in the compilation.

Walters, Helen B. *Hermann Oberth; Father of Space Travel.* New York: Macmillan, 1962. 169 p.
> Includes bibliography, pp. 161-164.

Who's Who in World Aviation and Astronautics. Washington: American Aviation Publications, 1955-58. 2 v.
> Volume 2 lists 3100 biographies and includes leading scientists and space experts who have come to the fore with the advent of satellites.

(4) ROCKET TECHNOLOGY

Abraham, Lewis H. *Structural Design of Missiles and Spacecraft.* New York: McGraw-Hill Book Company, 1962. 335 p.
> References accompany each chapter.

American Society for Testing Materials. Committee E-10 on Radioisotopes and Radiation Effects. *Space Radiation Effects on Materials.* Philadelphia, 1962. 61 p. (ASTM Special Technical Publication No. 330)
> References accompany parts II-IV. Part V, pp. 52-53, is entitled "Sources of Information" and lists journals, indexing and abstracting services, and

monograph series and proceedings of symposia which include information on this subject.

Anzalone, Alfred M. *Space Technology; a Partial Search of the Literature Concerning the Application of Orbital Space Satellites to Advanced Weapon Systems.* Dover, N. J.: Feltman Research and Engineering Laboratories, Picatinny Arsenal, 1959. 109 p. (Literature Search No. 9, Pt. 1)

 A list of annotated references to unclassified literature with a Uniterm index.

Balakrishnan, A. V., ed. *Space Communications.* New York: McGraw-Hill Book Company, 1963. 422 p. (University of California Engineering and Extension Series)

 References accompany each chapter.

Barrère, Marcel, *et al. Rocket Propulsion.* Amsterdam, New York: Elsevier Pub. Co., 1960. 829 p.

 Lists of references, some extensive, accompany each of twelve chapters.

Beardell, Anthony J. and C. J. Grelicki. *Soviet Research and Development on the Chemistry of Compounds of Nitrogen Related to Propulsion.* Washington: Office of Technical Services, 1961. 61 p.

 Bibliography, pp. 31-49, lists 238 references to Soviet technical literature published June 1955 through December 1960.

Bowman, Norman J. *The Handbook of Rockets and Guided Missiles.* 2d ed. Newton Square, Pa.: Perastadion Press, 1963. 1008 p.

 Includes extensive bibliography (2476 references), pp. 668-716.

Brown, Kenneth, and Lawrence D. Ely, eds. *Space Logistics Engineering.* New York: J. Wiley, 1962. 623 p. (University of California Engineering and Physical Sciences Extension Series)

 Most chapters include extensive bibliographies.

Bussard, R. W. *Nuclear Rocket Propulsion: a Selected Bibliography of the Unclassified Literature.* Los Alamos, N. Mex.: Los Alamos Scientific Laboratory, 1961. 22 p. (Atomic Energy Commission Report LAMS-2519)

 The bibliography, consisting of 171 references, is divided into three sections dealing with applications of fission energy to propulsion, specific studies of propulsion systems, and potential advanced systems.

Clauss, Francis J., ed. *Surface Effects on Spacecraft Materials; First Symposium, Held at Palo Alto, Calif., May 12 and 13, 1959, Sponsored by Air Research and Development Command, U. S. Air Force, and Missiles and Space Division, Lockheed Aircraft Corp.* New York: J. Wiley, 1960. 404 p.

 Lists of references, some extensive, accompany papers.

Corliss, William R. *Propulsion Systems for Spaceflight.* New York: McGraw-Hill Book Company, 1960. 300 p.

 Lists compilations of space abstracts issued regularly, p. 282, and periodicals which frequently include articles of interest to space technology, p. 283. Also includes an extensive bibliography of English-language references accompanying nine chapters, pp. 283-293.

Duncan, Robert C. *Dynamics of Atmospheric Entry.* New York: McGraw-Hill Book Company, 1962. 306 p. (McGraw-Hill Series in Missile and Space Technology)

 Includes bibliography (77 references), pp. 290-294, of materials published 1925-1959.

Ehricke, Krafft A. *Space Flight.* Princeton, N. J.: D. Van Nostrand, 1960. 2 v.

 Lists of references accompany each chapter.

Goddard, Robert H. *Rocket Development; Liquid-Fuel Rocket Research, 1929-1941.* Ed. by Esther C. Goddard and G. Edward Pendray. New York: Prentice-Hall, 1948. 219 p.

 Published also in 1961 (New York: Prentice-Hall, 1961, 222 p.) Consists of condensations of Goddard's own experimental notebooks for this period. The introduction, pp. viii-xx, is a biographical sketch of Goddard.

Goddard, Robert H. *Rockets*. New York: American Rocket Society, 1946. 100 p.
    Reprints of the author's *A Method of Reaching Extreme Altitudes* and
    Liquid-Propellant Rocket Development, originally published by the Smith-
    sonian Institution in 1919 and 1936 respectively.
"Guidance Issue," *ARS Journal*, v. 29 (December 1959), pp. 899-988.
    Consists of ten invited articles with numerous references appended to each.
"High Temperature Issue," *Aerospace Engineering*, v. 22 (January 1963), pp.
    3-209.
    Comprises seventeen articles, each accompanied by extensive bibliography.
Irvine, Thomas F., ed. "Rocket Heat-Transfer Literature," *Journal of Heat
    Transfer (ASME Transactions. Series C)*, v. 82 (August 1960), pp. 155-169.
    A six-part survey, each part accompanied by extensive list of references.
Kit, Boris, and Douglas S. Evered. *Rocket Propellant Handbook*. New York:
    Macmillan, 1960. 354 p.
    Each chapter accompanied by references and bibliography.
Kovacik, V. P. "Dynamic Engines for Space Power Systems," *ARS Journal*,
    v. 32 (October 1962), pp. 1511-1522.
    A survey article with 52 references, p. 1522.
Locke, Arthur S., et al. *Guidance*. Princeton, N. J.: D. Van Nostrand, 1955.
    729 p. (Principles of Guided Missile Design)
    Bibliographies accompany chapters. Chapter II, pp. 22-54, is entitled "Prior
    Developments."
Mueller, F. K. *A History of Inertial Guidance*. Huntsville, Ala.: Army Ballistic
    Missile Agency, 1960.
North Atlantic Treaty Organization. Advisory Group for Aeronautical Research
    and Development. Combustion and Propulsion Panel. *Advanced Propulsion
    Techniques; Proceedings of a Technical Meeting Sponsored by the AGARD
    Combustion and Propulsion Panel, Pasadena, California, August 24-26, 1960*.
    Edited by S. S. Penner. New York: Pergamon Press, 1961. 255 p.
    References accompany each chapter and a "Representative Bibliography on
    Spacecraft Propulsion" is included, pp. 233-234, with the paper by Addisson
    M. Rothrock entitled "Spacecraft Propulsion."
North Atlantic Treaty Organization. Advisory Group for Aeronautical Research
    and Development. Combustion and Propulsion Panel. *The Chemistry of Pro-
    pellants; a Meeting Organized by the AGARD Combustion and Propulsion
    Panel, Paris, France, June 8-12, 1959*. Editors: S. S. Penner and J. Ducarne.
    New York: Pergamon Press, 1960. 651 p.
    An extensive bibliography accompanies each paper.
Parker, Earle R. *Materials for Missiles and Spacecraft*. New York: McGraw-
    Hill Book Company, 1963. 442 p. (University of California Engineering
    Sciences Extension Series)
    Lists of references, some extensive, accompany each chapter.
Parvin, Richard H., et al. *Inertial Navigation*. Princeton, N. J.: D. Van
    Nostrand, 1962. 370 p. (Principles of Guided Missile Design)
    References at end of each chapter. Includes a history of rocket inertial guid-
    ance by Dr. Walter Haeussermann, pp. 5-13.
Paushkin, IA M. *The Chemical Composition and Properties of Fuels for Jet
    Propulsion*. Translated by William Jones. Edited by B. P. Mullins. Oxford,
    New York: Pergamon Press, 1962. 480 p.
    Literature references at end of each chapter.
Sandorff, Paul E. *Orbital and Ballistic Flight; an Introduction to Space
    Technology*. Cambridge, Mass.: Technical Publications Group of the Instru-
    mentation Laboratory of Massachusetts Institute of Technology, 1960.
    Includes bibliography (104 references), pp. 4-117-4-127.
Scala, S. M., A. C. Harrison, and M. Rogers, eds. *Symposium on Dynamics of
    Manned Lifting Planetary Entry; Proceedings*. New York: J. Wiley, 1963.
    980 p.

Lists of references, some extensive, accompany each paper.

Sosnitskii, Georgii G. and Galina M. Aleksandrova. *Rozvidnyky Vsesvitu* (Explorers of the Universe), Kiev: Derzhavna Respublikans'ska Biblioteka URSR Imeni KPRS, 1958. 68 p.

An annotated bibliography of books and articles, published 1956-1958, dealing with Russian development of artificial satellites, general rocket technology, and the problems of space flight.

Stockwell, Richard E. *Soviet Air Power*. New York: Pageant Press, 1956. 238 p. "Missiles; Soviet Super-Secrets," pp. 118-137, with footnotes and "Bibliography," pp. 227-231.

Sutherland, George S. "Recent Advances in Space Propulsion," *ARS Journal*, v. 29 (October 1959), pp. 698-705.

Lists 150 references, pp. 703-705, dealing with propulsion power sources, systems analyses, and space mechanics.

Sutton, George P. *Rocket Propulsion Elements; an Introduction to the Engineering of Rockets*. 3d ed. New York: J. Wiley, 1963. 464 p.

Includes lists of references, some extensive, at end of each chapter.

Sutton, George P. "Rocket Propulsion Progress; a Literature Survey," *Journal of the American Rocket Society*, v. 22 (January/February 1952), pp. 17-27, 31.

A bibliography listing 230 books and papers published 1919-1951. A classified summary of the references listed precedes the main list.

Sutton, George P. "Rocket Propulsion Systems for Interplanetary Flight," *Journal of Aerospace Sciences*, v. 26 (October 1959), pp. 609-625.

"References (41)": p. 625.

Sweitzer, Dorothy I. *Engineering Equipment and Processes Adaptable to Lunar and Planetary Exploration*. Pasadena, Calif.: California Institute of Technology, Jet Propulsion Laboratory, 1963. 335 p. (*Its* Literature Search No. 464)

A list of 2705 references, most annotated, to papers, periodical articles, and technical reports, some foreign, arranged under 25 subject categories and covering the pertinent literature through September 1962. Includes an author index.

Symposium of Soviet Research on Artificial Earth Satellites and Related Subjects. New York: U. S. Joint Publications Research Service, 1958. 2 v. (U. S. Joint Publications Research Service. Report No. 187. Project NY-1377)

A translation of v. 63, nos. 1-2 and 1-b of the Soviet periodical *Uspekhi Fizicheskikh Nauk* comprising seventeen research papers presented by Russian delegates to the conference on earth satellites held in Washington, D. C., Octobr 2-7, 1957. Papers are accompanied by bibliographies.

Symposium on Ballistic Missile and Aerospace Technology. Proceedings. New York: Academic Press, 1959 (4th) [first published] to date.

Issued annually. Many papers accompanied by lists of references, some extensive.

Temperature Control of Satellite and Space Vehicles; an Annotated Bibliography. Sunnyvale, Calif.: Lockheed Aircraft Corp., Missiles and Space Division, 1961. 32 p. (*Its* Special Bibliography SB-61-5).

Lists 88 references.

"Ten Years of Project SQUID—a Bibliography," *Jet Propulsion*, v. 26 (August 1956), pp. 660-680.

Complete list of unclassified literature resulting from SQUID research concerned primarily with combustion, fluid flow, and heat transfer.

Unterberg, Walter, and James Congelliere. "Zero Gravity Problems in Space Powerplants: a Status Survey," *ARS Journal*, v. 32 (June 1962), pp. 862-872.

A literature survey citing 75 references to English and German publications, 1916-1961.

Warren, Francis A. *Rocket Propellants*. New York: Reinhold Pub. Corp., 1958. 218 p.

Lists of references, some extensive, for period 1927-1957 accompany each chapter.

Williams, Edgar P., *et al. Long-Range Surface-to-Surface Rocket and Ramjet Missiles: Aerodynamics.* Santa Monica, Calif.: Rand Corp., 1959. 167 p. (Rand Report R-181)
  Includes bibliography and "References," pp. 161-167.

Zaehringer, Alfred J. "Solid Propellant Bibliography," *Jet Propulsion,* v. 27 (August 1957), pp. 900-927.
  Lists approximately 2000 entries for the period 1850-1956. Section 7 "History" has 65 entries.

Zaehringer, Alfred J. *Solid Propellant Rockets; an Introductory Handbook. Second Stage.* Wyandotte, Mich.: American Rocket Co., 1958. 366 p.
  Each chapter accompanied by references and bibliography. There is a section "History," pp. 7-36, and a "Solid Propellant Bibliography," pp. 245-300, listing references for the period 1956-1958.

Zaehringer, Alfred J. *Soviet Space Technology.* New York: Harper, 1961. 179 p.
  Includes "References," pp. 159-162; and "Russian Rocketry Roster," pp. 170-171.

Zucrow, Maurice J. *Aircraft Missile Propulsion.* New York. J. Wiley, 1958. 2 v.
  Extensive lists of references accompany each chapter.

(5) SPACE LAW

Goldsen, Joseph M., ed. *Outer Space in World Politics.* New York: Praeger, 1963. 180 p.
  Includes bibliography of related materials, pp. 175-178.

Griffith, Alison. *The National Aeronautics and Space Act; a Study of the Development of Public Policy.* Washington: Public Affairs Press, 1962. 119 p.
  Includes bibliography.

Haley, Andrew G. *Space Law and Government.* New York: Appleton-Century-Crofts, 1963. 584 p.
  Each chapter accompanied by numerous footnotes and references. Appendix V is a bibliography, pp. 528-539. Section V-A, p. 528, is entitled "Bibliographies of Space Literature," and V-B, pp. 529-539, "Selected and Partial Bibliography of the Works of the Author."

Hogan, John C. "A Guide to the Study of Space Law, Including a Selective Bibliography on the Legal and Political Aspects of Space," *St. Louis University Law Journal,* v. 5 (Spring 1958), pp. 79-107.
  Issued also as *Rand Corporation Paper P-1290* (Santa Monica, 1958) and reprinted in *Space Law; a Symposium,* committee print of the Senate Special Committee on Space and Astronautics (Washington, 1959), pp. 291-345. An extensive selected bibliography listing 256 titles from books, law reviews, political journals, scientific and technical journals, and American and foreign newspapers. Also includes brief list of scientific and general books, Rand publications on space flight, and periodical indexes, guides, and other reference works.

Hogan, John C. "Space Law Bibliography," *Journal of Air Law and Commerce,* v. 23 (Summer 1956), pp. 317-325.
  Early bibliography listing 72 items published in eight countries.

Jessup, Philip C., and Howard J. Taubenfeld. *Controls for Outer Space and the Antarctic Analogy.* New York: Columbia University Press, 1959. 379 p. (Columbia University Studies in International Organization, No. 1)
  Bibliographical references included in "Notes," pp. 285-354.

Lipson, Leon, and Nicholas deB. Katzenbach. *Report to the National Aeronautics*

and Space Administration on the Law of Outer Space. Chicago: American Bar
Foundation, 1961. 179 p.
   Includes bibliographies, pp. 155-179.
Oklahoma University. Law Library. *Bibliography of the Space Law Collection.*
Norman, 1959. 22 p.
   Lists 57 books and periodical articles published 1938-1958; also includes United
   Nations and Congressional documents published 1953-1959.
Pépin, Eugène. "Bibliographie des Travaux Publiés sur les Problèmes Juridiques
   de l'Espace et Questions Connexes (1910-15 Septembre 1959)," *Revue Française
   de Droit Aérien,* v. 13 (October/December 1959), pp. 325-352.
   References (1909) arranged chronologically under twelve broad subject cate-
   gories. Reprinted in the author's *Les Problèmes Juridiques de l'Espace* (Paris:
   Sirey, 1959), pp. 20-46.
"Selective Bibliography of Space Law," *New York Law Forum,* v. 4 (July 1958),
pp. 372-374.
   Lists 77 references published 1930-1958.
Smirnoff, Michel. "Bibliographie du Droit Astronautique," *Revue Générale de
   l'Air,* v. 21 (No. 4, 1958), pp. 392-398.
   Lists alphabetically by author 161 books and periodical articles published
   1943-1958.
Smirnoff, Michel. *Svetska Bibliografija Astronautickog Prava—World Bibliogra-
   phy of Space Law.* Belgrad: Institut za Medunaroddnu Politiku i Privredu,
   1962. 160 p.
   In English and Serbian. Covers the period 1910 through 1959. Arranged
   chronologically with alphabetical author and subject index.
Teclaff, Ludwik A. "Review of Space Law Literature and Activities," *Law
   Library Journal,* v. 54 (August 1961), pp. 208-217.
   The bibliography comprises: (1) an annotated list of 91 books and articles
   arranged alphabetically by author; (2) a classified index.
Union List of Air Law Literature in Libraries in Oxford, Cambridge, and London.
London: London University, Institute of Advanced Legal Studies, 1956. 54 p.
(Institute of Advanced Legal Studies Publication No. 4)
United Nations. Library. *A Bibliography of the Law of Outer Space* (Pre-
liminary Edition). New York, 1958. 35 p.
U. S. Air Force. Judge Advocate General. *Space Law Bibliography.* Washing-
ton: Dept. of the Air Force, 1961. 79 p. (Air Force Pamphlet AFP110-1-4)
   Lists alphabetically by author books, periodical and newspaper articles,
   official speeches, reports, diplomatic communications, and other official and
   semi-official documents readily available in libraries in the Washington area.
   Includes "Bibliographies on Space Law," pp. 6-9.
U. S. Congress. House. Select Committee on Astronautics and Space Exploration.
Survey of Space Law; Staff Report. Washington: U. S. Govt. Print. Off.,
1959. 60 p. (86th Cong., 1st Sess., House. Doc. No. 89)
   Includes "Bibliography of Space Law," prepared in the Office of the Judge
   Advocate General of the Air Force, pp. 38-60.
U. S. Dept. of State. *Documents on International Aspects of the Exploration
and Use of Outer Space, 1954-1962; Staff Report,* Prepared for the Committee
on Aeronautical and Space Sciences, United States Senate. Washington: U. S.
Govt. Print. Off., 1963. 407 p.
   Comprises pertinent acts, addresses, letters, messages, reports, and statements.
   An updating and expansion of a section entitled "International Negotiations
   Regarding the Use of Outer Space, 1957-60" which was part III of *Legal
   Problems of Space Exploration; a Symposium* cited below.
U. S. Library of Congress. Legislative Reference Service. *Legal Problems of
Space Exploration; a Symposium.* Washington: U. S. Govt. Print. Off., 1961.
1392 p. (87th Cong., 1st Sess. Senate. Doc. No. 20)

Includes numerous bibliographical references and an extensive bibliography entitled "Selected References on the Legal Problems of Space Exploration," compiled by Kenneth Anderson Finch, pp. 1329-1392.

Verplaetse, Julien G. *International Law in Vertical Space: Air, Outer Space, Ether.* Madrid: (Exclusive Distribution for North America: F. B. Rothman, South Hackensack, N. J.), 1960. 505 p.
  Includes bibliographical footnotes and "Sources," pp. 20-61.

Yale University. Law Library. *Bibliography of Materials in the Yale Law Pertaining to the Law of Outer Space* (Preliminary Draft). New Haven, 1959. 38 p.
  Current coverage of space law is provided in articles and in bibliographical sections in the three leading space law journals: (1) *Journal of Air Law and Commerce*, published quarterly by the School of Law, Southern Methodist University, Dallas, Texas; (2) *Revue Française de Droit Aérien*, published quarterly by Recueil Sirey, Paris; and (3) *Zeitschrift für Luftrecht and Weltraumrechtsfragen*, sponsored by the Institut für Luftrecht und Weltraumrechtsfragen der Universität Köln and published quarterly by Carl Heymanns Verlag, Berlin-Charlottenburg.

(6) SPACE SCIENCES

Artificial Earth Satellites. Translated from Russian. New York: Plenum Press, 1960 to date. 6 v. (current unbound issues published by Consultants Bureau)
  Translation from Soviet journal *Iskusstvennye Sputniki Zemli.* Each article accompanied by lists of citations to literature, some extensive.

Ashe, William F., *et al. Historical Survey of Inhabitable Artificial Atmospheres.* Columbus: Ohio State University Research Foundation, 1958. 154 p. (Wright Air Development Center Technical Report, WADC 58-154; PB Report 151 277; AD-155 901)
  Abstracts of articles disclosed in survey of world literature on production and control of artificial atmospheres for living organisms.

Baker, Robert M. L., Jr. "Recent Advances in Astrodynamics," *ARS Journal,* v. 30 (December 1960), pp. 1127-1140.
  Lists 276 astrodynamic papers.

Beischer, Dietrich E., and Alfred R. Fregly. *Animals and Man in Space; a Chronology and Annotated Bibliography Through the Year 1960.* Pensacola, Fla.: U. S. Naval School of Aviation Medicine, 1962. 97 p. (*Its* Monograph No. 5; ONR Report No. ACR-64)
  Lists pertinent bibliographies, monographs, technical publications, and periodical articles relating to biological experiments conducted during balloon and rocket flights and includes detailed tabluations of such flights.

Benson, Otis O., Jr., and Hubertus Strughold, eds. *Physics and Medicine of the Atmosphere and Space; the Proceedings of the Second International Symposium on the Physics and Atmosphere of Space, Held at San Antonio, Texas, November 10, 11, 12, 1959.* New York: Wiley, 1960. 645 p.
  Bibliographies, many extensive, accompany each of 42 papers presented at the meeting.

Benton, Mildred. "Artificial Satellites—a Bibliography of Recent Literature," *Jet Propulsion,* v. 28 (May-June 1958), pp. 301-302, 352-361; 399-401, 418-432.
  An annotated bibliography of about 340 references arranged alphabetically by author. Part 1 is for the year 1956 and part 2 covers the period 1957-1958.

Benton, Mildred C. *Use of High Altitude Rockets for Scientific Research; an Annotated Bibliography.* Washington: U. S. Naval Research Laboratory, 1959. 123 p. (Naval Research Laboratory. Bibliography No. 16)
  Chronological list of periodical articles, technical reports, and papers pub-

lished 1946 through June 1959. Arrangement is alphabetical within years with an author and subject index.

Berkner, Lloyd V. and Hugh Odishaw, eds. *Science in Space.* New York: McGraw-Hill Book Company, 1961. 458 p.

Each of twenty chapters accompanied by lists of references, some extensive.

Bethel, James S. *Motion of Artificial Satellites; a Bibliography of Periodical Literature.* White Sands Missile Range, N. M.: U. S. Army Signal Missile Support Agency, Missile Electronics Warfare Division, 1961. 25 p. (MEDW Report No. 1103)

Alphabetical list of 258 articles published 1946-1961 relating to various aspects of satellite mechanics.

Billik, B. "Survey of Current Literature on Satellite Lifetimes," *ARS Journal,* v. 32 (November 1962), pp. 1641-1650.

"References (30)," p. 1650, published 1954-1962.

Blythe, J. H. "Scientific Uses of Earth Satellites," *British Institute of Radio Engineers Journal,* v. 22 (November 1961) pp. 425-432.

Includes 35 references, p. 432.

Bradshaw, Nina H. *et al. Moon Explorations: Special Bibliography/Index.* Washington: Technical Information Service, 1963. 252 p.

A selected list of technical reports dealing with the moon and with lunar probes, selected from *U. S. Government Research Reports* and covering the period from June 1956 through October 1962.

Brown, John L., ed. *Sensory and Perceptual Problems Related to Space Flight; Report of a Working Group of the Panel on Psychology.* Washington: National Academy of Sciences, National Research Council, 1961. 51 p. (National Research Council. Publication 872)

Includes "Bibliography of the Literature Relevant to Sensory and Perceptual Problems in Space," pp. 28-41.

Flaherty, Bernard E., ed. *Psychophysiological Aspects of Space Flight.* New York: Columbia University Press, 1961. 393 p.

Bibliographies, some extensive, accompany each of 28 chapters.

Fogel, Lawrence J. *Biotechnology; Concepts and Applications.* Englewood Cliffs, N. J.: Prentice-Hall, 1963. 826 p.

A bibliography accompanies each chapter. Section F, "An Overview of Biotechnology," pp. 793-796, lists 48 references.

Goodman, B. D. "Psychological and Social Problems of Man in Space—a Literature Survey," *ARS Journal,* v. 31 (July 1961), pp. 863-872.

Lists 159 books, reports, and periodical articles published through the early part of 1961. Originally issued by Systems Development Corp., March 2, 1961, as its *Field Note* FN-5220.

Hendrickson, Ruth M. *Bibliography on Space Medicine.* Los Alamos, N. M.: Los Alamos Scientific Laboratory, 1958. 47 p. (Atomic Energy Commission. Report AECU-3914)

Covers period 1940-1957.

Hodgson, James G., and R. G. Tischer. "Space Feeding Problems; a Bibliography," *Food Technology,* v. 12 (September 1958), pp. 459-460, 461-463.

Classified list of references including general materials, space medicine, space psychology, space feeding systems, and algae as a source of food and oxygen.

IGY World Data Center A: Rockets and Satellites. *Catalogue of Data Received by WDC-A During the Period 1 July 1957-31 December 1961. Submitted to the Committee on Space Research (COSPAR) of the International Council of Scientific Unions.* Washington, 1962. 88 p.

Part C, pp. 15-49, is an author index and Part D, pp. 51-88, a subject index to reports and reprints received.

Jacobius, Arnold. "Bibliographic Control of Aviation and Space Medical Literature," *Aerospace Medicine,* v. 30 (July 1959), pp. 512-516.

A guide for the researcher in this field listing 69 pertinent references and sources in section entitled "Published Bibliographies of Aerospace Medicine and Related Fields," pp. 513-516.

Jacobius, Arnold J. "Bioastronautics Information Services and Publications in the United States," *Aerospace Medicine*, v. 45 (April 1963), pp. 344-348.

Part II entitled "Bibliographic Services in the United States Pertinent to the Space Life Sciences" lists 18 services published on a continuing basis with pertinent bibliographical data for each.

Kiss, Elemer. "Annotated Bibliography on Rocket Meteorology," *Meteorological and Geoastrophysical Abstracts*, v. 11 (September 1960), pp. 1480-1535.

Items are arranged chronologically and alphabetically by author within each year. A subject outline provides a guide to the subject matter. A geographic outline provides a guide to the locations of areas where observations and measurements were conducted.

Kiss, Elemer. "Bibliography on the Use of Satellites in Meteorology," *Meteorological and Geoastrophysical Abstracts*, v. 11 (October 1960), pp. 1683-1729.

References (201) for the period 1955-1960 are arranged alphabetically by author. A subject outline provides a guide to the subject matter.

Kiss, Elemer. "Supplementary Bibliography on the Use of Satellites in meteorology," *Meteorological and Geoastrophysical Abstracts*, v. 14 (March 1963), pp. 870-936.

Lists alphabetically by author 283 items published primarily during period 1961-1962. A geographic and a subject outline are included.

Krull, Alan R. "A History of the Artificial Satellite," *Jet Propulsion*, v. 26 (May 1956), pp. 369-383.

A chronological (1879-1955) bibliography of approximately 350 references to the significant published literature of artificial, manned or unmanned, satellites of the earth.

Le Galley, Donald P., ed. *Space Science*. New York: J. Wiley, 1963. 668 p. (University of California Engineering and Physical Sciences Extension Series)

Chapters accompanied by lists of references, some extensive.

Massachusetts Institute of Technology. Lincoln Laboratory. *Collection of Soviet Papers on Earth Satellites*. Cambridge, 1958. 182 p.

Bibliographies and references accompany papers.

Petrov, Viktor P. *Iskusstvennyi Sputnik Zemli* (Artificial Earth Satellite). Moscow: Voeizdat., 1958. 305 p.

Bibliography, pp. 301-303, lists 73 references.

Reiger, S. H. *A Study of Passive Communication Satellites; a Report Prepared for the National Aeronautics and Space Administration*. Santa Monica, Calif.: Rand Corp., 1963. 206 p. (Rand Corporation. Rand Report, R-415-NASA)

Includes bibliography, pp. 205-206.

The Russian Literature of Satellites. New York: International Physical Index, 1958. 2 v.

Translation of v. 63, no. 1, 1957, issue of the Soviet periodical *Uspekhi Fizicheskikh Nauk*. Each of eleven papers accompanied by bibliography.

Stafford, Walter H., and Robert M. Croft. *Artificial Earth Satellites and Successful Solar Probes, 1957-1960*. Washington: National Aeronautics and Space Administration, 1961. 602 p. (National Aeronautics and Space Administration. Technical Note D-601)

Section VI, pp. 585-602, comprises "References (237)."

Strughold, Hubertus. "From Aviation Medicine to Space Medicine," *Air University Quarterly Review*, v. 10 (Summer 1958), pp. 7-16.

Includes "References (55)," p. 16.

U. S. Air Force Missile Development Center, Holloman Air Force Base, N. M. *History of Research in Space Biology and Biodynamics at the Air Force Missile*

Development Center, Holloman Air Force Base, New Mexico, 1946-1958.
Holloman Air Force Base, N. M., 1958. 114 p.
   Numerous bibliographical references included in notes at end of each chapter.
U. S. Air University Library. *Earth Satellites; Selected References in the Air
University Library.* Maxwell Air Force Base, Ala., 1958. 10 p. (*Its* Special
Bibliography No. 118, Supplement No. 1)
U. S. Armed Services Technical Information Agency. *Bio-Astronautics: an
ASTIA Report Bibliography.* Arlington, Va., 1959. 164 p. (*Its* Report AD-211
755; PB Report 151 853)
   A selected list of references to reports originating primarily from Govern-
   ment-sponsored research programs relating to the biological problems of
   space flight. Entries are for period 1952 to 1958 and are grouped under
   ASTIA subject headings. A *Supplement* issued in 1960, 49 p., its Report AD-
   233 000, PB Report 161 653, lists 248 references and brings the subject matter
   up to date through 1959.
U. S. Armed Services Technical Information Agency. *Scientific Satellites; a
Report Bibliography*, compiled by Sara Bjorge. Arlington, Va., 1962. 24 p.
(ASTIA Report AD 290 800)
   A select annotated bibliography of reports prepared by Department of De-
   fense contractors covering the design and instrumentation of scientific satel-
   lites, properties of the ionosphere derived from satellite research, and meteoro-
   logical satellites.
U. S. Library of Congress. Science and Technology Division. *An Interim
Bibliography on the International Geophysical Year*, compiled by Fred S.
Howard. Washington: National Academy of Sciences, 1958. 56 p.
   Lists references from world literature under twelve large subject and
   discipline groups. Pertinent sections include " Rockets," pp. 37-40; " Satellites
   —USSR," pp. 41-46, and " Satellites—U. S.," pp. 46-53.
U. S. Library of Congress. Science and Technology Division. *United States IGY
Bibliography, 1953-1960; an Annotated Bibliography of United States Con-
tributions to the IGY and IGC (1957-1959).* Compiled by Frank M. Marson
and Janet R. Terner. Washington: National Academy of Sciences-National
Research Council, 1963. 391 p. (National Research Council. Publication 1087;
World Data Center A. IGY General Report No. 18)
   Section " Rockets and Satellites," pp. 297-354, lists 509 references, arranged
   alphabetically by author. Pertinent materials also listed under other disciplines.
U. S. National Science Foundation. *A Bibliography for the International Geo-
..physical Year.* Washington: U. S. Govt. Print. Off., 1957. (*Its* Publication
NSF 57-25)
   " Rockets and Satellites," pp. 35-50; " Earth Satellite Program," pp. 36-50.
   References, primarily articles and news releases, are arranged alphabetically
   by author.
U. S. National Library of Medicine. *Bibliography of Space Medicine.* Wash-
ington, 1958. 49 p. (U. S. Public Health Service. Publication No. 617. Bibli-
ography Series No. 21)
   Lists 381 references on various aspects of space medicine and related fields
   from 1950 to early 1958. Arranged in broad subject classes in inverse
   chronological order alphabetically by author within the years. A *Supplement
   No. 1* (Washington, 1958), 8 p., lists 50 additional items.
U. S. School of Aerospace Medicine. *Epitome of Space Medicine.* Randolph
AFB, Tex.: USAF School of Aviation Medicine, 1958.
   Comprises 41 papers prepared by SAM personnel on various aspects of
   space medicine, many accompanied by bibliographies.

(7) ABSTRACTING AND INDEXING SERVICES

AIAA Journal (formed by merger of *ARS Journal and Journal of the Aerospace Sciences*) New York: American Institute of Aeronautics and Astronautics, January 1963 to date. Monthly.

Contains section "Technical Literature Digest" (published in *Journal of the American Rocket,* September 1951-1953; in *Jet Propulsion,* January 1954-May 1959; in *ARS Journal,* June 1959-December 1962) listing pertinent books, periodical articles, symposium papers, and technical reports, arranged under broad subject categories.

"Abstracts of Current Literature," prepared by Science and Technology Division, Library of Congress, *Aerospace Medicine,* v. 29 (November 1958) to date.

About 1,000 informative abstracts a year are included from world-wide report, periodical, and monographic literature in the field of bioastronautics and related fields. Arrangement is by eleven broad subject categories with cumulated subject and author indexes in each December issue of the journal.

Aerospace Medicine and Biology: an Annotated Bibliography. Washington: Science and Technology Division, Library of Congress, 1956 to date (Vol. I, 1952 literature—Vol. VII, 1957 literature)

Issued irregularly. Provides comprehensive bibliographic coverage of the world literature on aviation and space biology and related topics. Each volume presently contains approximately 1,500 abstracts and has cumulated author, subject, and corporate source indexes.

Air University Periodical Index to Military Periodicals. Maxwell Air Force Base, Ala: Air University Library, 1949 to date. Quarterly.

Lists 18,000 references a year to significant articles, news items, and editorials from 68 English-language military and aeronautical periodicals. Arrangement is alphabetical by subject with annual and triennial cumulative indexes.

Astronautics Information Abstracts—Reports and Open Literature. Pasadena, Calif.: Jet Propulsion Laboratory, California Institute of Technology, 1959-August 1963. Monthly.

Contained about 1,200 abstracts a year of selective technical reports and open literature citations dealing with space flight and applicable data and techniques. Alphabetical subject arrangement with monthly author, subject and sources indexes cumulated to date of publication, annual cumulated indexes.

Bulletin Signalétique. Paris: Service de Documentation et d'Information Technique de l'Aéronautique, 1945 to date. Semimonthly.

Contains about 9,500 abstracts a year from world literature (including technical reports, memoranda, and papers) arranged by SDIT classification. Has section "Astronautique" and related topics.

Current Contents of Space, Electronic and Physical Sciences. Philadelphia: Institute for Scientific Information, January 1961 to date. Weekly.

Reproduces tables of contents of about 100 world journals. Each issue includes author address directory.

"Digest of Translated Russian Literature," *AIAA Journal,* v. 1 (January 1963) to date (included as "Russian Supplement" in *ARS Journal,* October 1959-December 1962). Monthly.

Comprises selected abstracts from translated Russian journals.

Index Aeronauticus; Journal of Aeronautical and Astronautical Abstracts. London: Technical Information and Library Services, Ministry of Aviation, 1945 to date. Monthly.

Contains about 3,500 abstracts a year from world literature, including articles in scientific and technical journals, patents, published papers, and reports, arranged by Universal decimal classification with monthly and annual author indexes.

International Aerospace Abstracts. New York: American Institute of Aeronautics and Astronautics, January 1961 to date. Monthly.

Includes 1,000 abstracts a year of world literature in the field of aeronautics and space science and technology. Materials abstracted include books, periodicals (including government-sponsored journals), meeting papers and conference proceedings issued by professional societies and academic organizations, translations of journals and journal articles. Subject classification with author index. Quarterly, semiannual and annual cumulative author and subject indexes.

Journal of the British Interplanetary Society. London: British Interplanetary Society, 1934 to date. Bimonthly.

Includes special section " Astronautical Abstracts," containing 2,000 abstracts a year to world literature with subject classification and annual author and subject indexes.

Journal of the Royal Aeronautical Society. London: Royal Aeronautical Society, 1866 to date. Monthly.

Includes section " The Library " containing 250 abstracts a year from world literature, including books, pamphlets, and technical reports, relating to rocket technology with annual author and subject index.

Pacific Aerospace Library Checklist of Periodical Titles. Los Angeles: Pacific Aerospace Library, 1941 to date. Semiweekly.

Contains 12,000 references a year from 300 world journals, papers, and reports with subject classification.

Pacific Aerospace Library Uniterm Index to Periodicals. Los Angeles: Pacific Aerospace Library, 1955 to date.

Accessions list weekly, posting list triweekly, quarterly cumulations, annual volume. Cites 12,000 references a year from 300 world journals with author and Uniterm index.

Referativnyi Zhurnal: Raketnaya Tekhnika i Apparaty Kosmicheskogo Poleta [Abstract Journal; Rocket Technology and Equipment for Space Flight] Moscow: Proizvodstvenno-izdatel'skii kombinat Vsesoyuznogo instituta nauchnoi i tekhnicheskoi informatsii, 1962 to date. Semimonthly.

Contains about 2,400 abstracts a year from world literature. Arranged by subject.

Scientific and Technical Aerospace Reports (supersedes its *Technical Publications Announcements*), compiled by Office of Scientific and Technical Information, National Aeronautics and Space Administration. Washington: U. S. Govt. Print. Off., January 8, 1963 to date. Semimonthly.

Announces, abstracts, and indexes reports issued by the National Aeronautics and Space Administration, as well as by other Government agencies, universities, industry, and research organizations both in the United States and abroad, and scientific and technical articles prepared by NASA contractor authors which appear in learned and technical journals. Separate cumulative indexes are published quarterly, semiannually, and annually.

U. S. Government Research Reports, Compiled by Office of Technical Services, Department of Commerce. Washington: U. S. Govt. Print. Off., 1946 to date. Semimonthly.

Contains about 40,000 abstracts and references a year to technical reports, many relating to rocket technology, from Government-sponsored research made available to industry and the general public. Arranged by subject with AD, report, number, and alphabetical subject index in each issue and semi-annual and annual cumulative descriptor and source indexes.

Voprosy Raketnoi Tekhniki [Problems of Rocket Technology] Moscow: Izda-tel'stvo Inostrannoi Literatury, 1951 to date. Monthly.
Includes section "Novosti Reaktivnoi Tekhniki" containing 300 abstracts a year from European and American literature.

Zentralblatt der Aero- und Astronautik (ZAA). *Abteilung 1, Deutschsprachiges Schriftum.* Munich: Alkos-Verlag, 1961 to date. Quarterly.
Cites about 1,000 references and abstracts a year relating to aerospace technology and bioastronautics from German books and over 700 German journals.

ADDENDA

History and Chronology

Emme, Eugene M. "Perspective on Space Exploration," *Airpower Historian*, v. 11 (January 1964), pp. 6-10.
Discusses the significance of the birth of the space age in October 1957 and its effect on the United States, the establishment of the National Aeronautics and Space Administration on October 1, 1958, its early years and accomplishments, and its role in the American space program.

Rosenthal, Alfred. *The Early Years of the Goddard Space Flight Center; Historical Origins and Activities Through December 1962.* Greenbelt, Md.: National Aeronautics and Space Administration, 1964. 273 p.
Prepared by the GSFC Historian, the volume contains chapters on the work of Robert H. Goddard, Project Vanguard, and the founding of this NASA Center. Seven appendices follow, including a list of GSFC satellite and space probe projects as of December 1962, a chronology March 1955-December 1962, a list of GSFC technical notes and reports, and a bibliography bearing on GSFC programs.

General Bibliography

Fry, Bernard M. and Foster E. Mohrhart, eds. *A Guide to Information Sources in Space Science and Technology.* New York, London Interscience Publishers, 1963. 579 p. (Guides to Information Sources in Science and Technology. Vol. 1)
Lists over 3500 published and 400 nonpublication sources and references, most English-language publications. Arranged in alphabetical order within major and subordinate subject groups. Subjects of the 19 major groups include specialized information centers and sources, Soviet astronautics, space law, International Geophysical Year, U. S. space programs, history and missile men and space centers. There are six appendices including a summary of satellites and planetoids, a list of U. S. missions utilizing large boosters, and a list of journals published in the space and astronautics fields. Has an author and detailed subject index. The guide is to be supplemented by an annual or biennial volume titled "Research Trends in Space Sciences and Technology: 1963-1964—A Guide to Sources of Information."

U. S. Air Force Academy. Library. *Outer Space.* Colorado Springs, 1963. 18 p. (*Its* Special Bibliography Series. No. 28)
Lists 121 books, articles, and government documents deemed pertinent for use by participants in the Sixth Air Force Academy Assembly, April 1-4, 1964.

U. S. Library of Congress. Science and Technology Division. *Aeronautical and Space Serial Publications; a World List.* Washington: U. S. Government Printing Office, 1962. 255 p.
Lists 4,551 titles originating in 76 countries.

Rocket Technology

Stuhlinger, Ernst,*et al*, eds. *Astronautical Engineering and Science; From Peene-münde to Planetary Space, Honoring the Fiftieth Birthday of Wernher von Braun*. New York: McGraw-Hill Book Company, 1963. 394 p.

Comprises 20 papers, many historical, and most accompanied by references, dealing with system and operations; advanced propulsion; guidance control, and tracking; spacecraft; and space physics and exploration. Chapter 3, pp. 43-66, is titled "A Chronology of Space Carrier Vehicle Launchings, 1957 Through 1962," by Frederick I. Ordway, III. Appendix I, pp. 365-375, is a biography of Wernher von Braun by James L. Daniels, Jr., and appendix II, pp. 377-384, is a bibliography of works by Wernher von Braun by Mitchell R. Sharpe, Jr.

Space Sciences

Rechtschaffen, Oscar H., ed. *Reflections on Space: Its Implications for Domestic and International Affairs*, with Foreword by the Secretary of the Air Force Eugene M. Zuckert. Colorado Springs: U. S. Air Force Academy, 1964. 345 p.

Compiled for use in conjunction with *Outer Space, Prospects for Man and Society*, Air Force Academy Assembly, the volume contains forty-eight selections by various specialists.

Young, Louise B., ed. *Exploring the Universe*. New York: McGraw-Hill Book Company, 1963. 457 p.

Prepared for the American Foundation for Continuing Education in its study-discussion program, the volume of readings contains selections from Galileo to the present day. Part 10 titled "Why Explore Space? " includes a chronology of space exploration and suggestions for further reading.

Index

A-4 (Experimental Rocket), 33, 38, 41, 43, 44
APL. *See* Johns Hopkins
Able & Able Star, 139
ASIS (Abort-sensing-and-implementation system), 230
Academy of Sciences, USSR, 275
Acceleration, 167-68
Accelerometer, 35
Adam, Project, 226
Advanced Research Projects Agency (ARPA), 118, 119, 120, 217
Aerobee, 64, 123, 125, 126, 127, 131, 259n, 262
Aerojet, 70, 74, 147, 168
Aerojet-General Corp. (formerly Aerojet Engineering Corp.), 46n, 53, 58, 64, 129, 244
Aerospace Industries Association, 261
Africano, A. P., 27
Agena, 160, 216
Air Force (USAF), 58, 69, 74, 83-91 *passim*, 128, 142n, 142-61 *passim*, 198-218 *passim*, 242, 263, 267; Western Development Division (WDD), 144, 147, 148, 150
— Air Research and Development Command (ARDC), 208, 209
— Arnold Engineering Development Center, 218
— Atlas D, 230, 231
— USAF Ballistic Missile Division (AFBMD), 214, 230, 231 USAF Man-in-Space, 217
— Project RAND, 69-77 *passim*, 85-92 *passim*; 78-88 *passim*
— School of Aviation Medicine, 267 Space Systems Division, 142n
— Strategic Air Command, 151
" Airacomet," 192
Akens, David S., 3, 107n, 227n
Alexander, George, 232n
Allegheny Ballistics Laboratory, 129, 138, 165
Allen, H. Julian, 214

Ambrose, Mary Stone, 214n
American Association for the Advancement of Science, 2, 29n, 122n
American Institute of Electrical Engineers (AIEE), 255, 256, 260, 261n, 267
American Rocket Society (ARS, formerly American Interplanetary Society), 3, 5, 19, 24-26, 48
Ames Aeronautical Laboratory. *See* NACA
Amneus, J. A., 61
Anderson, G. F., 263n
Anderson, David A., 39a
Antigua, 132
Apollo, 225n, 233
Apt, Milburn G., 205
Armed Services, U. S., 68, 79n
Armstrong, Neil A., 207
Army, U. S. 107, 110, 121, 123, 131, 162, 163, 217, 244, 247, 248, 279
— Air Corps (Force), 29n, 41, 44, 52-63 *passim*, 69-74 *passim*, 123, 192, 193, 195, 197; Air Material Command, 58, 60, 75, 81, 144 198; Air Technical Service Command, 59, 63; Bombing and Gunnery Range, 58; Underwater Propulsion Section, 59
— Chemical Corps, 108
— Hermes (project), 85, 108, 109, 127
— Ballistic Missile Agency, 65, 226; Joint Army Navy Ballistic Missile Committee (JANBMC), 163, 164. *See also* USAF
— Ordnance Dept., 60, 63, 65, 109; ABMA, 107, 112-20 *passim*, 163, 164, 165, 227; GMDD, 107, 111; journal, 65; Missile Command, 218n; OGMC, 107, 108, 109
— Signal Corps, 22, 63, 123
— Transportation Research and Engineering Command (TRECOM), 241, 244, 248n
Arnold, Henry H., 52, 61, 142, 192, 193
Arnold, Weld, 50, 51

309

The manuscript was prepared for publication by Ralph Busick. The book was designed by Peter Nothstein. The text type face is Linotype Janson designed by Nicholas Kis, 1690 and recut by Mergenthaler Linotype in 1932. The display face is Venus Bold cut by Bauer 1907-13.

Manufactured in the United States of America.